D0343223

Where's The Applause?

A true story of a child's fantastic survival

by

Louise F. Burnham

ISBN 1-880732-11-4

Garden Court Press
1001 Forest Avenue
Palo Alto, CA 94301

Dedicated to Dr. Barbara A. Barnett

A woman of ethics.
The owner of kind and "hold me steady" eyes.
The guide to my truth.
A woman who lives her courage and validates mine.
The constant reminder that there is already enough pain.
I feel grateful.
Always.

Special Acknowledgment to JoAnn Daugherty

Thank you for transcribing the tapes of this book into hard copy.
Thank you for being with me when I couldn't be there for
myself.
Thank you for the raucous laughter through this whole damn
thing.
Thank you my friend, for the love, and encouragement.

Caused by Gail

A woman with an enormous ability to love who did not know
abuse in our childhood causes many things, including serious
weight problems.
She wouldn't have thought of a self help book on abuse
because she didn't think of herself as abused.
She kept asking me why? Why? Why? Why aren't there stories
about abuse that the everyday reader could get and relate to.
I am so proud of your enduring, endearing self, even if it is your
damn fault I had to write this book and have it edited over and
over. To you — applause!

CONTENTS

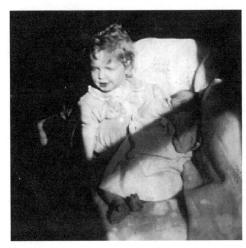

1945: With lil brother

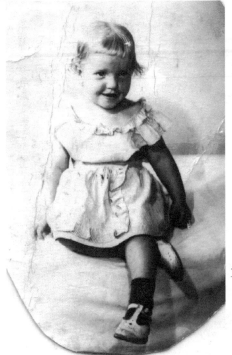

1949: Aged about 5 1/2

1946: "What happened?"

1946: With sister and lil brother

1949: Mom

1950: On Tom (I'm at the front)

1955: With lil brother

1957: At age 13

*1951: With big brother
and lil brother*

1965: With Jack

1965: In the Tetons

1966: With Baby Joseph

Part One

The Child

Spools and Strings

Yeah! They're going to school! No hitting today! The big boys went on the big yellow bus to school. I get to go when I'm bigger, mom says. The house we live in is called "the old school house." It has a loft that all the big boys sleep in. My lil brother and I sleep in the downstairs part and so does mom and dad.

I don't know why I don't get to sleep in the loft and go to school. Mom tells me to shut up about it. She says there are lots of things I don't know yet. I do get to go to school next year. My mom is the only one of the big people who never goes away. She stays home with me and my lil brother all the time.

Everyday we all go to the mailbox across the road from our house and get the mail. Mom gets so excited when there's anything in the mailbox. If she had a tail, she'd haul off and wag it.

Outside of our house there are acorn trees and maple trees. Mom makes us acorn men to play with. That's where you put acorns on sticks. One for a head and one for a body, some of them have little hats too. The maple trees have sweet stuff in them, and we put holes in the bark and a nail to hang the pails on and we get the sweet stuff out of the trees. Mom boils the maple sap, and then we store it in jars under the house — when it's boiled, mom calls it "syrup." I want that syrup cuz I like it.

We have lots of hills and trees and creeks and rocks and crabapples. We have those berries, too. I can just go outside and have them whenever they're ripe. There are red berries on the ground and black ones and blue berries and purple ones and very sour green berries. I can sit down in the middle of the red berries and pick until I'm full. The blackberries have thorns so I can't sit on them, I can stand up, pick and eat until I'm full.

The big boys slide down the hills on cardboards and they make wheel carts and they go down the road because the road has the biggest hill of all. They let me slide with them sometimes. Sometimes I don't ask them and I put me and my lil brother on a piece of cardboard and we slide down the grass hill by ourselves. We only do that once in a while because he screams in my ears and the cardboard rips and he goes one way and I go another. Mostly we go down the hills without anything under us but ourselves and get big grass stains on us. Mom hates that, and we get spanked.

We have two horses named Tom and Jerry. Mom calls Jerry a jackass. Tom comes right up to the window of the kitchen and mom feeds him with her hand. Jerry goes out in the road and we chase him around a lot and we get him back in, and mom screams at him that he's going to the glue factory if he doesn't stay in his damn pen. I don't know what a glue factory is but I bet it's bad, so I give him mean looks and chase him for mom.

Mom gave me some spools and some strings. The strings are different colors, so I tie them together and wind them around the spool. I want that. It's mine, and I can take it apart or not — whatever I want, I can do because it's mine.

Dad is out working so much that he doesn't come home lots of nights. Mom says he cuts pulp in the woods, and it's too far away. I don't miss him. Mom misses him and gets really excited when he comes home, even more than when there's mail in the mailbox. Dad looks like a giant next to mom. They both have fat bellies. I can hear mom cry at night sometimes when dad isn't home. I try to sleep with her but she won't let me.

When dad is home he does all the mean things and when he's not at home the big boys do all the mean things. The oldest of the boys just acts like he's the boss — but the next to oldest acts horrible, meaner even than dad. There are six of those big boys, and one lil brother. There's only one big girl who is gone most of the time. Mom really likes to talk to her when she comes home to visit.

The mean things that dad does are all the hitting and yelling and break-ing things. I hate it when he hits us but I really hate it when he beats up mom or throws things at her. When they get kinda calmed down he throws her in their bed and lays on her and makes her yelp and cry some, and then he goes to sleep. I like him best when he's asleep and I'm never gonna know why she ever misses him. I don't.

If it's daytime and any of those big boys or dad get mad, I grab lil brother and take off outside. If it's nighttime then I get him to help me wind and unwind my strings on the spools mom gave me. If we stay really quiet we might not get hit or nothing. We just work on the strings and spools.

When my dad goes to sleep and it's still daytime, mom gets up and makes bread — the best thing in the whole world! Bread that I can smell for a long ways outside. Bread that's brown on the outside, and white as snow on the inside. When dad isn't home and mom makes bread, we get to have some as soon as it's out of the oven. When he's home he gets the first of everything.

When dad isn't home and the big boys are acting like him, it's worse than having him home. Rusty, the oldest always makes me play house just like mom and dad do, and I hate it. I scream I hate it and he tells me that "girls have to do what boys say." I want mom to tell him to stop but she says nothing and she does nothing. I think if I were big like she is I'd slap those big boys silly. The reason I hate playing house is because of getting my legs crossed and hit and drug off to the bed and getting laid on. They're all so heavy and they take off my pants and squirm around and get me wet, and I hate it. Sometimes it's just my hands they get all sticky — that's better, though.

I get so mad that when they let me go, I just have to have fits, and if my lil brother makes me madder I drag him around by his hair until he does what I want. I just can't be happy for awhile and he just has to do what I say or stay away from me until I'm not so mad. I wish he'd do what I say and maybe I wouldn't yank on his hair.

My lil brother has a sickness and he gets stiff all over and stares at the ceiling and makes a sound like he's choking. Everyone gets scared when he does that — even dad. Mr. and Mrs. Breen showed us how to put my lil brother from a tub of hot water straight into a tub of cold water to help him get better. The Breens live a ways down the road, and they have a lot of cows. They have a car, and when my lil brother got p-monia they took him to the hospital. After he got out of the hospital he was too sick to come home so he went to some Aunt's house in a city. That Aunt lives fifty miles away and I didn't get to see my lil brother for a long long time.

I miss him when he is gone. I play with the spools and strings and sing his name, and about playing with acorns, and slide down the grass hills, and eat mom's bread. I get to sleep on his spot on the bed. I'm sorry I pulled his hair so much. I'm sorry he cries when I wipe his nose. I sing for him. I like that singing.

Magic Fat

Oh damn shit, I just don't want to walk over there. Daryl's gonna do something I won't like. He never does anything I like. He hates me and he always hurts me. Daryl is the next to the oldest boy, and since dad's been gone he gets meaner, and meaner. He does the most laying on me, too.

Again he tells me, "Get your ass over here."

If I don't go he'll get madder and then he'll hit me even more. He has to do his chores so there's more wood to get and he's already got the fire going in the potbelly. He's making that poker get red hot like he always does — now he's gonna make me go drag in the rest of the damnshit wood, I bet.

I go to him by the stove and he tells me to look up at the ceiling. I don't want to — I just don't. He slaps me on top of my head and tells me again to look up. I do it. I look up.

Hot! Horrible hotness all over me — everything is red in my eyes! I can't see anything! My neck snaps forward and then down like he's shoving my head to my belly! I think he killed me! Round and round, and blackness, hotness, redness.

I hear someone hollering my name — then I'm so cold, and I don't want to be here anymore. I want to sleep.

I wake up to my sister rubbing something on my throat. I can't see her but I can hear her. I hear her, she's crying. I don't know what's wrong but I can't wake up yet. They're mad and they hate me again. They tied my head down so I can't move it, and they tied my arms to the sides of the bed. I'm really gonna get it this time! What did I do?

I have to lay in the bed, my sister says. She's always making me be in bed. She's big like mom. My mom brings me soup. They tied my head down and I have to keep it back so far that I can't see anyone — I can only hear them. I don't feel good at all and nobody will tell me what I did wrong or why they keep me tied up.

This day is so long and it's dark out already. I want morning to come so I can go play. The sun will be out, the grass will still be wet, and the deer will be going back into the woods. I can see them in the morning.

Mom comes and the soup spoon is at my mouth — the soup goes drop by drop down my throat from the spoon and it's so hard to swallow. It seems like so many bowls of soup in one day.

Every time they wake me for the soup I can hear all that crying noise. Who is crying? Who is doing all that crying? Too many bowls of soup, and too much crying in one day.

My mom says she'll carry me outside when I feel better and I can eat my soup by myself. What? I thought she always said I was too big to carry. Hey! She must not be mad anymore.

I wake again and there's an ugly face over me. I don't know who this is but he's ugly. He pushes my hair back and rubs my forehead over and over and he makes all kinds of humming noises but he never sings a song, just lots of humming noises. He tells me to be still and be brave. He puts something on my throat and all I can feel is coolness. After he puts something on, takes it off, and puts it on again, I began to feel hotness on my throat. I scream and scream but I don't hear me, and the ugly man just keeps looking at me and humming and telling me to be quiet. He gives me something bitter to drink. He was right though when he kept saying, "Sleep is coming."

Sleep comes.

They wake me again and I'm tired of waking up. My mom brings the man something. He puts something warm on my throat. I hear him tell mom, "No scars."

The stuff for my throat smells really bad. It smells rotten. He wraps the stuff in a rag, and says, "Leave that on her."

He hums some more and my neck likes that humming.

Snow — it feels so good on my lips and my sister just rubs it back and forth so some of it goes down my throat and feels so cool and good. My sister doesn't like me. She's usually not around much. She feels kind of like a mom to me. I don't know why they're helping me, and tying me down too! Why are they so mad? What did I do? I bet they brought the ugly man to kill me! What's he putting on my throat? My big sister says it's animal fat.

Days, and days of soup and bad smelling stuff on my neck. They said they would untie me when my neck was better. I want to get up. I want to go outside. I want to go play. The ugly man tells me to think always of getting up and going outside to play — then my throat will get better. I think about outside.

I am going outside! My throat has to have that white stuff on it, a rag wrapped around it, and I have to wear Bluejay feathers or I can't play. That stuff on my throat smells so bad. If I take it off they'll haul off and hit me.

They set me outside, mom didn't carry me — one of the big boys did. My lil brother has the acorns and sticks but I can't walk around. I have to stay in one spot. I don't see the snow and mom says it has been going away for a couple of weeks now. She says I was in that sick bed a long time. While I was in the bed, the horses really did go in a truck to a glue factory, and they're never coming back.

My lil brother says, "Do you hate that stinky stuff on your neck?"

"Yes, and I hated being tied to the bed."

"Yeah, that's cuz Daryl sticked the hot poker on your neck."

Now I'm mad! Mad all over. Really mad. Damnshit assbite skunk boy! That's what he did! He stuck my neck! I remember! I told my lil brother I was really mad, and he said, "I knowed it cuz Daryl sticked the hot poker on your neck. You're gonna pull me around by my hair cuz he sticked you, and now you mad."

No! I'm gonna grow bigger and bigger, and kill him. I'll kill him. I won't have him around here anymore. I'm gonna kill that assbite big boy. My head aches, I throw up, so I go in to lay down again.

Mom says the stuff on my throat is pig fat, and it was grandpa's idea. Who's grandpa? She says he's her dad! She says I won't have any scars because of it. I asked her to tell me about this "grandpa" and she tells me to mind my own business, and shut my hell-yen mouth.

To the Shack

Dad moved us all to a shack. Mom hates the shack. It has four rooms, and two of them have cement floors and two of the rooms are just dirt that we can't dig holes in without getting slapped. Mom says dad thinks that moving us all to the shack is gonna make her move to Michigan with him. She says it ain't gonna work. Shack or not, she's staying. Good! I say.

Dad is leaving for work in Michigan. Mom begs him to not take those big boys with him. What? Don't take the six assbite boys? Mom is getting dumb, why would she want them to stay? I want mom to make all of them go to Michigan. Dad gives in and he's leaving, and the assbites boys are staying. I hear that, and run out to the woods to yell at the top of my lungs, "Dumb mom and assbite boys!" I yell till I can't yell anymore.

This new place has a cold water spring to get water for the house and lots of tall skinny trees (mom calls them poplars) and giant plants that are taller than me (mom calls them ferns). There are lots and lots of berries, and crab apples, and some giant things called gravel pits across the road from us.

A lake! There's a whole giant lake down the road just past the sheepherder's place. Mom says we can go swimming and fishing in that lake if we do our work. We can't go to the sheepherder's place though, cuz the fool's crazy and lives with sheep in his house. She says he sleeps with them. Better than sleeping with those assbite boys — I say.

We have to build an outhouse and put up clotheslines too. Some of the windows don't have glass in them either. We have to nail cardboard from boxes to the walls so it will be warmer. We can't go out the front door because there's no step, so we go out the side door. We have to clean up all the junk the other people left in the yard around the shack, and take it away. There are so many beer bottles and cans and mom says they draw flies. We have to drag them all the way down the road to this place called "the dump." Mom says everyone in the county throws all the stuff they don't want in the dump. I want to see this dump and maybe I want that stuff they don't want.

When this summer is over I get to go to school on the bus. Mom says I will get to color and read and paste. She says there'll be paper with no words or pictures — nothing will be on that paper and I will get to put on the words and pictures myself. I get a chair to sit on that's just mine and people aren't supposed to take it away from me. Well! If someone tries I'll just break it over their heads!

At the dump I can't believe my eyes. There's so much stuff that I can't even carry it all. I want to live at this dump. Mom says to bring back anything useful — I guess we'll have to come back a lot of times to get all of this. Jars, books, pictures of things I don't know about, dishes, clothes, even a chair, all sizes of everything — big and little things. I find more string than I ever saw before. I don't use the spool much now though. I stay outside all the time I can. I just play an play.

Mom won't let me go back to that dump every day. She says I have to help chop down the damn weeds all around the shack. She says that'll help keep the bugs and mosquitoes away. I ought to be glad, she says, cuz the bites are awful on me and the weeds make me sneeze my fool head off. Well, I say, I don't sneeze at the dump! But I end up chopping weeds anyway.

I like these days outside. All of the work is outside, and I don't have to be bothered by the big boys. I have to chop down the weeds and carry water to the house and collect wood. I have to do whatever else I'm told to do but I don't have to play any of the "assbite boys" games during the daytime. I like calling them assbites. I hate them, and their games because they always rub my legs raw, and get their icky stuff on me and they laugh at me when I cry, and I hate them. Mom just tells me to stay away from them. That's like staying away from the air, I say. She says she can't do anything about it. I hate that, too. Stay away from them — fat chance — there are a lot of them. She says she's the boss around here so why doesn't she boss them not to do that to me. She doesn't like anything about me. Maybe when I go to school I won't come back here.

The best thing about these days is that I work close to the house and mom and no one bothers me except at night. Three boys sleep on army beds. I can't breathe too well so lots of nights I sit up in a chair to help me breathe. My lil brother and me sleep at the foot of the big bed, and there's three of the big stinky footed big boys at the head of the bed.

Mom and I had to have a big fight because I say all girls should sleep in her room — in her bed. She says no! She says since I still wet the bed I can't sleep with her. I never know I wet the bed, so I try to stay awake, and not do that. I fall asleep, and wet the damn bed. Everybody hates it that I wet the bed. Now I have to sleep on one of the army beds, it's a good thing for me. When I wet the bed the boys hate coming near me and that's a great thing! Wet the bed I say.

On the days when I'm done with work, and I can breathe good, I run with our new dog Nicky to the lake, and find rocks (mom calls them agates) and try to catch fish, and play in the water with the dog. I still have to learn to swim so I don't drown. The lake is so big I can't see to the ends of it but I can see across it. I dig holes and make little lakes and then I build houses with rocks. I make boats out of bark like the Indians did and some sink and some don't. When I fish I use a can to try to sneak up on them and catch them in the can. Those are minnows, mom says, and too small to eat. I also put a piece of wire on some string and put a worm on that wire like I see other people who are fishing do. Sometimes I get a fish big enough for mom to cook. I have to cut off its head and clean it though, but I love that fish. Nicky goes everywhere I go. Mom thinks that Nicky is her dog — I say she's mine. These days when Nicky and me go to the lake I look for those things called "hooks" because they're attached to stronger wires and catch bigger fish.

At the lake there are all kinds of bugs and trees and squirrels and people. People that have kids I get to play with that don't hurt me so I don't hurt them. People that give me things to eat, too. Next time I go to the dump I'll get something to bring to the people, too. Sometimes I come to the lake at the wrong time and miss the people. I hate me when that happens! I haul off and slap myself in the head. The people do all that laughing and playing with kids! I want that laughing and playing and that food! Some of the people have things called inner tubes so they can float like boats in the water. They let me do that, too. Since all the fun is at the lake I work fast and hard at the shack so I can get there.

Mom says I'm getting bigger so I can do even more work. I tell her that getting bigger means more fun at the lake, and she should go with me every day. She tells me I'm crazy, and besides she can't swim. I can't swim either so mom says I can only go in the water as far as my tummy. Why in the hell can't she go in only up to her tummy? I'm gonna get bigger, and bigger, and have more fun at the lake, and if she wants to just sit in that stupid shack with those assbite boys, she can. Well, telling her that got my face slapped a lot so I'm not warning her again.

I pass that sheepherder's place every time I go to the lake. They call him Mr. N, and he's crazy but I think at least he never hurts anybody. When I start waving at him, he takes off. I don't know why he does that. I see the sheep go in and out of his house too because all of his doors are open. Our dog goes in and out of our shack and his sheep go in and out of his shack.

When I'm looking in the people's houses at the lake they tell me to go play or they ask me what I'm doing, and where I live. When I told mom about that she says to tell them nothing — absolutely nothing about our family "because it's none of their business." She says she'll beat me if I ever tell anyone our family business. When I tell them "it's none of your business," they get mad and don't talk to me.

Mom is bad at anything that's away from sitting around those rotten boys, and that damn shack. Know what? She says men are supposed to take care of women. Oh ha, I say! She swings, I duck, she misses.

I like these days at the lake and I don't like being at the shack. I like going to the dump, too. The dump has so many pretty colored clothes and I bring them home every time. Mom looks them over and keeps the ones she likes. I like the same ones so now I only let her see the ones I don't care about. She even gave some of the ones I got to those assbite boys. That did it. I don't bring her anymore big boys clothes.

I started to keep the clothes with the best colors hidden way up in the woods behind the house. I found a place back there that has the tallest of the ferns so it was easy to hide myself and there are some trees that I can climb. When I can tell that those big boys are gonna hurt me I take off, and hide there. Mom slaps me around because I'm gone or not working. I like mom slapping me better than what the boys do, so when I'm working and I see them coming — I hightail it, and hide at my place. I tied a rope between two of the trees to hang the nicest clothes on. Mom has a fit later cuz I didn't do my work — still it's better that way. I wonder if mom knows much at all. She just sits around, I can't figure why she doesn't ever go play with bigger people, like at the lake.

At the lake there's a lady named Mrs. Sawyer. She has four kids, and Mr. Sawyer. She talks to me and lets me play and eat with them. She told me where she lives and said I could come over whenever I want. I told her where I live and said she could come over anytime, too.

They came over! They're here! Yeah! Mom and Mrs. Sawyer have coffee! We play with their kids. What a day! I ask mom if she likes them and she says she likes Mr. Sawyer's cigarettes. I ask her if they can come over a lot. Mom tells me to stop bothering her and to shut the hell up.

I go to my clothes place in the woods. She's a pain in the ass, I think. I'm mad at her again. I button two of my pretty dresses together. Wait a damn minute! It works! I can button these clothes together. I can button them so they stay hangin' on the rope too. I work and work until I have a whole thing from tree to tree, from the rope to the ground of pretty colors. I put rocks along the bottom to hold them down. I make a whole house of pretty clothes I can live in.

I run back to the shack to tell mom the great news. Dumb me. Mom says nothing is great about a stupid kid tying rags to trees. She tells me I'm just gonna get rained on in my rag house.

I go outside cussin' her out. I yell back at her that I don't like her, and that I like getting rained on, and I'm gonna make a giant damn rag house and live in it, rain or not.

Indian Spring

Joe appears whenever he feels like it. He just shows up and gives me lessons on how to do things the way he says "OUR PEOPLE" did them. I never ever see any of "our people." I bet he made them up.

I don't know what he's talking about when he says "our people" and mom says he's just a damned old drunk. Mom says the town and all the neighbors think he's just crazy and she wishes he'd stop telling everyone that he's an Indian. He tells me I'm some Indian, too. Mom says she's really Jewish because she lived with the rich Jewish family in Detroit longer than anywhere else. Besides, mom also says, that no one likes Indians and I shouldn't be talking about it at all. She tells me that lots of people say the only good Indian is a dead Indian.

Everyone calls my Grandpa "Joe." Mom says he should go back to Canada or Michigan because no one will let him work here in Wisconsin. A lady named Ida owns a roadhouse and she lets him clean out the bar for one meal a day, and his booze. Mom gets mad cuz if he wouldn't have come here — if he stayed in Michigan or Canada — then no one would have to think we were any Indian at all. Mom says she could just get by being all French or just Jewish.

Well, mom is French, too, Joe says, but she's also Indian. So am I — I'm Indian a little bit and so is my lil brother. But guess what the best news is! Every one of the assbite boys are not one bit — not a little tiny bit — Indian! I'm happy to be anything they aren't. I'd be a wet sock on the clothesline for a whole winter if it meant I never had to see them again. They are not one bit of Indian because they were not born to mom. They were born to some other woman that was also stupid enough to marry my dad — that was before mom married him. One lucky thing is that me and my lil brother are mom's only kids and the only ones with Indian in us. All six of the assbite boys and my older sister are not the same as me. Their mom ran off. Smart I say!

Joe decided that since I was born in early winter when there wasn't much snow that he'd call me "Small Warm Wind." My killjoy mom howled when I told her all that. She said it just proves how dumb he is because there sure as hell is nothing warm about me. You can bet I ain't talking to her about this stuff Joe tells me again. I'd like to be the wind — I even like to climb up the poplar trees and hold on while the wind is blowing very hard. If I climb the real skinny trees I can hold on to two of them with my legs and arms wrapped around them and the wind blows me around.

Joe calls my lil brother "Blackbird" cuz he's dark like mom. But Joe can't get near him cuz mom told him to stay away from Joe, and he does it. I hate it — he gets to be dark like mom, and I have to be light like dreaded dad. Every time my lil brother says one word about how dark he is, I just go, and get his stuff out of his treasure place in the rag house and throw it as far as I can. If he swears he'll shut up about him being dark like mom and me being light like dad, then he can put all of the treasure back. That's the deal.

Joe says I have to learn some things now because it's spring time.

He tells me there are head and ear things to know, heart and belly things to feel, and hands and feet things to do and eye things to see. I have to know the difference and then do them for him just to prove I know. He says people with courage try to prove all they can. Just sayin' things means nothing to Joe. Everything I say, I have to know how to do.

Mom hates him, and won't say a word to him. When mom doesn't like a guy she just runs them off, but not Joe. She doesn't hit me for being with him, either. She just acts like it's all nothing — just nothing.

Joe takes me to the woods, and we walk all day long. We walk slow and steady and he tells me how to keep a steady sure pace. He tells me how to put my feet down with each step so I won't get as tired, and I won't make a lot of noise. It feels like I'm balancing on air but I'm on flat ground. When I come to a stop my feet have to feel planted like the roots of a tree — solid. I will practice all the time till he comes back, and then we do the next lesson.

Running, Joe says, will be just like walking, only fast on my toes. He tells me I can catch my sister "the wind" if I can run fast enough. For awhile I think he's crazy like mom says. The only sister I have isn't any one I'd like to catch, walking or running. My sister says that I'm not a lady. She's always telling me how to talk or act or something.

Climbing will be harder, Joe says because I have to watch a fly and a cat so I know what to do and if I watch both close and learn what they know then I'll be able to climb just about anything.

"Let me see if I got this straight — first I have to walk straight and quiet then I have to run fast on my toes then I have to watch some damn fly and a cat so I can climb. I get everywhere I want to go whether I'm walking or running and I climb lots of things. Well at least you can give me a good reason why I have to do this stuff, Joe."

Joe looked right in my eyes and said nothing. I hate it when he does that! I'm gonna get mad here in a minute. I want to know how come I have to do all this — why do I anyway? I'm tired and I'm mad and I think Joe should give me an answer.

Joe just made his sign that means "see ya later" and walked away. I feel like throwing a rock and bouncing it off the back of his head. He turns around real quick — I freeze — does he know what I'm thinking too?

I bet that old man is just making me do all this hard dumb stuff because my lil brother won't come and do this with him. I bet mom doesn't say anything cause she knows how much he's gonna make me do and she thinks hard work is good for me. Well, I wish she thought hard work was good for her too. Some hard work would wear all that fat off of her.

Joe's eyes drive me nuts. I feel like I have to do this Indian stuff! I guess I owe him since he fixed my throat.

I'm supposed to feel that I'm a part of the wind and the trees and the water and the animals and the earth and the sun and the moon and everything that's alive. Joe tells me that but he never tells me how I can do it. Why does it have to be hard? Joe says it's very important, so I guess important means it's gonna be hard.

A few days later Joe came back. He came so early in the morning that the sun was barely out. I got dressed and went outside with him and we started to walk again. He made the sign to go ahead of him and I knew I was supposed to show him how good I could walk — run — and then he'd want me to begin to climb like a fly or a cat.

Well, I'm ready for you, old man, I'm ready because I been practicing! As I walk ahead of him I step on a twig and you could hear it crack — shit shit, shit! I just keep walking. I put my feet down lightly and quietly and shift my body and soon I feel like I am and am not on the ground, at the same time. I'm doing it and I know it — I really am doing it and I can feel Joe, happy, behind me. I bet no one back at the shack could do this kind of walking and I'm not gonna tell anyone about it either. Joe says if I keep doing this walk I will be able to get within touching distance of birds and animals. He calls birds and animals my "brothers and sisters" — I just don't know why he says that. They're sure better than the brothers and sister I have now, so okay Joe, I say.

Running was the same as walking, only fast on my toes. I did it and he nodded an okay. I felt like the wind or a deer — I asked Joe if he could call me "wind deer" and he just shook his head no. Piss on it, I'll call myself that name and he just won't know it. He was staring at me again — I hate that, I bet he knows what I'm thinking. I'll just keep thinking it and see for once if he does know. He isn't saying anything but I still think he knows what I'm thinking sometimes. He'll be back and he says.

Joe shows me how to pick and how to dry wintergreen berries and leaves and dandelions and the leaves of all the berries and how to keep them safe from bugs and birds. He shows me the roots at the lake and says the cattails are for cuts, with a big leaf wrapped around it. Mud is for bee stings and cuts, too.

He shows me how to make fire and smoke from animal droppings — dried cow pies! I quit — a fire of shit — I mean it this time I quit. He's nuts! A shitfire with bugs to eat!

He tells me he won't be back again until many days later. I ask if I'm supposed to do all this while he's gone. He tells me yes.

I'm supposed to gather as many things to dry and store for the winter as I can and I found just the thing. Dried toads. I bet that old Indian didn't know I was smart enough to think of this. On this blacktop road there are so many flattened dried out toads that I can't even count them all. All I have to do is stack them up at my rag house and Joe will be really surprised. These toads tried to walk on the road and they're so slow that the cars ran right over them. Their lil legs are stretched out and perfectly flat — they look fried to me. Best part is I don't have to go kill anything.

I guess eight stacks of flat, fried looking toads will really show Joe that I can do this collecting thing.

Indian Winter

Joe stands looking at the big boys as if he were seeing "wasted meat" and to him anything wasted isn't good. Here we are in the cold and snow and ice, again with no food gathered and no way to get food now. I like it that Joe thinks they're a waste. He lets all of those good-for-nothin' boys know that he's disgusted with everything just with that look he gives them. Why doesn't he give them a trouncing or sock 'em cross the nose. Why doesn't he tie them all together and throw them in the lake like they do with the puppies and kittens around here. Well?

Joe doesn't much like my dad because he says my dad is weak. I don't think he's weak. My dad beats up everybody. Joe says that doesn't mean he's strong. A strong man takes good care of his people and doesn't brag about himself.

Joe is gonna drag me out and make me show him what I saved for winter. He says it's fine that I'm not gonna share anything I've saved with the assbite boys. Joe says family is an important thing! I figure that's because he doesn't live here. He thinks families should do all kinds of things together and help each other. He didn't like it when I told him the only thing I wanted to help those big boys do was die. Joe also gets cockeyed strange when I try to tell him what those boys do to me. He makes me shut right up and acts like he's gonna drop a litter on the spot. Since I told him about those boys he also never hums and rubs my chest anymore.

I watch mom nod at him and then she turns to me and motions me to get ready. Double damn, get ready to go out and freeze my ass off I bet. One thing good though, I do have some stash. Joe is good after everything is learned but he doesn't seem so good during all that learning stuff. What can we do out in the snow? I better not find out that Indians stay outside all winter. That'll be the end of this learning stuff. I'll quit and hide out for a long time. I mean it — the window is broken in the bedroom now and I wake up with snow on my hair sometimes and I'm not living outside all winter just so I can be Indian.

Joe never comes in our shack. I have to go outside and we start walking toward my rag house. I knew it! He does want to see what I stashed away this time.

We sat down in my rag house and Joe said that I have one big lesson for the winter and that's to feed deer out of my hand. I ask him how I'm supposed to do that. He tells me that's the lesson and I have to learn it. I ask him again, how do I do that — same answer comes out of his mouth. "That's the lesson."

"Piss on it," I say, "I'll figure it out myself."

Joe smiled at me — I like that smiling. If I can't figure out how to feed the deer, though, it will be his fault because he won't tell me how.

We're going to sleep outside! Snow up to my ass and he says we're going to sleep outside! I laugh cuz it must be a joke. It isn't a joke. He tells me that we can sleep outside and not freeze and not die. I figure my dad was right — it's a mistake to be born a girl. Prick-packers just get to do whatever they want to girls.

I'm not doing it and tell him. He tells me he'll be sleeping right beside me. Oh, now I get it! I ask him if he's gonna do that jumping up and down on me. He jerks his head back really hard and says no. He says he's gonna sleep beside me so he can make sure I don't freeze and I don't die. I don't believe him but if Joe doesn't keep his word I won't ever speak to him again.

First, though, he wants to see that I can build a fire. I ask him for matches. I should have known — we have to learn to build a fire with no matches. I say good luck. Joe takes a stick and shows me how dead it is. Then he crumbles it all up in a lil pile. He takes two lil rocks out and hits them against each other right by the pile he made. He makes some sparks in the pile and blows on them a bit and he makes a fire. We stoke it up lil by lil. Now I have to get a stick and practice a fire. I do it and I do it right. Sitting in my rag house with two fires. That crazy Indian takes lil pieces of things around my rag house (even cloth) and burns them in the fire. "Hey! What are you doing, Joe?"

"Showing you that many things burn."

Courage? Joe is telling me more about courage. He says my spirit guides will always be watching for my courage. I ask him over and over what that courage stuff is. He tells me that it's what I used when Daryl put the poker on my neck. I say I was sick when that happened and he says, "Yes, but you had the courage to fight to get well."

I tell him I don't know what made me get well. He asks me if I wanted to get well and go out and play. I try not to show him my eyes cuz he'll know that I think that's a dumb question. I just say yes I wanted to get well. He wants to know if I remember how hard it was and how I had to just use me and what's inside of me. That's courage.

I give Joe the rundown of all the stash I have. I have all the dried berries that the birds didn't eat or that didn't rot. I didn't have to catch and kill anything because the spirit gave me all those toads. But I don't mention them yet. What a surprise that'll be! I showed him the dried grasses and he told me which ones were for eating. The tall grass is for sitting and sleeping on. Cattails and acorns. I showed him the holes inside my rag house with apples in one and roots in another. Then I showed him the caches outside my house with dried cow pies and piles of wood.

We go back in and sit down by our fires.

"What's that smell? What has died here?" Joe stands and sniffs around.

Time for the surprise! I jump up and pull off the covers to my surprise of dried toads! I think he's too surprised to say anything. He's silent for awhile, staring at the stacks of toads. I tell him I'm storing them for food.

"These are not frogs," Joe says.

I say, "No, they aren't so you have to guess what they are."

Moving closer to them, he says again, "These are not frogs."

I can't wait for him to guess. I hop around in a dance while I tell him how I got all of these toads without killing anything. He looks at me like I'm stupid or something. I tell him how many stacks I stored and he just starts shaking his head. He says no one can eat those toads, eating toads is bad for you. My lil brother was right. I put the cover back over them. Joe takes the cover off again. Joe moved even closer — I see his shoulders shake and I wonder if toads have spirits that Joe cries for. He lifts up his head howling and laughing! I have never heard him laugh before.

"The sun and the road have left you only toad hides. Maybe you'll wear a toad hide dress in the spring!"

"A toad hide dress?"

We howled and laughed some more. A toad dress! Toad leggings! Toad bed! I stopped laughing — what are they good for? Joe put his hand on my face and no hitting. "They have served their purpose. They were your work, now they're our laughter." I hugged Joe — I told that old Indian I liked him and he put his hands to his chest and then moved them toward me. He's saying "I like you," I think. We have to throw them out he says. He lifts up the rag wall by my stacked up worthless toads. Putting a rag around his hand he just shoves them, stack by stack, outside. We walk out where the toads are and he picked one up with his raggy hand and sails it toward the sky. The damn thing spins and flies just great. I try it! Great! Those toads fly and spin just right. After sailing a few, Joe signals us back in the rag house.

Now we look at all the dried berries and leaves and roots I stored. He shows me how to use the cans I saved to heat snow and make tea of the berry leaves, and he shows me how to mix the roots and berries and dandelion leaves for soup. We mix the soup stuff while we drink our tea. The water for the soup has melted and we put in the mixture and I throw in the rocks like I do for my brother's soup. Joe practically jumped in the soup after those rocks. "What are you doing?"

I tell him how I keep my lil brother from bitching about "no potatoes" by throwing rocks in the soup I made. He shakes his head and leaves the rocks in the soup. He didn't try to eat them either.

He shows me how to pack up some food and we head outside. It's really dark now and we walk towards the woods. I feel like throwing a fit and I don't know why I'm not throwing it. I'm scared and it's so cold and I just don't want to sleep with Joe. I don't want to freeze my ass off either.

In the woods Joe starts digging in the snow. He makes a big deep place. Then I make one for me right beside his with snow between them. I feel better that we'll have snow between us. I'd rather freeze to death alone then get laid on. Joe pulls a lot of pine bows and needles down and puts them all around where he says his feet are gonna be. I have to do the same. We put as many pine bows and needles on the bottom of the beds as we can. Then he tells me to build a fire.

After I get the fire going and put snow on to melt, Joe shows me a north star. I stare at the sky a lot but he doesn't think I know where that north star is. He draws the Big Dipper in the snow by the fire and shows me again. After he thinks I know where the North Star is, he asks me if I remember the Indian name he gave to me. I say yes. He tells me that when I die, my name is never to be repeated again. I ask him, "Okay, freeze-my-ass-off Joe, does that mean if you freeze to death in the goddamn snow that I can never say the name 'Joe' again?"

He make the sign that means "this is true." Then Joe tells his Indian name to me and I think that's a good name for Joe.

He shows me how to put pine bows to shield our heads from the north wind by sticking them in the snow around the top of the snow bed. After we get the branches put up we pile snow around them.

We have more tea and more soup. Joe tells me about how spirits and animals and people should live together. I know what he's saying about all of it but the spirits. He tells me to think of spirits like I think of wind and then think of a kind of wind that can also think better than people. Only the wind spirit can think more and see more and know more than everyone. I can think about that.

It's time to get in the snow beds and freeze our asses off. I don't care if I die sometimes. I won't have to live with those rotten boys, at least.

Joe shows me how to put pine bows and layers of my clothes on top of me in the bed. Then we pile on snow and make a tunnel a little bigger than me — lots of snow — snow all the way up to my neck. How am I supposed to stay warm with snow all the hell over me? Joe helps me get all snowed up and shows me how to put one of my shirts over my face but I tell him I can't breathe and I cry. He tells me to stop crying and he puts two sticks in to hold the shirt over my head but away from my face. I ask him how I can get out to help him with his bed. Joe tells me I can't get out of this bed before morning. I ask him what do I do if I have to pee. He never answered me.

I lay still and think of the wind spirits, then of everyone having a spirit like that. I'm feeling good in this snow bed now. It isn't so cold. I can feel sleepy. But I don't believe everyone has one of those spirits — not those skunk boys. Maybe Joe doesn't know about people with no wind spirit.

Later I wake up in the dark screaming for Joe. He said, "I am beside you — I won't leave."

I can't go back to sleep. I'm so cold now cuz I kicked a lot and messed up the snow bed. I wait a long time but I just get colder. I call to see if Joe is still there. He is — I tell him I'm freezing. Joe tells me to get out of the bed. I do it and tell him I have to pee. He says do it. I finish and he tells me to come to the edge of his bed. I do cuz I'm just too cold. Joe digs out his arm and then digs out a place for me to crawl in beside him. I do it and my heart is pounding so hard and I'm feeling really hot. I might throw up. Joe puts my head down on his chest and pulls more snow on top of us with a branch. I listen to Joe's heart in his chest.

It's light and Joe is out of the snow bed and beside the fire. He tells me to get up and makes me tea in one of my cans and puts on soup in the other can. The fire he made is much bigger than yesterday. Joe tells me to take off all the layers of clothes and he shows me how to hang them on branches by the fire then we stood and turned and turned to dry all the clothes we were wearing. It worked — it all worked!

I don't know why Joe didn't do any of that jumping up and down on me. Maybe he doesn't like me or maybe he's afraid of women. Better yet — maybe he's really the wind spirit.

When we get to the shack Joe just has to remind me of the deer lesson. Then he leaves. Mom starts telling me to do my chores and be quick about it. I get the wood and some water and then I help mom wring out the clothes and take them to the clothesline to hang up. I can't hang them cuz I'm too short. Lucky me — I'm short.

Joe told me my task was to get the deer to eat out of my hand. All damn winter I tried to feed them grass from under the snow and tree bark and not once did they even try to eat out of my hand. That damn Indian would come around and ask me if I did it yet. Sometimes he'd just watch me try. I got sick of it and mad at the deer for not being friendly and I told Joe that I quit. He asked me what I had done to try and feed the deer. I told him about the grasses and the tree bark. He said, "Why would they take from your hands what they can reach for themselves?"

I'm gonna be a deer. No one knows but I am gonna have a baby fawn when I grow up. I have to so I can be a good mom. Deer are the best to their babies, of all the animals, I've ever seen. They teach them and never hurt them, and the dads and boys never even come around. Joe says family is most important and he says you can grow up and just choose anyone for your family. I'm having my very own family of fawns. I have to get a family and live in my rag house and never be a bad mom with assbite boys. I made that promise to the spirit guides.

Later I went and took some horse feed from a neighbor. A lot of days of trying. A lot of days of crying and cussing. More trying and a couple of deer did it! I had made little trails of feed shorter. They finally took the feed from my hand. I kept feeding them so I could show Joe. He said he was pleased I had finished my task. He asked me how I was gonna repay the feed? I said, "Work, I guess."

I tell 'em, he's mean — it was his idea. He should repay the goddamn horse feed.

Shopping

My lil brother and I leave the shack as soon as the grass is dry from the night. We're always happy when we get to go to the dump. Mom always says that's where the rich people throw away perfectly good things. She says they have so much that they don't have to care about anything, so if they get tired of stuff they just throw it away and get new stuff.

When we go to the dump mom says we're shopping. I want all the colors of the clothes there. I can't wear most of the stuff but I can use it for my rag house. My rag house gets bigger and bigger.

I sit down at this dump and I find this shoe box of pictures of other people. There's one picture — a big picture. This picture has a boy dressed up in a suit like he's gonna go to church. He's as big as the big boys. In front of him is a lil girl dressed up like she's gonna go to church too. The boy in the picture has one of his arms around the lil girl and is holding her hand. I want this picture. They look like they like each other. Maybe there are some big boys who don't hate lil girls.

Once we found an old stove. It was green and white and the oven door wouldn't close. I messed around on it and found out that I could make what sounded to me like a lot of horses! I wanted that green stove to be back at my rag house. My lil brother said he wasn't gonna help me drag that damn thing all the way home. I asked him what he wanted to make him do the job and he said nothing could make him do it. He was wrong — a few smacks from me and we were figuring ways to tie it up to drag it home.

It took us three days to get that stove back to my rag house. One of the assbite boys showed us how to put little logs under it to make it roll. I never can figure those boys out — just when I'm sure they're gonna die of rotten insides they do a thing that's smart and good. Maybe they do that to confuse me like a dark string on a hook confuses fish and they bite it and get their dumb selves caught. Anyway, I never do figure it out for sure.

While we were rolling the stove along the trail to my rag house I see mom walking down the trail from my rag house in a pretty pink and white checked dress. I holler, "Hey! Dumb mom! That's my door!"

She's walking around in my door! She found my rag house. I got that pretty pink dress for my rag house a while back and she's wearing it! "Hey mom, gimme that, that's my door to my rag house, so just get it off!"

She tells me to "shut the hell up" or she'll wear the whole rag house. She would do that because she says she's the boss around here.

My lil brother and I love my rag house. We make different rooms in it by putting up a cross branch and making a wall with the clothes and holding them down tight with rocks. Outside of the rag house is the pig and chicken farm. We make fences of sticks and we put out old rusted pails for the water. Every day we pull up grass and weeds to feed them.

Inside the house I made furniture out of stuff from the dump. I even stuffed some big clothes to be people we liked to live in our house. One of the stuffed people was a long gray coat with red buttons. That gray coat person was the wife like Mrs. Sawyer. She's happy and does lots of things. I do the waltz with her sometimes. One of the other people was a shirt and some dress-up pants and he was a farm hand. He helps everybody with all the hard work. He never hits anyone or makes them take off their clothes. My brother and I made a deal to never make a dad or any assbite boys. Because of what Joe taught me food in the rag house was good. We had only a little fighting in that rag house.

Pigs and Chickens

The pail is just too heavy and it's dark outside and it gets me all wet. That's why they call it a slop pail because everyone throws slop in it all day and uses it for the outhouse at night. If the damn thing wasn't so big I'd throw it so far they would never find it. I told mom when I grow up I'm not having a stinking damn slop pail. Mom just starts screaming and swinging whenever I tell her what I'm gonna or not gonna do when I get bigger. She tells me I don't know what I'm talking about. I do too. I do know lots of stuff. When my lil brother and I go to the dump I see all kinds of different things. There are pictures of things I have never seen anywhere at all. What about the cars that go by our shack? What about those big trucks? What about the clothes I find at the dump? Mom yells at me that when I live in some fancy house then I can say what I'm gonna and not gonna do. I just tell her again what I already said, and I ain't in no fancy house either. I live in my rag house. She slaps me and throws me around. I don't care — I hate her and all the people in that shack and I still hate that stinking slop pail.

Tomorrow when I get up I'm gonna go right out to my rag house. I like it back in the woods where no one shows up except my lil brother. I can add onto my house and make it bigger and prettier. Lots of times we find stuff for mom, too. We drag it home and some things she likes and takes and the rest I put in my rag house. I don't show anybody the stuff I really like cuz they would take it away from me. It makes me so mad when they do that so I wait and wait for my chance and I just take whatever it is right up to my house.

In my rag house I also made a place for the horses. I made horses out of sticks. I smoothed out the knots on those sticks cuz they tore my legs up. My lil brother is such a pain in the ass — worse than the knots were on the stick horses sometimes — because whenever I make him help me round up the pigs and chickens he says he can't see them. He's blind till I smack him some then he says he can see them.

Suddenly I see Daryl coming and I run, run for my life. The assbite is coming! Off towards the woods — go legs! Where did the fool come from anyway. I always keep a look out for that skunk but I missed him this time.

I try going up a tree but I'm too damn small and too slow. He has me by the tail of my new long coat. I just got this coat from the dump and it has great lil orange and black checks on it. "It's my fawn skin," I yell at him, "Let go and don't rip my coat." He tells me that if I get my ass down out of the tree, he won't rip it. I come down. "I hate you, you skunk, and when I get big enough I'm gonna kill ya."

He tells me, "No goddamn woman ever gets big enough to hurt a man."

He starts to yank my clothes off me and two of the other big boys come through the trees. There are three of the boys that usually do this shit and they need to be dead.

"Hey, you guys want some?" he bellows.

They just stand there and I think they might say no. Arnie shakes his head no and walks away but Fred heads toward us.

"Arnie's such a wimp," Daryl yells out.

They push me to the ground. One holds my legs crossed real tight and the other one puts his ugly dumb thing between my legs and jumps and wiggles around a lot. I scream and scream for him to kill me! I hit and bite but I don't win. He makes some snorting noises and stops. Then Fred does the same thing but without the noises. I start to cry cuz they got that sticky jazz all over my new coat. I hate them and when I get big I'm gonna kill them

I rip the inside out of the coat to get rid of that sticky stuff, but I rip too hard and tear the coat up. I get so mad I just leave the coat right there.

I head for the gravel pit across the road from our shack. The road workers come out all the time and dig out gravel and leave these high ridges. I stand on the top of the pit and sing and sing at the top of my lungs. Mrs. Sawyer says the people who sing on the radio get a lot of money for it, plus they get to make records for the radio. I like the sound of my singing in that gravel pit but I don't get any money or make any records. Mrs. Sawyer says maybe I will one day.

She lets me sing at her house all the time. Everyone at my house says I sound like a dying cow. Since they're skunks I don't think they know anything — especially not more than Mrs. Sawyer. Anyway, singing makes me feel good. I even make up my own songs. My mom says it's okay if I sing there because it's far enough away from the shack so she can't hear it.

Glad's and Food

Mom is sitting in the middle of the gladiolus garden yelling to me that one of the glads is purple! I yell that you can't eat a purple glad. Mom yells for me to shut my smart mouth.

I love summer. Everything grows and I get to walk out there and eat it, just like Joe showed me. Wintergreen berries, strawberries, the tender green buds on the tree, the grasses if I pull them up right - they have tender parts at the base, the roots to the tall plants along the lake, and the tops of clover. If I want milk I can go to the neighbor's cow cuz I learned how to milk. It's too cold in the winter to walk that far but not in the summer.

I can go to the Sawyers and help with the canning and picking and planting, best of all the eating. Mrs. Sawyer said I could call her mom, so I do. She shows me how to do things that she knows. Like how to put my clothes back together when they rip. She knows just about everything.

"How long can you stay today?"

She always asks me that. I always say I don't know cuz I don't know what she means really. I stay as long as she acts like it's okay, unless I've been told I'll get whipped if I'm not back at dark.

I wanted to plant a garden at my own house but mom won't do it, and she won't make those lazy boys do it. Mrs. Sawyer gave me some seeds and I planted them like she said, but my mom pulled them up and planted her damn gladiolus's. Mom does that every time spring comes but she won't plant food and I hate that. I threw a fit and she slapped me around and screamed at me and I lost and so I don't have my own garden at my own house. Mom said if I give her any more trouble that I can't go down to Sawyers anymore. She wins! I told Mrs. Sawyer all about it and she said I should never yell at mom. But she doesn't know mom. Now Mrs. Sawyer lets me plant my own garden beside her big corn garden. She gave me peas, corn, tomatoes and beans. She told me to get a lot of jars from the dump to can them in the fall. I hated carrying the jars all the way from the dump in the gunny sack to the bottom of our road and then the next day I drag them to Sawyers. The Sawyers send me home with food sometimes and mom always tells me to thank them. I get up with the sun and I do all of the chores mom tells me to do and then I go to the Sawyers. I help water the garden and help pick the berries. Mrs. Sawyer makes jam and jelly out of all the berries. I tell mom about it and she tells me to just shut up — she doesn't want to hear one more thing about Mrs. Sawyer.

I try one more thing. I go and pick a lot of strawberries and I bring them to mom with some jars. I tell her there are strawberries, raspberries, blueberries, juneberries, gooseberries, and blackberries, and I get slapped around and thrown outside and she doesn't let me go to the Sawyers for a long time. Instead I go to the lake to fish and swim. I ask my dog Nicky (who really belongs to mom) just what the hell I did all of that for? The dog never answers. I feel like beating up mom but Mrs. Sawyer says I shouldn't even yell at her.

Mom always waters the gladiolus flowers — she even carries the water for them from the spring herself. She watches them every day and she digs up the ground around them and pulls the weeds. That's what you do for food plants too. I tell her. Mom likes jam and other foods and she's always bitching that my dad doesn't care enough to keep us in food. Dad isn't good. I wish he'd stay gone forever. The boys could do a lot if mom would just make them get at it. I think she's afraid of them too. She just likes the dog and her flowers. She even talks to them. I know she likes coffee and cigarettes too, but she can't grow those. Any men who come around always bring her that stuff and canned store food. I heard the constable tell mom and my oldest brother that we couldn't have any money because our dad was still alive. Shoot him, I say.

School

The giant yellow bus is coming and this time I get to get on it. I'm going to school! I had to wait till I was seven to start first grade because my birthday is after September. Now I'm seven. Now I get my own desk and books that even I can read. I will get lunch every day and also play on the swings with a bunch of kids my own size.

Mom is telling us to get down the driveway so we don't miss the bus. My lil brother is yelling his head off because he can't go too. Mom says he can go down and wait with us till the bus comes.

At the bus stop the boys do their usual rotten stuff like spitting and hitting and my lil brother asks me if I'll bring him some school stuff. I tell him I will. The bus pulls up! I love this bus!

My lil brother starts crying and hollering so hard all you can see is his wide open mouth. I grab him and throw him up the bus steps with me. They can have one more damn kid at school.

Then Daryl grabs me and I get slapped into a seat on the bus and my lil brother gets slapped right off the bus. I watch him crying and running towards the house as the bus pulls away. I feel awful when anyone does anything to him except me.

This bus is something big! There are two or three of us in most seats but some seats only have one kid in them. One of the assbite big boys is sitting between me and fun. I won't stay in this seat with him. I jump over the iron bar on the back of the seat and right in with a kid more my size. The bus driver stops the bus and comes back and yells at me not to get up or jump the seats — he says I will have to get off the bus if I don't sit still. Okay, I'll sit still if I don't have to sit with any damn boys. Everyone laughs. Everyone except the big boys. The one in front of me turns around and says, "You just wait till we get home."

The bus driver says I have to sit by myself right up behind his seat. I followed him up to the seat and he started moving the bus again. I don't know why I want to just wail and have a fit. I can't because I'll never get to school.

I can see everything from this seat. The bus seems to be going fast —
not as fast as riding in a tire down a big hill but almost that fast.

We pull up in front of the school. The bus driver opens the door and
everyone gets out before me. He tells me to get out and be a good girl. I just
don't know what to say to that. What is being a good girl? I just tell him to "be
a good man."

I walk into the school and the brother who is supposed to show me
where to go points to the room right at the bottom of the stairs. I'm afraid to
go in all of a sudden. He just grabs my arm and throws me into the room. I run
into another kid and we both fall down. The kid starts yelling really loudly so
I jump up and try to help her up. She won't let me. The teacher comes up to
help her, so I just stand there. The teacher looks upset — she tells me that
there's no running in the school.

Everyone is waiting for the teacher to tell them which desk is theirs.
As she tells each of us to sit down, she's also telling us which grade we're in.
There are three other kids in this first grade with me - one girl named Edith
and two boys named Johnny and Mike.

Edith has yellow hair, so does Mike. Johnny is kinda pudgy and has
dark hair. Johnny is going to sit right next to me. Edith gave me this smartass
look. I think she isn't gonna like me.

The teacher, Mrs. Yanich, is telling everyone that if they want to talk
to her they have to raise their hand and wait for her to call on them. She says
when the bell rings we get a recess to go to the lavatory and play outside. I
ask, "What's a lavatory?"

Everyone laughs. I don't get an answer.

Mrs. Yanich picks an older kid to give books and paper to everyone.
Another kid gets to give out pencils and crayons. We're not to touch these
things till the teacher says to. I want to get on with the playing outside.

As the teacher stands by her desk in the front of the room she tells us
a lot of "rules." We have to sharpen the pencil she gave us. One of the older
kids shows me how to make a point on my pencil at the sharpener on the wall.

The first thing the first grade gets to do is color all the #1's on a paper
— red. They look like three flowers to me. Then we color all the #2's — green.
They're flowers!

The second thing we get to do is make an "A" on a paper with lines on
it. "A" goes on the big lines and "a" only goes on half of the line. The teacher
is reading with some of the big kids while we do all the "A's."

The bell rings — what a pretty sounding bell! I jump up and run for
the door. The teacher calls me back. The rule is that we stand at our desks and
leave the room by grades — 1, 2, 3, and 4. Out the front door we go. I head
right for the swings. I sit down on it and it goes back and forth a little, then it

just stops. I get off and run at it and sit down again and it goes back and forth a little — then it stops. Johnny is on a swing going really hard back and forth — he's high and swinging. I ask him, "What the hell is wrong with the damn swing I'm on?"

Johnny jumps out of his swing and lands on his feet. I grab his swing and get on it — it goes back and forth a little and stops. I stand up.

Johnny says, "You have to pump it up."

Geez, I don't know how you "pump" it up. Johnny tells me to sit on the swing and he begins pushing me from behind and telling me to put my feet back under the swing and then swing my feet forward and that's "pumping." I hear the bell ring but I just learned this and I want to stay outside and swing. Johnny runs for the school yelling back at me that I'm going to get in trouble if I don't come in. So I jump from the swing like Johnny did. Straight out of the swing and flat on my ass. Ripped my pants and tore my skin. I walk back to the school crying and cussing.

When I get in the room the teacher is right at the door telling me I'm to come in as soon as the bell rings. I say okay and start to walk to my desk. Mrs. Yanich calls me back to the door.

"Aw shit," I say, "my ass is broken."

Mrs. Yanich tells me not to cuss one more time or I'll have to go to the principal's office. Then she checks my broken rear.

"Your poor dear, how did this happen?"

"I jumped out of the swing."

She tells one of the older kids to watch the class and takes me to the room up the stairs where the first aid cabinet is. She gets some stuff out of the cabinet and tells me that she's going to clean me off and put on some medicine. I just stand there. I chuckle at her washing off my broken ass. Mom is gonna scream a lot cause I ripped these pants. Mrs. Yanich tells me she's going to put on some medicine now, and that it will hurt a little but I must hold still. I do it.

I yell, "Jesus Christ that stings — Holy shit — oh damn."

That teacher slaps my mouth. "Young lady, you're never to cuss in my school again or I'll send you back home to stay. Do you understand me?"

"Okay, I won't!"

"Now let's go to the lavatory and wash those hands of yours and that face."

The lavatory is a room that has sinks with water that comes out of some silver pipes, and toilets that you push a handle on and everything goes somewhere else. The toilets get used like the outhouse at home. They have stuff called toilet paper that you wash your rear on when you're finished. The teacher tells me that since I don't have that at home "I will stink if I don't learn to wipe good." I tell her we don't have that paper at home but sometimes we have old catalogs and books from the dump that we use.

Back in the classroom I sit at my desk. Now we get to write on some more papers. I love these crayons and they're mine with no big boys to take them away from me. The pencil drives me crazy because it tears up my paper. Johnny says not to push so hard. My pencil breaks. What happens when you break your pencil — do they send you home? No! You get to go sharpen it. I love that pencil cause it makes a new lead every time.

I get in trouble because I talk to Johnny, and because I like to walk around the room. The teacher tells me to be still. I can't do that very well - I don't like sitting still at all.

The wonderful bell rings and now we're gonna go eat. But first we have to go wash in the lavatory. I wash really fast and go push the handle on the toilet to watch it a while.

We walk down the stairs to where the lunch is. We get our lunch stuff on trays and then we all sit at a table. While we're eating the teacher keeps looking at me and telling me not to use my fingers. Edith says, "More like using her whole hand. She has no manners." I take a swat at her but the teacher stops me. I don't like the way Edith's voice sounds.

I like this food. I see the older kids come in and get their trays. I don't have to eat with those assbite boys. I can hardly believe my luck.

We put our trays away and finally we get to go outside. I head right for the swings. I pump and pump and I'm going faster and higher. Yelling as hard as I can feels so good it makes me laugh really hard. Pumping and yelling and laughing. I think of a toad hide dress and laugh even harder. Johnny stands up on his swing. I stand up. I stand the hell up on nothing and then I'm on the ground trying to figure it out. I only got scraped a little. Johnny stops his swing and tells me he'll show me how to stand up right.

The bell rings and we go back into the room. I don't want to do all of this sitting. My ass goes to sleep and makes me feel weird. I want to get up and run as fast as a deer. I want to swing. I love the crayons and that pencil but not all this sitting.

Lunch

The bell rang and it's lunch time. I'm gonna be the first to get my hands washed and get right at that lunch. Washing our hands is dumb enough because we aren't even dirty but then the teacher runs around the tables and taps us on the head if we touch our food. I never get to know why we have to wash our hands if we can't touch anything. The teacher says that it's just good manners. She says I better learn them manners before I get too old.

This lunch is a lot better since I learned the lunch rules. Just awhile back the teacher would've liked to strangle me at every lunch time.

At our shack whoever finishes first takes what they want off of anybody else's plate. I eat with my arms around the plate so no assbite boys can take anything. I eat with my hands so I can hurry up — at the shack that's fine but at the school lunch that's not fine. I get tired of trying to figure out these "manners."

I'm next to the smallest and I'd like not to get hit so I never take anything off of anyone's plate but my lil brother's, and I mostly don't do that because he screams and gets me hit a lot. Besides mom says that he's sickly and will die if he doesn't eat his own food. I'd like it if he doesn't die.

At school, though, I'm not the only small one and I get done with my food fast. So around those tables I go — I get what I can carry and high tail it out to the swings. I swing and eat and swing and eat — I like lunch time and I like to swing.

Then out of the school comes the dreaded teacher, principal, and some kids. I don't want to talk about the "manners" and the "right things to do," so I swing as fast as I can because they can't get me then. They stand around yelling at me and telling me to come down. I finally get kinda sick — I think from eating too fast and swinging — so I jump from the swing and run for the woods around the school. If they catch me then I have to listen to a lot of words and sit in the principal's office until it's time to go to my hated desk. If they don't catch me I get to play. Of course I have to do all that listening and sitting later anyway.

Sharing

It's bitter cold and the bus is winding up the driveway to the school. Christmas vacation is over. My mother had all but cheered when the bus picked us up. All the way from the house to the bus the seven of us did cheer. Mom couldn't have been happier than we were. I loved learning about Christmas from my teacher. I had not loved the Christmas vacation. I knew there was another one of those holidays coming so we could give each other gifts again and I just wanted to get back to school and get going on them. Mom wasn't into Christmas or any holidays — she calls it begging. I call it fun.

As we all fly off the bus and run into the school I make the right turn into my classroom. Kind of skidding up to the teacher's desk — hollering at the top of my lungs, "When do we start the valentines?"

The teacher is about to tell me to sit at my hated desk when Edith walks up next to me. She's wobbling her dumb head back and forth like she's trying to shake the fleas out of it. I still think there's something live running around between her ears but my teacher assures me firmly that isn't true and I shouldn't mention it again. I wish Edith would go home forever. She thinks she knows all about everything. She's always telling me what's what. I teach her something she doesn't know, like how to fight. She doesn't like the lesson and I spend recess at my hated desk. Edith isn't worth teaching.

"Teacher, I got a pretty new sweater for Christmas — see!" Edith chirped.

"That's lovely, dear," the teacher said, escorting Edith to her desk. "We're all going to share our Christmases." Edith is gonna share her sweater with me too! I'm worried because the teacher never heard Edith swear she wouldn't ever let me touch anything of hers because I always came to school dirty! I sit down at my hated desk — Edith isn't gonna like this! She'll probably flip her head back and forth so hard it will fall right off. The bell is ringing.

"That's it!" I squealed. "Time for the sharing and the playing!"

The teacher said for that impolite outburst we'd all sit for five minutes in silence. Oh! I could just kill myself. I sit wishing Edith had done that instead of me.

"Now, children," the teacher says, "come up and make a circle on the floor and we'll share what our Christmas was like."

Making sure I don't sit by Edith I find a place in the circle. The sharing begins. When I was making sure I didn't sit next to Edith I ended up next to the teacher. Now I really have to watch it or I'll be back at my hated desk. The teacher is sitting in a chair and I ask her why she isn't in the circle on the floor. A mistake question if ever I asked one. She tells me not to be impolite or I will have to go to my desk. Close call, I think. I just can't keep up with all these impolitenesses.

"We had cherry and pumpkin pies and a ham for our Christmas dinner. We played button-button and drank hot apple cider after dinner. We then went to our neighbors and joined them in singing Christmas carols. My husband gave me a new coat and I gave him a new watch."

I listened and listened — when was she going to share her stuff? I know her coat is going to be too big for me. Hey! What am I gonna share? I didn't know this was gonna happen. I didn't even check at the dump!

The teacher looked down at me and said it was my turn to share. I looked up at her and told her she didn't really share yet and also asked her if she wanted me to get her coat out.

She looked at me as if she had never seen such a thing in her life. "Whatever would I want you to get my coat out for?"

I was looking at her as if she were stupid or something. "So we can share it — but I bet it will be way too big for any of us."

Everyone laughed and the teacher just smacked her lips together and said, "We're sharing by just telling our Christmas stories. We're just going to tell each other what happened at our own homes at Christmas. Now it's your turn."

We're not gonna do anything but talk? Why did she call that sharing? Just talking is sharing? Well at least I won't be the only one with nothing to share. Anyone can talk.

"Well mom doesn't like Christmas, she says it's begging. We just did our dinner and that was every day and didn't have pies at all. My dad came to visit and so we had to play his games. The big boys have to practice on me. That's all."

The teacher asked what we all played and what my big boys practiced on me. Sometimes I really think my teacher doesn't know a lot.

"Well, my dad's games are fighting games and wrestling. Then the big boys have to practice making their things get bigger by putting them between my legs and then there's this sticky stuff that gets on me after they..."

My teacher grabs me by the arm so hard I bit my tongue. We're out the door and heading for the principal's office before I can do anything. The teacher is so mad she has tears in her eyes. She pushes me towards the principal's secretary and lets go of me.

"Stand right there, young lady!"

She disappears into his office. The secretary just stares at me.

"What did you do this time?" she asks.

I cry and tell her I was sharing.

She said, "Must have been pretty bad."

I can't stop shaking and would give anything to go home no matter how much I'll get whipped. Mom told me I better not cause any trouble at school.

My teacher came out of the office wiping her eyes and shaking her head as she passed me and went out the door. I was gonna follow her but the principal said, "Just a minute — you're going with me!"

He quickly put on his overcoat and hat and motioned me out the door. As we passed my classroom I saw all of my things by the door. The principal told me to pick them up and come with him. I did. We got in his car — I sat in back. He started the car and turned to me.

"You should be ashamed of yourself. You can't come back to school until you learn not to say filthy things. Such a bad, bad girl" he ended, shaking his head.

I was gonna say something but he told me I'd ride all the way home in silence. I did that.

When we got to my house the principal told me to wait in the car. After a bit he came out and told me to go on in. He drove away. I stood there — just stood there. I guess I'll go down and stay in the neighbor's hayloft till she's not so mad. I looked at mom standing in the window — she hates me I bet. Bet Edith thinks it's about time someone got me in trouble. Maybe I can make some more snow tunnels in the snowbanks. Maybe I could go to the dump and find something for mom so she won't be so mad. Maybe I could go out west like the pioneers did and get some gold and make my own school.

Suddenly mom came flying out the door screaming, "You rotten little bitch, you hell-yen."

Slapping me and socking me and screaming, "You were nothing but trouble from birth. I told you your rotten mouth is always gonna be trouble."

My nose started to bleed and she yanked me by my hair into the house and straight to the bed. I wait till she's gone and climb out the window and go down to the neighbor's hayloft. I lay down in the hay and think, "She never misses my damn nose."

When to Read

School has been fun since the teacher started reading us part of a story every day. She reads and we all put our heads down on the desk top. We have to be quiet. The teacher reads and I listen. My head feels so good, just like the bedroom dirt floor at home must feel when I sweep the top and dampen it. My head is really like that, clean and smooth, while the teacher reads the story to us. The kids who know how to read have to get up in front of the room and read out loud. The teacher says I have to learn my ABC's so I can learn to read. I decided that I'm only gonna listen to stories and I'm never gonna read. No ABC's for me. That makes the teacher mad at me every day but I still get to hear the story she reads. I'm never gonna tell anyone I like those stories because when people find out you like something they take it away. Besides the kids always make fun of my clothes, they tell me I'm dirty, so I'm never gonna get up in front of the room to read. Not ever- even if I learn to read. They will just laugh at me.

Every night now I get my chores done really fast and go to bed. When I get in bed I lay with my arms crossed under my head. I whisper the parts of the story from school that I can remember. With my arms and head like that I can hear me and no one else can hear me. I make up my own stories, too. I tell myself about how I'm gonna take a bag of corn seeds like other Indians and tomato seeds cuz I like them and go out west like the pioneers in the teacher's story do. My mom won't plant a garden even if the pioneers did, she says they were nuts and most of them died anyway. I hate talking to her — she makes me worry about every damn thing I want to do. I just tell her I don't care if it's nuts and I gonna be one of them pioneers that lives.

When I go shopping at the dump mom asks me to bring home any of the books with "Mickey" written on the cover. I don't know why she likes those "Mickey" books cuz there are no pictures. She sits all day reading and smoking. When she isn't in that kitchen chair in the winter when we get home from school that means she's sick and in her bed. It's a certainty that we don't catch her doing anything else. On Mondays she washes clothes in the washer with a ringer on it. She just got that this fall so now she does the wash part and then we hang all the clothes outside for a day or so. The clothes freeze as stiff as boards. Then we bring the clothes in and they finish drying in the house. My mom hates sewing and cooking and cleaning so we have to do it, the big boys hate the work so I end up doing it all. I hate the work and all of them too. With the irons off the stove I make creases in the pant legs — mom said I make the best creases.

At the dump last summer I found some of those Mickey books and brought them home for mom. I'm not doing that again cuz then she was too busy reading to water her damn gladiolus's and I ended up with that job too.

Something in those books made her chuckle a bit and she was so interested in them I was dying to known what they said. After the teacher started reading to us at school I asked mom to read some of the Mickey book to me. She said I was too young to hear those mystery stories and then she said she wasn't a very good reader anyway. She only went to the fourth grade and learned to read better after she went to be a maid at the rich Jewish family's house. I don't what she means or what it has to do with reading me the damn Mickey book.

No More Indian

The school bus comes to a screeching halt and the doors open and the bus driver jumps out and yells behind himself for everyone to stay on the bus.

My brother Arnie tells me not to look out the window. I said it was too late I already looked. I walked right off that bus. The driver is shaking Joe and telling him to wake up. I take that damn old Indian's hands and try to sit him up but he won't.

My brother put his hand on my shoulder and said that Joe looked dead to him. It was true so I didn't kick at him or nothing. I sat down by Joe and took off my coat to put over him cuz I knew he was cold. Arnie asked me if I was gonna stay with him and I nodded yes. Arnie told the bus driver that not one thing on earth was gonna move me. The bus driver said he couldn't leave me there alone. Arnie said he'd stay. The bus driver got back on the bus and left.

I don't know why I said, "You can't be here cuz ya didn't ever even like him."

Arnie just nodded and said, "I liked him."

We sat and sat until the people came to take him away.

Now I can't say his real name again. I'm not sure why but that's the rule he told me.

When Arnie told mom that Joe was dead, mom said and did nothing. Just nothing.

One Less Mouth

Mom cried as we all start going to go to bed. She told us we could eat in the morning. I know I can sleep this night — my stomach has finally quit hurting. Mom says that we are starving because dad doesn't send money to feed us. That is why our stomach hurt so bad and all we do is lay down. The times mom cries, I ain't mad at her anymore.

I curl up next to my lil brother and I tell him mom said we can eat in the morning. In the winter, like now, it's warm with my lil brother in the bed. I wish I knew if mom is warm by herself. She's always crying these days. I ask her if she's warm and she asks me what do I care? I don't know what to tell her when she says that.

Dad's not ever gonna take care of us. It has been two years. Mom didn't win. Dad didn't come back. Why won't mom make a garden, not even a root cellar? Mrs. Sawyer and her family never go hungry because they work at making the food from the garden. When I grow up I'm gonna be a good mom, make lots of gardens and feed my baby fawns.

I think Nicky ran away cuz there's no food. I tried to find her but I can't. If she's smart she went where there's food.

We all just lay around and sleep all day and all night. Everybody is tired — too tired. We don't do anything. We eat that cornmeal stuff.

The constable came out and told mom again that we can't have any money because dad is still alive (again, I say, kill him). He has to take care of us. But now we can't have more of the surplus food because some of the assbite boys are old enough to go to work on the dairy farms. I wanna know when they're leaving? I wanna know the wonderful day when those assbite boys are leaving! I want to see them work their lazy asses off on the dairy farms. I told mom I will be very happy when the assbites leave me alone and go away to work. She tells me to dream about it in my sleep and shut the hell up. I ask the guides that Joe says I have to send me some dreams like that and also to hurry up and make me into a deer so I can have a family.

My lil brother is having those fits again and one of the big boys went to get a neighbor. This time we're all sick but he's having the fits bad. All stiff and staring at the ceiling.

I don't know why they're putting me, my lil brother and one older boy in a car. We aren't having fits. I'm too tired to fight with 'em. I just want to sleep. I don't even care if I dream now or not. I like to dream most of the time.

This hospital thing is pretty good. I just lay here and they bring me everything. The room I like to go to is the bathroom. You make your mess and pull on a chain thing and it puts some water in there and away goes the whole mess — just like at school. Mom says they had that kind of bathroom at the mansion she used to work at in Michigan, and the paper to wipe any of the mess off of your "butt." That's the funniest word I ever heard, "butt." Ass! They don't know about ass, wait till I tell them! This nurse tells us what to do and brings us stuff to make us feel better. She's always washing me off whether I'm dirty or not. She also combs my hair and doesn't pull it hard. I want to go live with her; she says I can't. We'll see about that later cuz maybe she'll want me if I tell her I will work hard.

The nurse took me to see my lil brother too. His eyes look so creepy and black that I decided to go back to my bed. The nurse says I can see him later, when he's better.

I want to go home where the nurse lives. Mom wouldn't care — she's always saying she wishes we had a few less mouths to feed. I think this nurse is good for me.

That nurse says we're going home in a couple more days. That isn't okay with me. I could stay here and clean up the place or do something. No matter what I say the nurse just tells me that we're going home. I like huggin' that good old nurse. She hates it when I try to jump on her back from the bed. I hate it when I miss her and land on the floor. She says I'm gonna break something if I keep that up. I told her that it was my ass! She said they know about that word already but they don't think it's nice to say it. Who can guess stuff like that? Not me. I make up a song of, "In the hospital it's butt and home it's ass — la la la la."

The nurse tells me that if we could eat solid foods we were well and then we could eat at home.

"Nurse, you're so dumb — we don't eat that at home. We eat corn-meal mush — cause of my dad being gone and my mom being lazy."

The nurse tells me things were going to be different now and we were going to eat better food.

"Nurse, it's all snowy and cold outside and we can't make any food even if my mom would let us."

"Your mom will get surplus food from now on. At least, until they find your dad and he can take care of you and your brothers."

"I just want to stay here. If they find my dad he won't take care of us anyway and he'll hit mom and lay on her and make her scream and cry. He won't stop the assbite boys from laying on me and getting sticky stuff on me either. So why find him?"

I start jumping on the bed and yelling that I wanted to stay here and that my dad is worse than anything, except the assbite boys.

I throw my pillows at the nurse cuz now I'm mad — she catches them and comes over to me and tells me to lay down. I stop jumping and yelling. I hate myself cuz the nurse looks like she doesn't like me. I hate my damn dad.

The nurse fixes me in the bed and tells me I have to be quiet. I try to hug her but she won't let me. She looks so mad. When I ask her if she's mad at me, she says no, but she acts mad. I tell her I won't jump and yell anymore. She tells me that's good because the other people are sick and need it to be quiet, too.

Pretty soon it will be time for the hag nurse to be here and my best nurse has to go to her house. I decided I'm even gonna be nice to the hag today so my best nurse won't be mad at me.

It isn't easy to be nice to the hag — she calls me "a filthy little rat" and asks me all kinds of dumb things like "does mom have men sleep with her?" She tells me that "good little girls" do not talk the way I do. Why does she ask "bad little questions" for me to answer? She says good little girls like to have their hair washed and combed.

She makes me so mad and I tell her I'm never gonna be one of those good little girls I'm gonna be a deer. She always says "You can't be anything but a girl, and not a good one at that!" That's when I start throwing pillows and jumping on the bed and running around yelling "Hag! Help! A hag is here!" She wins when she says she's gonna tie me to the bed. She'd do it, too. I saw her do that to one of the other girls in here — that's the girl who named her hag nurse.

I ate all the food they gave me today and I didn't throw any of it back up. But my best nurse didn't come today at all. The new nurse says she's a friend of my best nurse. Where's my best nurse?

I ask the new nurse when my nurse is coming back and she told me she doesn't know. I decide I'll do everything I'm supposed to (except liking the hag) so my nurse will be happy about me when she comes back. I wish I had not thrown that fit.

The hag is here again and I'm not gonna do anything wrong. I get my hair washed and soap in my eyes and let her comb it out by the roots and lay down in my bed and stay there. Hag asks me if I decided I was gonna be a good girl and I tell her that I'm being good so my best nurse will be glad to see me when she comes back.

Hag laughs and says: "Your nurse doesn't want to come back until you're gone. You make up such awful things to say that just make her sick."

Hag said, "It makes me sick, too."

Back home and we aren't as hungry now because the welfare gives mom more of those boxes of surplus food. But no one is any happier and there's still fighting all the time. Those assbite boys still do all the same things they always did to me, hitting, laying on me.

I got a birthday card from my Aunt Sara with little rabbits on it. I don't know this aunt, mom says I saw her but I was too young to remember her. I like this card. Mom took the money out and kept it for the food. Aunt Sara lives in the city and she says she wishes I could visit. I wonder why? Bet mom forgot to tell her I'm a hell-yen.

Mom sits in her usual spot, staring out the window like she always does. She had a fight awhile ago with one of the assbite boys about him living on some farm and working there. Rip-roaring idea, I say! Dumb mom argues with him that he should work for that farm but come home with the money and help her too. I got an idea! He can just never come home and send all that money in a card like my aunt did! I yell out the idea and get slapped for my trouble.

That boy is gonna leave anyway and mom screams at him how ungrateful he is and that it will be just fine to have "one less mouth to feed."

I think about that. I hate these boys and I hate the way mom just sits and lets them get away with everything. I think about that when my aunt said to visit her and that my mom likes the idea of "one less mouth to feed." I might visit that aunt in the city.

I walk into the kitchen and put my foot up on a chair like that damn dad does when he's telling everyone what to do. It works for him.

"Well, what do you want?" mom says.

"Would you like one less mouth to feed?" I ask.

"Of course I would, you stupid shit."

"Well, then, how 'bout I go to Aunt Sara's and work and send you all the money in a card?"

"I suppose you're gonna fly there — it's fifty miles from here!"

"I can't fly, dumb sitting mom but why can't I hitch a ride like Rusty is gonna with the guys who go to the city to work on the railroad every morning?"

"So go," mom says.

I went to bed planning how to get to California (it's out west) from my aunt's when the snow goes away. I thought of how I won't have to be in this room with these assbites jumping up and down on me. I just can't get to sleep. I talk to the Indian spirits and tell them I need a job in the city.

It's getting light out a bit — I have to hurry and get out to the road to catch a ride.

I throw on the warmest stuff I can and I go into mom's room to tell her I'm going. She tells me good-bye from the bed.

It's so cold that I think about going right back home. I don't see any of those railroad workers in cars. All I see is the road and all I feel is cold. Mrs. Sawyer isn't too far away so at least I can get some of that coffee from her. I like that stuff and she and I drink it and talk together.

After awhile of walking I have to take off some of my warm stuff because I'm sweating. I'm glad I'm not cold anymore.

Mrs. Sawyer is moving around in her house and I can hear that western music that she likes. I walk in and she looks surprised to see me. She hugs me hello and tells me to take off my warm stuff. She's pours some coffee.

I tell her all the news and that I'm going to the city. She gets really upset and asks me if I know how far away that is. She asks me if I want to stay with her and go with Mr. Sawyer when he leaves tomorrow. I think that's a good idea, but then the boys might see me and make me go to school or back home. I'm not taking any chances.

I tell Mrs. Sawyer no and I tell her why. She tells me someday things are gonna be better for me. I ask her how she knows that, and she says she just thinks that's true. I'm gonna think that too, cuz Mrs. Sawyer knows a lot of good things that really do work out.

Mrs. Sawyer asks me how I'm gonna know where my aunt is in the city. I pull out the card that my aunt sent.

"She's right here." I point at the address my mom showed me on the envelope.

"Well, how are you going to know where that is?" Mrs. Sawyer asks me. I get a little mad cuz I think she might be tricking me. Then she draws all these lines on a paper and tells me they're called streets — kinda like the road out here but there are a lot more of them and they're shorter. Well, hell, I don't know how to get to those things. Mrs. Sawyer tells me that I have to go to a gas station and when I get there I should show them this card and ask them to help me find my aunt. I tell her I'll do that.

After we eat lunch Mrs. Sawyer makes me a bag of food to take with me to the city. We walk out to the road and she tells me which way to go when I get to the big road with the 50 sign on it. She hands me a surprise! It's a smaller than Mr. Sawyer's thermos bottle, the one he keeps his tea warm in when he works on the railroad. Mrs. Sawyer says to bring it back with me when I come back this way. I get to take it! I get to have the warm coffee right with me. I tell her thank you! When she hugs me good-bye she looks sick. I ask her if her belly hurts and she smiles a little and tells me no. We wave these silly waves at each other as I go down the road and she goes to her house. That waving at each other makes me laugh a lot and feel good in my tummy.

When I get to the 50 road I turn and go the opposite way from the way the school bus goes. I see only one car coming at me and I can't flag it down because it's not going to the city. I'll have to walk the whole goddamn way, I bet. Might as well have a swig of that coffee. I sit down in the snowbank and drink some. I'm only gonna drink a little at a time to make it last. Snow is cold on your ass and that's that.

It's starting to get dark. Dark isn't okay with me. Freezing my ass off is also not okay with me. How far is damn fifty miles anyway? Fuck it — at least I know how to sleep in the snow.

Walking and walking. That's all I can do. I can hear a car but I can't see it and I have been hearing it for awhile. Maybe my head is just thinking up a car like Mrs. Sawyer thinks things up.

Lights are coming behind me. It's a car, a big one! I start waving my arms back and forth to flag it down. I hope to hell it stops.

It stopped! I see it's a truck. I climb up and show the guy the envelope from my aunt. I tell him that's where I'm going. I sit down on the seat and he starts to drive away but he says he isn't so sure that he should drive me all the way to the city. He wants to know where my mother is and does she know I'm going to the city. She thought it was a good idea, I tell him. He says that seems strange to him. I say who cares how it seems to you, that's the way it is. I ask him what's it to ya anyhow. He tells me that he's worried because I'm so small. Small?! I ask him if he thinks I'm going to the city to pick a fight or something? He wants me to tell him what I mean. I mean who cares if I'm small if I don't have to fight anybody. He laughs. He better be telling me what he's laughing at real soon — I hate that. I tell him, too. He says he wasn't talking about a fight and that he thinks that since I'm so small I might be running away from home or lost and then mom will worry. My turn to laugh. Mom doesn't worry, silly, and she said I should go because then she'd have one less mouth to feed.

We didn't talk for awhile and I ate the lunch Mrs. Sawyer gave me and I asked him if he wanted some but he didn't. I didn't offer him any of my coffee.

He asked me a lot of questions and I answered some and told him "none of your business" to others.

When we got to the city I told him I had to go to a gas station. He pulled off to one. I started to get out and he pointed to the side of the station and said, "It's right over there. I'll wait right here."

I don't know what he's talking about! I ask him what the hell is "right over there." He says the washroom.

"I don't care about the washroom — I have to get someone to tell where to go now so I can get to my aunt's."

He says, "I'll take you to your aunt's."

I look at him — there's another "good man," just like Mr. Sawyer says. I get back in the truck.

When we get to my aunt's house the man tells me to be a good girl and pats me on the head. Maybe that's the way good men touch girls, so I pat him back, tell him to be a good man and jump out of the truck, telling him thank you.

The City

I try to open the door, but it just won't open. I start to rattle the door knob a lot and the door opens. There's a little woman standing there. She's so little and she has a big lump on her shoulder — she stands crooked. She looks at me and says, "Can I help you, dear?"

I tell her who I am and that I came to get a job and live with her. She asks me to come into her house. I think this must be Aunt Sara.

We go into the kitchen and there's food all over the table! She says she's my aunt. Aunt Sara tells the two people at the table what I told her. The girl looks surprised and the man says, "She can't stay and that's that!"

Aunt Sara tells me to sit down and have something to eat. The girl's name is Jodie. Jodie is real friendly and offers me some of everything on the table. The fat man doesn't even look up — he makes all these snorting sounds as he eats. Kinda like a pig but quieter. Jodie tells me that Aunt Sara is my dad's aunt, too. Well, I don't know about that stuff!

I feel like throwing up! I tell my aunt I have to go outside and I make a run for the door. I get to the porch and I'm sick. I can't eat that many peanut butter sandwiches ever again.

When I'm done my aunt leads me upstairs. She takes all of my clothes off and puts a long soft dress on me for bed — she calls it a nightie. That tickles me — a nightie. She puts me in a big bed that has sheets and pillows like Mrs. Sawyer has on her beds. Aunt Sara says we'll get everything settled in the morning. She pats my hand and kisses my head. I watch her turn off the light, go out and close the door. I just can't do anything now till I wake up. I bet tomorrow I'll have to leave because that man downstairs says I can't stay. Maybe if I get a job I can stay.

In the morning she says I can live with them in this city called Duluth. Aunt Sara's friendly, her daughter Jodie's funny, and her son Charlie's huge and mean looking. Aunt Sara and Jodie laugh a lot and make me laugh a lot. The man's just big, fat, and mean. Aunt Sara makes breakfast and everybody sits and eats it and nobody takes anything off of anybody's plate and nobody screams at each other and she doesn't have a big laundry stick like mom and she doesn't hit people on top of their heads. Her son just sits, doesn't talk, and grunts. I think he's practicing to be a pig. Jodie takes me around and shows me the streets and shows me the corner store. At the corner store you just go in if you have some pennies and buy things and keep 'em. You have to give them the pennies.

We have to share all kinds of stuff at the house. I have to learn to clean things different ways because they have a vacuum cleaner that takes dust off of the floor. They don't have any dirt floors like back home. I think of mom.

Aunt Sara never yells at anything. Except the time she showed me how to do the vacuum cleaner and it tried to eat the curtains. I was vacuuming along the rug at the edge of the wall. It got by the curtains and it ate them. Sucked 'em in its mouth and I was running around yanking on it and then I yanked the curtains off the... I can't believe this. I can't make it stop eating the things and I can't get away from it so I pick up the vacuum cleaner and run with it into the other room. It stopped eating the curtains and it stopped running at all. But it still has the curtains in its mouth and I'm in big trouble. Aunt Sara is yelling and laughing at me. Then she gave a big lesson on how not to eat things you don't want to eat with that vacuum cleaner. I had to help her put the curtains back up. Jodie just sat and laughed and laughed and pretty soon I was laughing too. We put everything back together but that roaring mouthed vacuum ripped the bottom of the curtain where it bit it. I don't know about vacuum cleaners. I don't want one. I don't like 'em.

Her son Charlie came home from work after that vacuum cleaner tried to eat the curtains and told her to send me home immediately and I had to go up to my room and just sit there while he screamed and yelled about sending me home. I didn't even do anything to him. He doesn't touch me, though. One neat thing, he doesn't touch me.

They have a coal bin in the basement to keep the house warm and you have to put the coals from the bin into a thing called the furnace and it makes you all black. I have a pair of pants they gave me and I wanted these black squares on it like a coal is so I went down and I printed a coal thing all over my pants and I loved it. I want you to know nobody else loved it. They get upstairs, they yank the damn things off me, and they're laughing the whole time and telling me it has to go into the washing machine. Do you know, they have a washing machine that goes around and around by itself and rinses clothes and dries them out? You don't have to put it through the wringer and catch your hands in it like at home and you don't have to put it in the tub and you don't have to wring out the clothes and when you've put 'em on the line, they're almost dry already. I like that washing machine. I'm gonna get one when I get bigger. Besides, you know what I found out, I found out that mom is wrong. She said all that stuff I saw in books at the dump isn't true, but it's true. All that stuff like cars and tables of food and pretty rooms with pretty things in them and smiling people. It's all right here in this place called Duluth.

Even at the corner store here I can go down and just sit around and talk to them and sometimes I help them stack boxes and I sort things, and they like me! They said so. They don't talk to me like mom does and they don't act like they want to slap me around. They gave me a popsicle. A popsicle sits on two sticks and you suck on it and suck on it and it's like the best thing in the whole world and it gets littler and littler and comes off in your mouth and you get to eat it and you get to keep the sticks. Jodie showed me how to break them in half and share 'em so every time I get one now I bring one half to her unless it melts and falls off which really pisses me off. I hate that. I stomp on it and swear at it.

I have to go to school here since I'm too little to get a job. Mom's not going to like that. I think she wanted me to make some money and send it to her so that it would be even better than one less mouth to feed. It would be more money like my dad's supposed to do but he's not gonna do it. They show me the school and I meet people and I meet my teacher and they take me back home. The day comes when I'm supposed to go to school and I get all dressed and I know the way to walk so I go out the door and I don't go to school. There's a park really close called Lincoln Park and I go play there. It has squirrels and deer, all the things I like, and a little river running through it, and so I play all day cuz I'm not going to that school. Cuz the teacher will make me sit in the chair and be bored to death. I'm playing in the park every day. At night when I come home we have dinner and we have laughter and we play cards and we play games and I want a mom like this. I want one that talks to me. One that likes me. I want dinners like this where no one hits anybody and nobody takes food off your plate and you don't have to eat with your hands. At Aunt Sara's you can't eat with your hands unless it's bread. You have to eat everything else with spoons and forks and cut things with knives. This must be more of that manners thing that the school at home was telling me about. I didn't know that lots of people do this at home. I only thought you did it at school. I guess I'll catch on to this manners things pretty soon.

They have a thing called a bathtub. At home we have a round tub that sometimes we take a bath in, one right after another, and the boys pee in the water and laugh about it before mom slaps me into it and I hate it. But here they have a bathtub and the water comes out of the wall. You fill up the bathtub and then Jodie puts in some stuff and these bubbles get really high and you get in the bathtub and you're covered up with bubbles. I play in there until my skin wrinkles up. The water gets cold and the bubbles go away and they make me get out. But I think that's ok cuz tomorrow I get to do this again. I like that bathtub and those bubbles.

Jodie has records that go around on a record player and I get to listen and sing at the top of my lungs. Nobody slaps me and nobody tells me to shut up. I get to sing and sing. I can't do it after everybody turns the lights out. I did that one night. There was all hell to pay. Everybody got up and everybody told me to shut up. But they only wanted me to shut up not cuz my singing's bad but because they're trying to sleep. Okay then.

Aunt Sara runs around doing her cleaning and her mending and her mailing letters. She mails a lot of letters. I told her she should send some to mom cuz mom loves that mailbox so much. But mostly she does her own stuff and once in a while — this is really strange — once in a while she runs over and hugs me. She thinks I'm sweet, she says. Sweet? Wait till mom hears that!

Aunt Sara's grunting son hates me. But he doesn't touch me. At night he brings home people and jumps up and down on them like my dad does. I wonder if there are any people who don't do that who are men? Why do women let 'em do that? It looks awful, feels awful, sounds awful and I hate it.

Days and days go by and I play in the park and I run around the neighborhood and I love it and everybody asks me if I should be in school and I tell 'em no because I don't think I should be in school. I came home one day and Aunt Sara is sitting very, very quiet. I don't like this. I walk in, and Aunt Sara sits me down and tells me that I'm not going to school and I tell her I knew that. I was the one not going. She says I have to go, it's a law. She says if I don't go to school the authorities will come and get me. I ask her who these authorities are and she says, "They're the welfare department."

The welfare department is gonna come and get me if I don't go to school? I ask her why they care if I go to school and she says because it's really important that I learn that reading, writing, and arithmetic stuff. If I don't go to school they'll get mad at her because they'll think she's not doing her job. I don't want them mad at her. I don't care if they're mad at me, I don't even know 'em, and I don't like 'em. They have a dumb law but I don't want them to be mad at Aunt Sara. I tell her that I'll go to school and the next day I walk all the way to the school. I don't go to the park and play. I get to the school but I can't remember where I'm supposed to go and it's too big. A big place with lots of long halls and I don't know what to do so I just stand in this school. At least I'm at the school. Now they won't be mad at Aunt Sara. When all the kids come outside then I go outside and play with 'em.

Aunt Sara's big hump on her back is from falling out of an apple tree when she was little and breaking her back, that's what she told me. I like help-ing her because there's a lot of things she can't lift and lots of things she can't do, not cuz she's dumb or lazy, and she loves it when I help her. She doesn't get mad or anything. She thanks me and I like that. I like that thanking stuff.

Jodie and I do lots of things, too. One day she took me roller skating. All that slinging around on wheels and falling down I thought I'd bust my ass. Jodie fell down a few times too so we laughed a lot but it's really painful to when you land. To top it all everybody's zooming around you and your broken ass and trying to run over you. She says I'll get better and better at it. She took me to the ice skating rink, too — that was fun. That's so close to flying. I thought I was gonna leave the ground. You can go so fast, and then you fall and you bust your ass again. But when I'm skating I feel like I'm gonna fly any minute. I like that.

The dreaded social worker is talking to Aunt Sara in the kitchen. I think I'm in trouble. These are those authorities she was talking about. I hate authorities. I'm not ever gonna be an authority. They're mean, they make me crazy, I want them gone. Aunt Sara comes out with the authority and tells me I have to go back home because as long as my parents are living, I have to stay with 'em. How did the authorities know I was here? Now I have to go home in the spring when the school is over. I go back up to my room and cry. I don't know why I'm crying except I don't want to go home and I don't want to hear that yelling and I don't want to feel that badness.

I have an idea. That authority says it's because my parents are living then I should kill 'em. I should, I should kill all those people except my lil brother — anyway they're bad and mean and they hate themselves and they hate me and I hate them and so as long as they're living I have to live with them then maybe they shouldn't be living. I tell that to Aunt Sara. I asked if she'd help me kill 'em and she says no and she cried too. That was making her sad. I don't know why it felt better that she was sad too, but it did, and Jodie, she cried and hollered. She thought it was terrible. The fat son who grunts and jumps on people, he didn't do anything and he was glad and I knew it. Aunt Sara likes him, though. He's her son, she says, everybody likes their son. I tell her, Oh, ha, you don't live at my house then, because nobody likes anybody at my house.

Every day that I'm supposed to go to school now, but I don't go, cuz I have to go back home anyway so it's not gonna make any difference.

I go play at the park and I make friends with the people there and I go to the corner store and I help them out and I go home and help Aunt Sara and listen to records and take bubble baths. When I grow up I'm gonna do this. My mom's wrong, she doesn't really know anything. Grown-up people can have whatever they want.

The only thing good about going home is that I'll get to see the dog and the lake and all the fish and all the things in the woods and I'll get to see my rag house again and my lil brother. Those assbite boys probably found and tore it up my stuff by now.

I ask Aunt Sara a lot of questions about mom and how come I can't talk to her and why she hates me and Aunt Sara says that she doesn't know about any of that. She doesn't understand it; I don't either. She says some people just don't want to be talked to and they don't wanna do anything except what they're doing. They don't care about anything else. They're just gonna do what they do. Well, if that's true, why do I keep trying to talk to 'em? I think about this for days and days when I play in the park and when I'm gonna sleep at night. I think, why do I talk to them then? Maybe they just really don't want to be talked to. Maybe I should just shut up. When I go home I'm gonna shut up. I am, I'm not gonna say anything.

Going Back to Wisconsin

Aunt Sara wakes me up early, packs up all my stuff, talks to me for awhile, and makes me a big breakfast. I can't eat it. I try to think of ways not to go. I try to get her to tell the authorities I'm lost and I'll disappear to the park until they go away. She said the authorities can make a lot of trouble for her. They could even put her in jail. I give it up. I'll go home. She tells me when I get older I don't have to stay at home. All I have to do is wait to get bigger and older. Seems like everything is that you have to wait to get bigger. I can't wait till that bigness happens. I'll be gone like a bat out of hell. I don't want to, but I have to wait to get bigger. Aunt Sara says in order to get big enough, you have to eat and work really hard and just get bigger. I'm gonna do that. I'm gonna just go home and get bigger and go away.

The authorities are here. They're putting my stuff in the car and I'm hugging Aunt Sara for all I'm worth. I feel such a good thing inside me about her. I feel the same way about animals in the woods and my dog. I just like her. She's good to me. I'm gonna really hate not laughing with her and Jodie.

I get in the car and we go. Across the bridge and into Wisconsin. There's a man and a woman in the front seat and me and my stuff in the back and they talk to me and I decide I'm gonna practice not talking cuz it doesn't make any difference anyway. They don't even care that I don't want to go home so I'm not saying anything.

The woman in the front seat tells me that it's bad manners not to answer questions when you're asked. I don't care. I just don't wanna talk anymore. Since I wasn't talking, I guess they thought they would talk to each other but they were talking to each other about me. I thought, Do they think I can't hear them? What a couple of dummies. I can't wait to get out of this car.

After awhile, after a long time, we pull up at mom's house. I don't want to be here. Mom comes out the front door and just stands there. Her eyes are so dark, you can't see in them. They look black to me. They're dark brown, she says. She just stands there. I just stand there. I take off for the woods.

I go visit my rag house — it's still there — but I've got a lot of work to do on it. It's been a long time and it's falling over. I have to go to the dump right away and get some stuff to prop it back up and get some more cloth for the parts that ripped away. The fences for my pigs and chickens and my horses are still there. Oh, what a break! None of it disappeared. I have to go to the lake to see if it's still there, too. I'll run like the wind dragging my lil brother with me and when we get to the lake, it's still there. Everything is just like it used to be.

Now I get to sing a lot more songs in the woods because of Jodie's records. I know more words, and now I can sing 'em. I don't have to be in the house and hear the radio anymore. I memorized the songs.

I go home, it's dark, and I go in the house and mom is sitting as usual at the kitchen table, coffee and cigarettes, staring out the window. She spends her life like that. She doesn't say a word to me except "Go to bed." I think to myself, I'd rather be shot. I go in the bedroom and climb out the window and go back to my rag house to sleep. From now on I'm gonna sleep in my rag house so I can stay away from those assbite boys. I'll go back, the sun will come up, I'll climb back in the bedroom window, and nobody will know.

I like the outside. I get to be in my rag house, I get to be alone, I get to have all of my stuff here, I get to listen to all the noises, watch the moon and watch the clouds and get rained on. I don't mind getting rained on and it sure beats whatever they do in that shack. I'm pretty happy here. Now if I can just sneak in every morning and not get caught, I'll be even happier.

The sun comes up and I romp back to the house. I can't go in. I don't know why. I don't want to. I sit on the step. The big boys tell mom I haven't been in that bed all night and they should know, the pukes. They really should know because they don't have anyone to do weird things to. Why don't they use each other if they like it so much? I guess it's because they want a girl to do it.

Mom says who gives a shit where she sleeps and I think, "Way to go, mom!"

I don't say anything to anyone. I like this quietness that I do.

I start to have trouble breathing again. When I was at Aunt Sara's I didn't have any trouble breathing. Maybe Duluth, Minnesota is better for me than Wisconsin. Maybe I breathe better in the city. When I get bigger I'm leaving here and going somewhere I can breathe better.

Nothing's changed, except I don't talk much at all. I stay gone almost all the time I can possibly stay gone. I eat at lots of the neighbors root cellars. I know I'm not supposed to. I feel like telling them I'm sorry I have to eat your food, but then they probably wouldn't let me do it. I can't stay out of my house if I don't eat their food. Pretty soon there'll be berries, everything will start to get ripe and I can eat in everybody's garden again. Pretty soon. Maybe this time even when it snows and winter comes, maybe I can sleep outside like Joe showed me. He said you can't do that for a long time because it will make you sick. I could do it sometimes, though.

Since I don't say anything these days, everybody slaps me to make me answer their questions. They ask me if the cat's got my tongue. I don't answer them and I don't talk to them and they slap me, but they slap me anyway and I like it better getting slapped when I don't say anything than when I did. I just think it now. I don't say it.

I stay outside and I run around and I go further and further. There are so many things I didn't know were out there. If you walk past the blackberry patch you get to these giant trees. They're pine trees, but there's hundreds of 'em, and you can just walk and walk and walk and there's no brush and there's deer in there. They just stand in it.

This year mom says that we have to pick all our berries and make jam. I can't believe my ears. She's gonna make something. Whoa, what a trip! She's gonna make jam. We have these pails and buckets and I help her pick the berries. One day we were picking blackberries and a black bear wobbles up to the blackberry patch where we are. I've seen him lots of times. He just wobbles around and makes growling noises, he's just eating berries, and he licks rotten logs. He does! I've seen him, he tears those logs apart and licks 'em a lot. Slivers in his tongue! But he doesn't bother anybody. Mom goes nuts. She goes batshit crazy. She slings the berries she picked in the air and starts running at me. I think, what the hell? I took off — I'm having none of this and I'm not lettin' her catch me, she's probably gonna slap me cuz this bear showed up. That bear doesn't do what I tell it to do. I take off around the blackberry patch, she takes off after me. This is crazy. Now we're running around and running around and run right into the ass end of that bear. It's just standing there picking berries. Mom is screaming and running in circles. I take off into the woods, the hell with this berry picking with a batshit mom. She takes off for the house, screaming at me. I mean, she acts like I went out and asked that bear to show up.

Later on I can hear her screaming my name so I go see what she wants. She hands me all the pails and tells me I can just get my ass out there and pick those berries myself, since I'm such a smartass and if that black bear shows up then I can just deal with it. I always deal with it, you dumb mom! I take the pails and go and the black bear isn't there anymore. I pick berries and more berries till I have lots of 'em and I take 'em back to the house and she just takes 'em from me. Aunt Sara would have thanked me, just like that. I want to hear those thank you's. I like 'em.

When I was at Aunt Sara's, Jodie told me that the people who sing get up on a big stage. She showed me on the TV. They get on the big stage and then they sing to people. I decided that the gravel pit across the road from us is gonna be the stage. I get up on the high part of the gravel pit and there's all these giant rocks and I decide I'll pretend they're people. I get up there and I sing and sing and sing and I pretend they like it. I like that singing and I like my gravel pit audience. Jodie says audiences are people who listen to you cuz they like you.

I miss Jodie and Aunt Sara. I still laugh when I think about that vacuum cleaner eating the curtains. Aunt Sara sends me cards sometimes, and it has a dollar in it, and mom takes the dollar and I get the card and that's fine with me. The cards have pictures on them and Aunt Sara writes me words I can read. She says she misses me and guess what! She says she loves me! I write her and tell her I love her too. I miss her too. I ask mom to send 'em and she just gets mad and she says she can't afford to send my letters. I go to my rag house and cry. I never understand this crying thing. I guess I cry because I can't...Aunt Sara will think I don't care about her and mom won't send the letters. Maybe Mrs. Sawyer would.

This morning I'll go to Mrs. Sawyer's and tell her I need to get this note to Aunt Sara so she won't think I don't care about her. I have to tell her those I-love-you's and misses-you things. It's important to her, I know it is. Mrs. Sawyer writes an envelope. That's what she called it, an "envelope," and she puts a stamp on it and writes Aunt Sara's name and address on it. We put it in the mailbox, we put up the flag, and we wait and we have a cup of coffee and we watch for the mailman. He took the letter. It's on its way to Aunt Sara's! Now she'll know I feel the same way she does.

All of a sudden I feel that thing Aunt Sara calls love to Mrs. Sawyer so I hug her and she hugs me back. What a deal! This loving thing must be good for other people. We don't have it at our house but everybody else has it.

Mrs. Sawyer says she loves her family, and when her babies cry, or they want something, or if they're in a fight or whatever, she doesn't hit them. She talks to them and she slaps their hands, though, if they're gonna do something that's gonna hurt them. What an idea! Maybe I could be a mom like Mrs. Sawyer when I grow up, instead of being a deer. I'm ten years old now and the spirit guides haven't made me be a deer. Mrs. Sawyer says that won't work anyway and I will just have to have babies like other people do. I will, I'll have my own baby and be good to it. Then I'll finally have a family that loves me.

I need to get bigger, go to the dump, make my rag house stay up, do all my outside berries and animals and Mrs. Sawyer says that'll keep me happy and I'll grow up and be a happy person. I'm gonna do it. I'm gonna stay out of my house as much as I can. Mrs. Sawyer says one of the ways to really be happy is to remember all the good things that people do for you. I tell her okay, let's see, mom, she tries to get us to go to school and she tries to get us things, like she goes and gets groceries sometimes and she washes clothes and once in a while she brings us this candy called "bananas" or something — it's yellow, shaped like a peanut or something. It tastes good. She does that and she chuckles when she reads those Mickey books, and she's nice to the dog Nicky, and she doesn't tear down my rag house. She wears things off of it if she likes 'em, but she doesn't rip it all up.

She doesn't hit me as much anymore cuz I don't come home. She says she doesn't care what I do or if I talk at all, which is better than before when she was hitting me all the time and caring what I did. I don't ever try to sleep with her anymore because I found out how to get outside and not have to sleep with anybody. But she does some good things, like she came home one time with a red coat for me. A bright red coat for winter. Somebody gave it to her and it's my size and I get to have it. It has wooden buttons. She did that. I'm gonna like what she does so maybe I won't be unhappy like her when I grow up. I keep thinking about going out to the highway and getting a truck driver to give me a ride so I can go back to Duluth and hug Aunt Sara and laugh with Jodie. I can't do it now, though — the authorities will get us all in trouble.

I keep thinking that somehow I can go away. Maybe if I didn't go to Aunt Sara's nobody would know where I was. Mom lets me know all the time that it didn't help to have one less mouth to feed, not to mention she hopes I learned my lesson cuz I'm too young to get a job and I thought I was so smart and I'm not. I keep thinking I know a lot of things she doesn't know. I'll know how (when I get bigger) to do all of that stuff, and just because I'm too small now that's why I didn't do it, not because I can't. I'll have to get bigger first. But she talks like it's never gonna happen. She could do it. She could go to the city and get a job, and she's not going to. But that's because she's dumb. I mean it, I don't think she knows anything. There are a lot of trucks in the summertime that go right by our house. Maybe I should get on one of those and go somewhere. Maybe I got here by mistake. Maybe I'm not supposed to be here. Maybe that's why everybody hates me. They don't want me here and I don't wanna be here. Maybe if I go other places, maybe I'll find out where I'm supposed to be. But I can't go to Aunt Sara's because of the damned authorities. Pretty soon I'll be big enough to just go and go.

I'm saving rocks in the ditch by the driveway so I can practice my dead eye aim on the assbite boys. I need a big pile of these rocks so I can bounce them off those assbite boys all the way down the driveway to the school bus. Then they'll get on the bus and I won't. That'll be a happy rock throwing day.

Every Winter, Every Summer

Getting from one room in our house to another is just like getting through the outhouse without flies jumpin' ya. First of all you have to get in the door if they'll let you in, and they don't slam your hands in it or yank on your arms or pull your hair. And then when you get inside everybody is slapping, kicking, punching, whacking, I don't know what the hell the problem is but when I go from the front door to the bedroom, I'm tired! All that hitting and poking and kicking and what are they doing, anyway? That's how you get from the front door of mom's house to the bedroom, the dreaded bedroom, where all the shitass stuff happens. You know what? One time I walked in and the big boys had brought home a ruler from school and they had their things out and they were pumping them up and measuring which one of their things was the longest. The oldest boy didn't win, and since he was older, he thought his thing should be the longest so he promptly stood up and beat up the brother who did win. A flock of flapping assbites, I say.

I can't believe these guys, they slap everything, they hit everything, they step on everything, they choke everything. They do it every damn day. I mean, it just never, never is different. One time Daryl was playing with a calf and it started sucking on his finger...and he put his thing in its mouth. But he didn't like it because that calf wouldn't let go. I laughed, everybody laughed. When I hate Daryl, I remember that trusty calf and it makes me feel better. Because the calf's tongue was too rough and so his thing was really sore - he was hollering! Better him than me, for once, I say.

Every winter and every summer it's the same. In the summer I live outside, and in the winter I have to stay inside a lot. Joe's sleeping outside in winter doesn't work. I can't do it, I get too cold and the bed gets wrecked up. Then I wet the bed and freeze my ass off.

Awhile ago, dreaded dad came home, and while he was home, making everybody miserable, somebody died. An uncle or something, I didn't know him, but I walked in the house and everybody was sitting down quiet. You know what? That made me feel so very crazy, like sitting on an ant hill. I romped right into that living room, punched an assbite dead in the face, and the fight was on. I felt a lot better, cuz I know they were gonna hit me, I just want them to hurry up. I always want them hurry up when they're gonna hit me.

When I start the hitting to get it over with it seems to make everybody extra pissed. I run for my life! Awhile back I was hiding in a shed and there was this window that some cats kept coming in and I kept on throwing them out — first out the door then out the window. I wasn't trying to be mean, cats make my eyes swell shut. The cats were clawing and howling and climbing up the side of the shed. A woman started yelling from outside, "What are you doing?" Then she saw my face — my face was puffed up and my eyes were almost swollen shut — and she stopped dead and said, "Well hello!" We recognized each other from the lake. It was Mrs. Sawyer.

Later Mrs. Sawyer's husband went down the road to talk to my mother, and she told him that "the little bitch always runs away, and that's just the way it is." I heard this because I was hiding outside. I knew he was going to mom's house, and I was scared that he was gonna bring my mother back with him. When I saw he was alone, I crept up to the windowsill and listened to him talking to Mrs. Sawyer. I was so glad that was what mom said. Mrs. Sawyer came outside to talk to me and said, "You can't sleep in the barn anymore."

Well, I figured as much. Looks like I have to go home after all. But then she said, "You come in this house this instant and take a bath and get into bed." Mrs. Sawyer doesn't usually talk like that, but she did that time. Well I'll be dipped in shit, what a surprise!

That was the beginning of me going to Sawyer's.

We had to do something about the cats because they made me sneeze so much, and Mrs. Sawyer didn't have the heart to keep them out of the house. I had my own little roll-up bed that was wrapped in a sheet during the day. I couldn't lay on the floor — I couldn't even sit anywhere where cats had been. I had my own chair that was covered in a sheet. They even bought me my own coffee cup. Mrs. Sawyer bought it for me.

She said, "Oh, I'm so glad you're here! I have a present for you" and she gave me the coffee cup. I wish I lived there all the time.

Some people came by today and asked mom if they could take my lil brother and me to Sunday School. My mom said yes, so we have to get dressed in clean clothes on Sunday and they'll come by and we'll get in the car and go to Sunday School. I like that Sunday School, they tell us stories. I love stories. They sing and I love to sing, at the top of my lungs, my Sunday School teacher says. She says I could sing quieter, and I say I don't want to. I sing on my stage, every winter, every summer, no matter where I'm living, inside or out, it doesn't matter, I just go to my stage and sing and sing and sing and it makes me feel better. At Sunday School I get to hear stories and I get to sing. The only part I don't like is that the ladies that pick us up ask me all kinds of questions about mom. Just question after question, and I just tell 'em it's none of their business. I don't talk.

Inside mom's house there's no laughing. When I'm outside I laugh at a lot of things. I laugh when I remember Jodie and Aunt Sara and I laugh when I think of stories Mrs. Sawyer told me. Every time I go to school, Johnny and I play — Johnny is my boyfriend at school, he's my best buddy. I like that best buddy, he shares his guns with me. He has two of 'em. I put one on a rope and wear it and he wears the other one with the belt it came with it. It has bullets in it but it's not a real gun. We play and we play and we play. He tells me that he lives with his grampa and tells me about his grampa and grandma. His grampa is always sick. It really bothers Johnny so he cries some. He tells me everyday how hard his grampa coughed and how sick he is. I tell him, when I grow up I'm gonna take him someplace where people aren't sick. He tells me we're gonna rent one of those giant Mack trucks, the ones with the big trailers, and build a house in the back and travel all over and take care of each other. We just lay on the grass and look at the clouds changing and we talk about where we're gonna go and what we're gonna do. Every day, I play with Johnny and every day, I just like him and he likes me.

I don't have too much trouble at school anymore since I learned not to do things that aren't manners, and since I learned not to talk about "disgusting" things very much at all. I tell them to Johnny, though. He's really nice to me. He says we're gonna dig a tunnel from his house to mine because we never get to see each other except at school. He started digging and I started digging. We don't know how long it's gonna take. But we're just gonna keep digging until we get to each other then people can't stop us cuz we'll be underground in the tunnel, they won't even know we're doing that.

They told me at Sunday School that God is good to all little children. I'm a little children, they said. I don't think he's good to me. I tried to shoot him with our old twelve-gauge. The big boys shoot at me with that twelve-gauge. They count to ten and I run into the woods and they just shoot and they always miss me. I think they miss me on purpose because when they do try to shoot other things, they hit 'em. But I never know if they're really gonna shoot me or not. I'm mad at God now cuz he doesn't take care of my lil brother and me, I got out the twelve-gauge and I propped it up like they do and I pull the trigger and it knocked me on my ass and I couldn't move my arms forever. I thought the damn thing killed me for a minute, so I just as soon not be shooting that twelve-gauge until I get a lot bigger. I'm gettin' a lot bigger, though.

I'm getting bigger every day. Year after year I will keep getting bigger — pretty soon I can go away.

I make up my own songs on my stage now, and when I'm really mad I make up songs about the boys. Then I sing, "You skunk boys, you make too much noise, you hate everybody, and I hate yourselves, you skunk boys."

I sing on and on and on. I sing "Peggy Sue," "Bye Bye Love," and "Rave On" from the trusty radio. Makes me feel good. I sing "Jesus Loves Me" songs from Sunday School, too. Maybe if I sing it enough then God will take care of me since it says he takes care of all the little children. He better hurry up because I'm growing. Pretty soon I won't be a little children.

Mom still sits, every summer and every winter, and bitches about dad and calls him names and calls me names cuz I look like him and tells me that everything's wrong because he doesn't take care of us. But she just still sits there. There's a guy who comes around a lot now. His name's Tom. He comes around and brings groceries. He brings me things sometimes. He says he likes me. He hugs me sometimes, too. The good kind of hugging. He talks to mom and he brings her wine. She likes it, and she keeps it under her bed. I tasted it, I don't like it, it tastes terrible. Otherwise I'd've drank it. Why not, she wears the door off my rag house.

When Tom goes home from work mom says that little horn honking is him going by. Every night at ten. I have to be in bed at ten. One time I went to bed outside. My mom didn't know I was outside, and I heard that honking, and I got up to look, and I walked down the trail from my rag house, and I saw this Tom man sneaking in our house. I go see what he's doin'. Oh, ick, what he's doing is going in mom's room. He's doing that jumpin' up and down. Hey! Mom's not hollering or cryin'. No wonder she doesn't want me to sleep with her, he's in the bed with her! He stays with her for awhile, and then he gets up and goes home. She really likes him, I can tell. I like him, he's a nice guy, and he brings us stuff, and he doesn't hit me. He doesn't jump up and down on me. He doesn't make my mom mad or holler.

Now my mom cleans Tom's house. Tom has a wife named Angie and Angie can't move much, she had a stroke, so my mom cleans the house and takes care of Angie. That must be why he brings presents and food. Mom took me down there lots of times cuz I have to clean out the toilets and scrub the floors and help her. Angie gives me candy and smiles at me. I like her. She can't walk very good and she's sick a lot. Tom likes her, too — when he comes home and we're still cleaning, he's very nice to her. He kisses her hello and he talks to her and he makes a drink of wine and mom has some and Tom has some and Angie has some. Tom always gives me a taste. I always take the taste but I never like it.

But there's trouble. Everybody found out that Tom comes to see mom and sleeps with her for awhile and everybody at school is calling mom a whore. I have to beat 'em up. I don't know why but when they call her names I get mad and hit 'em. I'm in trouble half the damn time again. I don't say anything, I just hit 'em a lot. Jesus, I shouldn't listen to 'em but they make me so mad. I don't go to Sunday School, I'm not going anymore cuz at Sunday School when the ladies are taking us home, they wanna know if Tom stays at our house and they make it sound really terrible so I told them off. I don't care about God anymore, either. He's a pain in the ass. If he loves little children, he has a dumb way of showing it. Not to mention the fact that he sends me to Sunday School with icky people who make mom worse than she already is. If they don't like what she does, how come they don't help her like Tom does? The teacher at Sunday School class says we're all supposed to love each other and be nice and they aren't. I mean, they lean over the back seat with their porky faces in my face askin' me "none of their business" questions that I'm not supposed to answer and that make mom mad too. I'm not going anymore. I'm not gonna talk to God. I'm gonna get a different God. Like Joe says, I'm gonna have my spirit guides and I'm not gonna have a God like theirs cuz he's really not funny and anyways he lied. Take care of little children, my ass! He never does take care of me. Teacher said maybe some children have a rougher time so that they can learn something. Can you stand that? I can learn something? I can learn how to get jumped up and down on, and slapped and screamed at and choked and go hungry and I can learn all this! This is stupid. Every summer and every winter, it's the same. If God doesn't see that, then why should I talk to him? He doesn't know anything either. He's probably as dumb as mom.

I talked to my spirit guides instead. I feel good when I talk to them. I tell them all the singing I do is for them. I think my spirit guides like me because they don't do anything, they don't tell me things that aren't true, like that Sunday School stuff. At Sunday School they have that written down in a book and it's not even true! I wonder when they're all gonna find out it's a big lie. I bet everybody's gonna be mad about that!

Instead of Sunday School, now I get up really early and go to Mrs. Sawyer's. Sunday at Mrs. Sawyer's is wonderful. Sometimes they go to the lake and I go, and we always eat and I get to eat. I love that food! Mrs. Sawyer is really wonderful. I carry water and I bring in wood and I help her clean and I help her with the kids. She calls me the new word of "wonderful." She has four kids and I like helpin' her. She thanks me. She's like Aunt Sara, she likes it when you do things. When I carry wood and water at home, my Mom just thinks I should, so I do, but she never thanks me. I thanked her for dinner once and she told me to shut my goddamn mouth and quit being a smartass.

I don't thank her anymore, either. I don't know why home is so different from other places. I tell her that it's a lot more fun when you're laughing and happy and singing and she tells me to shut up, so I do. I just think it anyway.

Yesterday mom was down cleaning Tom's and Angie's place, and my big boys stood me on the table like they always do and took off all my clothes. I hate it when they do that! They make fun of me and they try to put things inside of me like straws and sticks and stuff. They're assbites! Yesterday, I leaped off the table onto the oldest big boy's fat stomach and bit him as hard as I could. I don't argue with 'em anymore. But I still fight with 'em. I don't care if they kill me, it feels so good to hit 'em. I know they're gonna hit me back, I don't care. I just don't care. Haul off and kill me, I say.

After they do these things to me I'm so mad. I take off and run around and go visit people or go to the woods or go to my rag house or go shopping at the dump. I'm just waiting. Year after year, I'll just get bigger. Mrs. Sawyer says that's how it goes. Pretty soon, I'll be big enough to leave here.

Today is time for my trusty rock slinging. When those assbites go for the bus I'll do my dead eye rock bouncing off their heads. I get in the ditch where I have stashed lots and lots of rocks. I'll lay low and when they run for the bus I'll start peppering them with my stash. I wait and I also know they have to go to school for some important practice today — pretty damn smart of my dumb self, I say. I'm slinging rocks and hitting my targets and those assbite boys are hollering and telling me they're gonna kill my ass tonight. I don't care. I feel better with every rock that hits them. Not to goddamn mention I'm not gonna be here tonight. The other kids on the bus are hanging out the window hollering. I like this. They leave rocked proper by me and all I have to do is go stay away for some days and come back and get a beating that I can feel good about for once.

I stay in Johnson's barn for a few days and come back and get my beatings from the skunk boys who still have some welts on them from my wonderful dead eye rocking I gave them. Good for me, I say.

Pretty soon I can go and work for somebody. I can chop wood and I can carry wood and I can carry water now. I can do all those things and I can cook some things and I can take care of kids. I'm gonna ask mom if I can go live at Mrs. Sawyer's because then she won't have to feed me, and Mrs. Sawyer said it would be fine with her. I'm gonna ask.

That was a waste of time. Mom says I can't go live with Mrs. Sawyer. That does it. I'm leaving. I'm going out to the damn road and take off. I'm gonna go up to the city and I don't care where I live anymore, but I'm not staying here. This is dumb. She doesn't care what happens to me, and those damn boys make me miserable every day, every time they catch me. I don't get it. She doesn't want me and I know it. She doesn't even like me. Why won't she just let me go somewhere? I have to go somewhere she doesn't know about. I told her I was leaving anyway and she said that the damned authorities would come and get me and put me in jail. It would be better than here, I bet you. I'm gonna try it. The worst that could happen is that I end up back here. I'll have to take all my dried things, all my dried berries and all my dried leaves for tea. I'll wrap them up in a rag and take it with me. I'm gonna start. I'm gonna get all packed up and I'm gonna go and get on a truck and go to the city. I'm not even gonna tell Mrs. Sawyer this time, though, so the damned authorities can't know. Cuz Mrs. Sawyer says she couldn't lie. That it's not good for people to lie, she says. So this time I won't tell her.

Bread Trucks, Stealing and Liars

I got all my stuff wrapped up in a shirt and tied and I'm carrying it and going down the road. I think it's gonna take me forever. It's five miles to that little store with the gas pump. I can get there; people come there all the time. They could take me someplace. It's so hot, walking and walking. I better just keep walking and get to that store. It's gonna be almost night by the time I get there, I bet.

Well, that wasn't a chortling good time. It took me all day and then I had to sleep in the back of the store so nobody would know I was there and today everybody tells me when I ask them for a ride that I'm too little and where's mom? Why would I want mom? What's wrong with these people? Anyway, nobody's giving me a ride but there's a guy who has a truck. It has a picture of bread on the side and I'm gonna sit on the back of it or get in it or something, cuz I'm going on that truck. That truck's supposed to go to Superior, he said. That's close to Duluth. There are lots of people — I could just live there. I get inside of the bread truck when he's unloading some stuff and I hunker down behind the stacks of things he has in there and I wait, and he shuts the doors. I'm going. I can't believe my luck. I am hungry so I start opening and eating. I quit eating because nothing more would go down my throat. When he gets to the city, he opens those doors and takes something out and sees me. Boy, is he mad! Screaming at me. I get out of the truck and take off.

I'm walking down the street. I'm just here — lost.

There's store after store after store after store! Where are the people's houses? How am I gonna get a job carrying water and wood and taking care of kids if all they have is stores? I go in and there's this store that has this square bunch of windows for candy in 'em. I want that. I'm standing there, thinking to myself, if I stick my hand around this corner, I can have that. I stick my hand around the corner when the lady has her back turned and just as I'm ready to pop those candies in my mouth she grabs my hand. She's big. Very big, and has red hair. She's huge and she looks down in my face and she says, "You don't want to do that. You don't want to be a thief."

I tell her I do too. I love candy. She says, no, if you steal it you go to jail, or you could work for the candy. What kind of work? I'll do it. She puts the candy in a bag and she says, "Now, come with me," and she shows me a back room where I have to unload these bags and boxes and then I can have the candy. I do it. I work and work and work and she comes back and she says, "That's good enough" and she hands me my bag of candy. She asks me where my mother is. Why does everybody want to know where my mother is? They wouldn't like her even if they found her.

The lady at that store says again that if I take things it's called stealing because it belongs to somebody else and they didn't tell me I could have it, so then I could go to jail, and I can't get out. I'm not gonna do that stealing, then. I don't wanna go anywhere I can't get out. That's worse than being at home. Dreaded home.

The Authorities

I don't get it! I've been in the city awhile and I found the people's houses, and this woman says I could stay with her for awhile, and now she's called the authorities. They're comin' to get me! I'm so mad at her. What a liar! She said I could stay with her, she didn't say she was gonna call the authorities. She tells me I'm too small to be away from my mother. She doesn't know my mother! It's good for people to be away from her. Damn it! I'm so mad at 'em, I run around screaming and throwing her stuff around. This time I've had it! I'm not gonna be nice. I'm not gonna be happy. I'm not gonna be anything. I'm mad. I'm mad at everybody! Besides that, Mrs. Sawyer lied, she said if you tell the truth and you're good to people, they won't do rotten dumb things to you, and that's not true. She must think that because she doesn't do rotten things. She doesn't know about the rest of this. She lied. Being good doesn't mean other people will be good.

Here comes the damned authorities. This is Miss Grubb. I'm supposed to say hello to this? I'm not talking to it. It's big and gray and fat and wears thick glasses, and I don't like it already. It's the authorities! Miss Grubb puts me in her car, yanks me around to get me in there cuz I'm not real happy about going, gets me to her office and sits me down. She tells me that if I'll tell her my last name and where I live, that she'll get me back home. Why in hell would I wanna go back home? Is this woman nuts? I tell her about what goes on at home. I tell her I never want to go home. I tell her about the big boys always doing things to me and jumping up and down on me and mom and... I tell her everything at the top of my lungs, and then she says, "You have a foul mouth and a horrible imagination!"

What's an imagination? I mean...what's wrong with her? She tells me I better not tell horrible stories. Horrible stories?

I tell her, "You asked me and I told you."

She says "Yes, but I didn't ask you to lie to me and make things up." Then she says, "From now on you better not tell anybody those things."

This is just like the hag at the hospital! That nurse, she didn't like the story either. I hate those imaginations myself, whatever they are. Why does everybody ask me to tell 'em and then get mad? I tell her, fine, I'm not gonna tell you my name or nothing. I'll just sit there. So...after a long time, she puts me in the car and takes me to this place called a "children's home" that has lots of kids in it and lots of food. I like this! There are a lot of kids who don't like their moms either or their moms are gone or something. Anyways, so we all get to stay together. This is a good idea!

At this children's home, you have chores you have to do but nobody runs around jumping on you and hitting you and screaming at you unless you're a brat. I was a brat for awhile, and I quit it because they might not let me stay. Miss Grubb came. Ick and yuck! The woman who called her and blabbed that I was there found my pack and found Aunt Sara's letters to me. Now they know where I live. Miss Grubb said mom said, "Don't bring her back cuz she's a pain in the ass"

They're calling my dad! Dreaded dad in Michigan! I'm gonna die! He's gonna kill me! I told this Miss Grubb-authority that my dad would kill me if I go there and she says, "Oh, don't be ridiculous."

Miss Grubb says I shouldn't be such a big baby and I don't need to live with mom. This woman is stupid. She's as much a dumb person as mom. Why am I telling her that? It's true! It's not ridiculous! If she sends me to my dad's he'll pull my head right off my damn body. Then she comes back a couple of days later and tells me that my dad said to send me on the bus to Michigan.

Oh, I don't want to do this. I don't want to do this at all. Fine, great, fuckit, I'm on the bus, headed to dreaded Michigan and dreaded dad and death. When I get off this bus in Michigan, I'm not going to his place. No! I say No!

This bus is fun, though. You can see out the windows and people talk to you and they share stuff with me and I tell them things but I don't have anything to share with them. The bus driver gets me food when it's mealtime because the social worker gave him money for that. At least I'm not hungry. The social worker gave me my pack back but she took out all my dried things. I don't know why she did that. What about stealin' — those were mine.

It's a long, long ride, the bus driver says. He told me that this bridge we're gonna go over goes over a big giant water. It's called a Mackinaw Bridge. I don't know about that kind of bridge. I ask him what a Mackinaw is. He doesn't know, he says, it's just some Indian name. Well, that's weird. I can't wait, though. He says by night we'll be going over it. It has lots of lights and pretty water and I can't wait.

He was right, the bridge, that Mackinaw Bridge, is really neat. The biggest water I ever crossed. We went across it, it really was fun. He let me sit up in the front seat so I could see really good because everybody else was trying to sleep and I don't want to. I tell them I'd like to get up off the bus before we get to my dreaded dad's and he said that he'd get in a lot of trouble if I do that. I like him. I don't want him to get in a lot of trouble, but I don't want to live with my dad. I don't want dad to kill me. Maybe I can think of a way to die before I get there. I ask the driver what kills people. One thing, he said, is "if they don't breathe, they die." I spent all night holding my breath. Dumb me — it didn't work. Goddamn never mind, I say.

Dreaded Dad

I must have gone to sleep cuz I'm waking up and it's daylight. We're in Michigan, heading for the place called Flint. That is the place I was born. Mom told me I was born in Flint, and I went to Wisconsin when I was two. At the bus depot I see my dreaded dad. He gets my stuff and puts me in the car and he doesn't hit me and he doesn't touch me and he tells me he's taking me to some friends. We go to some people's house and they're called Andersons. They have a mom and dad and a daughter. I like her. They have this cat and they have this dog and I hate the dog cuz he jumps on you and nips at you...he's really stupid and then he rolls over and pees on your shoe. I don't play with him. The cat makes me sneeze a lot.

But they have a big giant house and I live in the basement. Dad left without hitting me! He didn't even scream at me! What a lucky break! Mrs. Anderson says my dad's gonna be back in a couple of weeks and I have to learn how to cook some things for him if I'm gonna live in the basement with them. I'd rather live anywhere else. I don't want to live with him at all. I learn how to fry eggs and potatoes and I learn how to make coffee by myself and make toast. Mrs. Anderson taught me how to put some meat in the pan and put carrots and potatoes in it and cook them and then make this gravy. She says my dad will like that. She taught me how to make sandwiches, because he'll want to take them to work when he comes back. I have to do this stuff. Maybe he won't do anything to me if I do it right. I keep working and practicing and working and practicing and I can do it. I do it just fine. Mrs. Anderson has me make a bunch of food for them every day, so I can learn how to do it for dreaded dad. I can't believe I have to feed him! I'd rather kill him! But if he's not gonna hit me or anything, then I can make this food and then I can't go back home. I don't want to be here either.

After my dad comes back, I cook for him and it isn't right yet and throws the plate at me and the food gets all over me. I get so tired. I stay in the basement and I don't go and play. I don't know why I don't play, but I try to make him breakfast and he gets all mad and throws things and breaks plates and stuff, and when he leaves I just lay down. I sleep. Mrs. Anderson comes down and checks on me, but I tell her I just want to sleep. She checks my head to see if it's hot, but it's not, so she just lets me sleep. She tells me it's not really good for me to sleep that much, but I can't help it. I just want to sleep. I get up and I try to make dinner for dad and hope he doesn't throw it all at me.

Dammit it! I heard dad talking to Mrs. Anderson and he said Daryl's coming here! Dreaded, assbite, skunk Daryl, the meanest of all the big boys on earth is coming here! Oh, fuckit. I better get out of here. If he comes here, he's gonna jump on me and make my legs raw and make me mad and slap me. What? My lil brother, he's coming too? He's gonna be here? I can't leave! Somebody will have to take care of him. I guess I have to stay.

I go upstairs and I talk to Mrs. Anderson. I tell Mrs. Anderson how much I don't want to be here when Daryl gets here, I tell her all the reasons and how much I have to stay because of my little brother. Mrs. Anderson's eyes practically popped out of her head. She asked me a lot of questions and I answered them and she didn't tell me not to make up horrible imaginations. She said I don't have to sleep downstairs with dad and Daryl when they come, I can sleep upstairs with her daughter. I feel better. At least at night I can rest.

Mr. Anderson comes home and Mrs. Anderson brings me upstairs and wants me to tell him about how Daryl jumps on me and what he does so I tell him. He just raises all sorts of hell. He's really mad! He says not in his house! Nobody's gonna do that Daryl stuff in his house! He says that's awful, that's terrible, my dad should know about it. I told him my dad does know about it. He doesn't believe it. He said if he knew about it, that my dad would stop it. I thought, Oh ha, you must know a different dad than I know.

When my dad comes home, they tell him. What a horrible thing. The way he looked at me scared me all the way to my toes. After they talked for awhile he took me downstairs and he just paced back and forth and back and forth and back and forth. I feel like screaming. Then he stopped and looked at me and said, "What the hell is the matter with you? You're not dead or anything, why are you complaining all the time?"

I said cuz I hate what that jumping on me and what Daryl does and he says, "Well, he's my son. You're not hurt. I want you to shut up about this. It isn't like you're pregnant, you know. You can sleep upstairs. You say another word to Mrs. Anderson about this, I'll knock your head off."

I tell him I won't say anything. So that's that.

They put me in school here. I hate school. I'm not gonna go. I don't feel right. I feel like I'm really different from everybody. I miss Johnny. I miss playing with him and talking to him and I don't want to be friends with anybody anymore. I just want to sleep.

Daryl and my little brother get here. I show my little brother Mrs. Anderson's daughter Jeannie. Jeannie's really nice and my little brother likes me and her and so we play and we play. It works out really good.

We were playing outside when my dad got home and I ran in to get dinner stuff and I could hear Daryl and my dad hollering at each other and Daryl is saying what a raving little shit I was and how rotten of me to tell all that and he's not staying here. My dad comes in the house and slaps me around a lot. He says I wrecked the whole family and I'm a troublemaker. What good news! Even if I do get slapped around and I wreck the whole family, Daryl's not gonna stay here, what a deal!

Mrs. Anderson talked my dad into sending me to somebody, a minister, she said, and I get to talk to him about all this stuff, and he won't lock me up, and he won't beat me up. No problem, I can just talk to him. Mrs. Anderson said that all this stuff that's happened to me is why I don't go to school very much and why I want to sleep all the time and why I'm so unhappy. No kidding, I say. No kidding!

I go to the minister's office after school, it's on the way home. I didn't really go to school. I went to the school grounds and then I walked around a lot and sat a lot but I have to make them think I'm going to school. I go to the minister's office and he lets me in and he says to sit down and he says a prayer and then he asks me what happened. I tell him a lot of it and he tells me he'll see me again tomorrow and I go home. The next day I see him and he says a prayer and he asked me what happened and I tell him the same things again. He asked me a lot of questions so I have to tell him exactly what happened. I start hating that because I have to say every little thing. This makes me feel like a crawlin' snake. He acts like he likes these stories. I don't like this. I wonder if he has the same God those Sunday school people had, and they just like sickening things, and pretend to like good things.

I go home and tell Mrs. Anderson I don't want to see the minister anymore, and she says I have to. She asks me why I don't want to see him, and I said he makes me feel weird — kinda sick, cuz he asks me for all these little details to everything, and she says, well, that's the way he's gonna help me. Well, I don't understand that, but Mrs. Anderson is okay. I don't think she'd lie to me. I'll try.

The minister says he wants to see the things I call scars from the boys jumping on me, doing weird things, and I tell him I can't show him the scars because I have to take off my clothes and he says, "We'll say a prayer and it'll be okay."

We say a prayer and I take off my shirt. He doesn't want to see the scars. He wants to do the same things my big boys do! I hightail it out of there, yelling at the top of my lungs. He told everybody after that how sick inside I was and how I'd never tell the truth. Now Mrs. Anderson doesn't like me anymore. I heard her talking to my dad and she said she was worried about me, and she was really upset, and my dad said, "See? I told you. She's always been like that."

He said I've always been a strange kid. I have always been strange! They are the ones who are strange! Strange, strange, strange. Anyway, he told 'em that I always lied all my life and that I've always been sick. Nothing was ever the same with Mrs. Anderson. No more talking and no more sleeping upstairs. No more good things. They say hello to me but they don't talk to me anymore and they don't invite me up to see TV and they don't invite me up ever. Mom was right when she said, "You little hell-yen, your goddamn mouth is gonna get you in serious trouble, smartass."

When am I gonna learn?

I heard Mrs. Anderson talking to Mr. Anderson and they said my dad had to keep us kids, otherwise the authorities would get him in trouble. I liked that! He deserves some damned trouble! They talked about my how dad's gonna move us out to a lake. We're gonna live in a trailer house. I wonder what that is. I still have to do the cooking and taking care of my little brother. But the cooking's better and dad doesn't throw the food or plates at me anymore, so I must be doing it right, I guess.

Part Two

The Adolescent

Butch

It's true, we're moving up to a lake in a trailer house. We have everything loaded up in dad's truck, and we're moving. We get to the lake and we drive into this place that's called a trailer park and we get to ours and we unload all our stuff.

I feel a lot happier these days. I am gonna be twelve years old in three months but people tell me I look sixteen. Sylvia lives in one of these trailer houses, and so does Butch. Butch is my friend and Sylvia is my friend too. We get to run around and laugh and climb trees by the lake and jump out of them into the lake. I love that. I still have to clean the trailer house and make them meals and do the laundry, but I don't mind. This isn't bad. Dad is gone most all the time. He comes home to eat and scream at me, and then he goes away. All right with me! My little brother has some friends to play with. He looks good. He doesn't look so sick anymore. He misses mom all the time, though. At night I hold him, and he cries himself to sleep cuz he misses mom. I don't know why he misses her. I don't miss her. Maybe that's cuz I'm sick and strange.

Butch says he's gonna marry me when we grow up, and I told him I'm never marrying anybody. I told him I hate that stuff married people do. Butch says he likes that kissing married people do. I want to know what that is. I don't know about this kissing thing. He tells me, you put your lips together and just wiggle 'em and you like it. We tried it. He was right, I liked it. He didn't do anything else, or I'd have to pull off his arm and beat him with the bloody end, like mom says she'll do to me all the time. We just do a lot of hugging and that kissing thing. I loved it! Sylvia was doing it with her boyfriend, David, she said that she loved it too. Whoa, maybe I will get married if kissing is all they do. I like this.

Butch is so much fun. We run around and run around and run around and we go everywhere and we get in the lake and we get in other people's boats and we get in trouble because one of 'em broke away from the shore and it drifted out and somebody had to come and get us and we thought it was great but they didn't. We climbed this big tree and we sit in the tree and talk and when we're not sitting in the tree and talking, we're leaping off the branch into the water. It's a fun time, a fun good time.

I found out mom got rid of all the kids. Most of 'em are working cuz they're out of school, and she's pregnant, she's gonna have a baby. A baby! She hates everybody, why does she want to have a baby? I'm the one who should have a baby. I want a family.

I was putting the food back in the morning and cleaning up the dishes and in the door walks Daryl. Here we go. He slaps around and yanks off my clothes. I'm not staying here. I'm not gonna live in any place he lives. He's a rotten assbite son-of-a-bitch! I want to kill him. He does horrifying things. He always does and he calls me all kinds of names and he tells me if I tell anybody this time he'll kill me. I don't care. I hit him and kick him and bite his arm and I just keep fighting him and fighting him and he does what he does and he goes away. Kill me, I say. Get it over with!

I think of going to see Butch but all of a sudden I hate the idea of kissing and I guess I hate everything. I get up and wash myself all over. I hate that fucking Daryl. Mrs. Sawyer says you have to think of good things. I don't know any good things about him. Mrs. Sawyer says you have to be happy or you'll grow up like your mom, very unhappy. I'm not gonna do it. I'm gonna be happy. I don't wanna be like them. Any of 'em. I don't even wanna be like my lovable little brother. I don't wanna be here.

The summer is over and I have to start school again anyway so I might as well go away. I'm gonna try it again and see if it works. This time was really bad, assbite really hit me a lot. I don't feel very good, either, for many days now. I don't think I'm gonna take much of my stuff from here. I don't know who's gonna take care of my lil brother, but everybody here likes him. He likes them. He'll be okay. I'll sing him those spirit songs.

The Dead Family

I get my favorite little things, wrapped up in a shirt and tied, and I walk down the road past the lake. I don't even know where I'm going this time. I don't know the area. At home I knew where every tree in the place was. But here I don't know much. I'm just gonna walk and walk and get a ride on a truck again.

I walk and walk but nobody picks me up and I don't see any trucks yet. I don't know why but I don't think living is very much fun because you get happy and you romp and frolic and then some fucker come along and hurts you really bad. Because you're a girl and because you're smaller than they are. Maybe mom was right. I'm not as smart as I think I am. If she's right, I don't see why people keep breathing. I mean, why do this damn life — why? I should just swim out in this lake so far that I can't come back. A guy did that this summer, and he died. It only took a little while. I don't know. I'm gonna think about laughing with Butch. Maybe people stay alive for those kind of things. I don't know. Joe told me that it's my life and I can get to do what I want with it. He's wrong. People just come and wreck your days and hurt your body and the things they say to you make you feel terrible.

What if it's true that I caused all of this? What if I dreamt it. That authority person, Miss Grubb, and everybody ends up thinking I made it up. Why did I make it up and keep it in my head? Just walking and walking and walking and walking and no trucks. This must be the kind of road that trucks can't go on. I don't feel very good. I never felt like this before.

Now what's wrong? I'm awake and I'm in a hospital. I know hospitals when I see 'em. They have all these white sheets and they have me laying down and then they're just standing there and a man is standing there. The people have white things on, too. This is a hospital. I've been eating good. I shouldn't be in a hospital.

I tried to get up and they made me lay down again. The man says his name is Dr. Larkin. He doesn't have that "hit-you" look. Dr. Larkin asked me how old I was and I told him almost twelve years old. He asked what happened to me out on the road.

I tell him, "I was walking on the road and now I'm here."

He said, "Were you running away?"

I said, "How did you know that?"

He said, "Because you have your things all wrapped up here."

I said, "Yes, I'm running away, and I'm gonna keep running away so let me out of this goddamn hospital."

He says, "Such talk for a young lady!"

Young lady! Of all the things people call me, I hate the most! Such talk, my ass!

"How come I can't get out of this bed?" I tell him.

He says, "You were found on the road."

"I was found on the road? No kidding, that's where I was walking."

He said, "No, you were laying down, unconscious."

"What's unconscious?"

"Where you go to sleep when you don't want to. You fainted."

"Well, I don't know what you're talking about. I was just running away, I wasn't trying to faint."

He said, "What are all these bruises and cuts on you?"

I said, "Those are not cuts — can't you tell anything? That's from Daryl jumping up and down on me."

"What do you mean?"

"I'm gonna tell you this story, and you're gonna say, 'Oh, don't make up such rotten ugly stories,' aren't you? Everybody tells me I have an ugly mind and I make up bad stories and I have a nasty mouth and, fuck you people, I don't care if I have a nasty everything!"

He said, "What do you mean, jumping up and down on you?"

The nurse is patting my head. Pretty soon they'll start yelling, "Stop making up these stories," right? Oh, hell. I might as well tell 'em so they can hurry up and say it so I can hurry up and get off this bed, tear up this room, and pull off my own stupid head and get it over with.

"Crosses my legs and then takes his thing and puts 'em between 'em and then he jumps up and down a whole lot and it takes all the skin off me."

"Oh," the doctor says.

Oh. Like that. I never heard anybody do that before. This is where they finally leave the room. But they're not leaving the room. This is a different place, this Michigan. Maybe people here don't — well, people here do too, the minister did that thing and Mrs. Anderson didn't let — I don't know anything anymore. I just don't know anything at all. I just want out of this bed.

He says, "No, you have to stay right here. Where do you live?"

I told him I don't live anywhere.

He says, "Now come on, you have to tell us where you live so we can contact your parents."

"I don't have any parents, they're dead."

I couldn't believe my own ears. Ah ha, I told 'em they were dead. Chortle goddamn chortle. What an idea! From now on, all my life I can just say, Blamo, they're dead and people will just stand there like Dr. Larkin is now, looking at the ceiling wondering what the hell to do. I have dead parents! Louise, you're so smart! Dead parents, what a deal! Dead parents. Dead assbite boys. Yeah!

Okay, I don't have any family, period. Dr. Larkin said, "Where were you living when you packed your stuff and got on the road?"

"I don't remember."

Dr. Larkin says, "You're gonna be real hard to handle, aren't you?"

I thought, You haven't seen half of it. If you don't let me out of this bed I'm gonna be even harder to handle. I tell him that and he tells me "Okay, let's do this. Let's make a deal."

A deal? "Yes, let's make a deal that you stay in this bed for me and we'll feed you really good and we'll fix all your sore places and then we'll find you a place to stay. Okay?"

I wonder what the real deal is, but I say okay because I really don't feel very good and I'm hungry and the sores on my legs and hips and face and arms make me really hurt, so laying down for awhile is an all right idea.

The nurse's name is Charlotte. Charlotte's nice to me, for now. There's something about her that makes me feel warm. I ask her if she's a mom. She says yes.

I say, "Do you hit your kids and scream at 'em too?"

She says, "No."

I say, "Do they do what you tell 'em?"

She says yes. I think, oh good. Mom's wrong — you really don't have to hit people. Mom is always saying you have to hit people because they don't listen, that's why she hits me. She hits me so I will do my chores and I tell Charlotte, "I always did my chores anyway. But she always hit me anyway, too."

Charlotte says, "Well, not everybody does the same thing." Charlotte has a lot of everybody's she hasn't seen yet, I say.

I ask her if she knows as much about my bruises and everything as the doctor and she says, "I know a lot but not as much as the doctor."

Then I ask her how long you have to hold your breath before you die, and she started laughing, she said, "That's not possible. You can't just hold your breath and die."

"Why?"

I want to know why you can't just hold your breath. If you can't breathe, then you die, right?

She says, "Yes."

I said, "How long do you have to hold your breath?"

She says, "Well, there's some facts you need to know."

"Facts. What's a fact?"

"It's something that's real true. It's always true."

"Oh."

"Well, the fact is," Charlotte says, "if you hold your breath, you would go unconscious. You would faint, just like you already did. But you wouldn't die. Your body would save you because it wants to live."

My body wants to live, so it won't die on purpose. I'd have to do something bad to it? Yes. Well, they do bad things to it all the time and it doesn't die.

She said, "Yes, luckily they don't do things that are bad enough to kill you."

"Oh."

Then I think of Mrs. Sawyer's think-of-the-good-things, so the good thing is that they never do anything bad enough to kill me. I get it, Mrs. Sawyer was right! I tell that to Charlotte. She hugs me. Some people do this hugging, and some people don't. I really can't tell who's doing what. The minister hugged me right before he started rubbing my chest and stuck his hands down my pants, but that's a bad hugging. I tell that to her. She says, yes, that's bad hugging. There's good hugging and bad hugging, I say. She says yes. Then she tells me, "Now you close your eyes and go back to sleep. I'll see you in the morning."

I ask her, "Are you gonna send a hag nurse in, cuz I told you all this stuff? When I was in the hospital before they had a nurse who really liked me and I told her all this stuff and she never came back to my bed and then hag nurse told me it was because of those stories. Everybody hates those stories and they tell me I make them up."

Charlotte says, "You just close your eyes. I will be here in the morning."

The sun is coming up and Charlotte isn't here. She lied to me. So what. Some woman is gonna come in here and scream at me again.

I sit up in my bed and scream, "Hey! Who the hell is out there?"

The nurse comes in and I think, uh oh, is this a hag nurse?

The nurse comes in and says, "Charlotte just called and said she'll be here in a minute. Do you want any breakfast before she comes or when she comes?"

"When she comes," I tell her.

She leaves and turns around at the door and says, "Just push that little button, you don't have to holler."

At the top of my lungs I scream, "I like to holler! I'm a filthy little rat that hollers."

She came over to the bed and she said, "Please. You're gonna wake up other sick people."

"Oh, all right. I'll push the buzzer, but I like to holler."

Charlotte comes and we have breakfast and she talks to me and talks to me and talks to me. I like talking to her. We talk about other things, like she asks me how far I walked and I tell her, "I don't know, but back home — "

She says, "Where's back home?"

I tell her, "Wisconsin, silly. Anyway, back home I walked miles and miles. I like to walk. I don't know why I laid down and went to sleep. I didn't know I was gonna do it."

She says she knows that. It's called fainting. Fainting.

"That's when your body is so tired or sick that it goes to sleep whether you want it to or not."

Okay. It can do things I don't want it to do. That makes me nervous. I don't want my body running around doing stuff I don't want it to do. But she says that happens when you're really hurt and I was really hurt. Oh.

She says it's time for her to go and she'd be back every day. I said, "Who picked me up? Who is the person?"

She says, "It was me, I was on my way to work. I saw you and brought you to Dr. Larkin's. I work at his office."

"Oh. Well, it was nice of you to not leave me on the road. Something might have run over me."

She says, "I know, and you're too little to be running around by yourself."

I sat up in the bed and I tell her at the top of my lungs, "I'm not damn little! I'm getting bigger every year! Pretty soon I'll be big enough to live by myself and get my own job and you take back 'I'm little'. I'm not very little."

She stood up and put her hands on my shoulders and she says, "Okay. You're not that little."

"Thank-you, yellow-haired Charlotte," I say.

For a couple of days, I rest and eat and I'm tired of the bed. I get out of it and I put on my clothes. I want to go home.

She says, "Where's home?"

I said, "I told you I was looking for one."

She says, "You have to stay here until we find a good place for you to be."

I told her, "You know what? I work really hard. I can carry water now and not spill it all over myself and I can carry wood and I can make meals and I can clean a house...I'm good at that stuff. I'm good with taking care of Mrs. Sawyer's babies."

"Who's Mrs. Sawyer?" she asked. "She's my neighbor in Wisconsin. I mean Michigan. Also I don't get to see her."

"Was she your mother?"

"No. I told you my parents are dead."

A woman walks in my room and asks me my name and I tell it. I don't like the looks of her. Behind her comes Charlotte, and she says, "This is a social worker."

I'm out of bed. Out of bed scrambling for my clothes and trying to get out of the room. An authority! That's what she did. Charlotte brought an authority. There's a big wrestling match, and I didn't win. Charlotte put her arms around me and held on and I couldn't even hit her. She had me in a hug lock of some kind. I didn't know what the hell happened but I couldn't do anything but holler. I yelled and hollered and yelled and hollered. She didn't let go of me. Then I sat down, I'm tired again.

She brought me back to the bed and the horrible authority wants to know where I live and I told her, "I don't live anywhere, I was looking for a place, you guys, you must be deaf or something. I already told you this."

She says, "Where's your mother?"

"I don't have one, she's dead. I told you, everybody's dead."

She says, "Well, we're going to let you go home with Charlotte."

What? Home with Charlotte? "You can help Charlotte with the house and the babies, then we'll see what to do after that."

They left the room and a few minutes later Charlotte comes back and she says, "I had to bring an authority. It's against the law for me to just take you home without telling anybody."

"I hate authorities, Charlotte, I hate them, they do mean things to me, and they won't let me live with Mrs. Sawyer, and they drag me where I don't want to go."

Charlotte said, "Well, we'll deal with that later. Right now what I want you to do is put these on." She hands me a new shirt and new pants. Underwear! I get underwear! I sing an underwear song. What a deal! Everybody's always had underwear, I don't.

I sat back down on the bed and tell Charlotte, "I can't go home with you. Because I wet the bed."

She says, "I know you wet the bed. We can wash the sheets. Put on your clothes."

I put on my clothes and guess what, in a box she has socks and shoes. My size! Brand new! I can't believe it! More singing and singing.

Charlotte's House

We go to Charlotte's house and she has two kids, Cathy and Ricky. And a husband named Dick. Dick's going to school and Cathy and Ricky are too little to go to school, and Charlotte works as a nurse at the Dr. Larkin's office. Charlotte gave me a room upstairs, an attic-like room, and they're all downstairs. My room has my own bed and my own stuff to read and my own stuff to do and a little radio of my own. A little radio! I can sing and sing and sing. I miss my audience at the gravel pit. I miss singing at the top of my lungs. I miss that. I'm going to miss some swearing cuz I can't swear around here. My trusty feel good swearing will just have to be done alone, to myself, again.

One time I was singing at the top of my lungs upstairs and Charlotte came up and knocked on the door, opened the door and started clapping. I felt really weird, I shut up, and she said, "That song rates applause. You rate applause. You're quite a little girl."

I said, "I'm not so little. What's applause?"

"Where people are glad that you did what you did. If you sing a good song or you do something neat, then they clap. You know, you provided something for them, gave them some entertainment." .

"What's entertainment?"

"Oh, if I danced for you, and you liked it, then you would clap and that's called applause and the dance was entertainment."

I said, "You know what? I should be getting applause for all of my life. I've been entertainment forever. Not the kind of entertainment I want to be — I'd like to have applause for singing. I love to sing."

She said, "You're very good singer."

"I am?"

"Yes!"

"I've been singing forever, Charlotte, and all it ever gets me is slapped and hollered at."

She said, "Well, I like your singing. I think it's worth applauding," and then she said, "Dinner is ready."

I went downstairs to dinner. She likes my singing! It's worth applauding! I've been singing forever. Where's the applause? I've been entertaining everybody forever. I entertain my lil brother and make him feel better, and I'm entertainment for the assbite boys, whether I like it or not. I want to know where the damned applause has been.

I have lots of jobs here. I do the dishes after dinner, clean up the kitchen, and I take care of the babies and I watch 'em in their baths so they don't fall in. They have a bathtub and bubble bath stuff too. I get to take a bath that way, too. First I have to watch the babies, then I dry 'em off, and put on their pajamas. I have pajamas now, too. I put on their pajamas and then they go and their mom talks to 'em and their dad talks to 'em and puts 'em to bed. They don't hit these kids, either. They hug 'em and hold 'em and tell 'em stories, and kiss them "goodnight." That's a new one.

Charlotte plays the piano beautifully. Dick sings. They go to church called Baptist church. I go too. But I don't go to Sunday school and get asked weird questions. I like church and I like that singing. Sometimes Charlotte plays the piano and I sing. They applaud. I love applause. It's good for me. That applauding is just right. When they sing, I applaud them too, and when the little girls, Cathy and Ricky sing, I applaud them too. At night, after I do what I'm supposed to do, I go up into my room and I do a lot of crying and I still don't know about this crying stuff. I miss mom, for some reason. Actually, I don't know if it's mom but I miss all of my trees and my animals and my dog and my lake and my rag house and my dump. I wish mom were like these other moms and there was no hitting and they're happy with what their children do. That's how I miss mom. I wish she was like that.

I hope my lil brother's okay. I still don't tell 'em I have a family. That authority woman came twice to see if I'll tell her where my family is. Charlotte says that Dick's going to graduate pretty soon and if they have to move away, they want to take me with 'em. But they can't take me with 'em unless the authorities says it's okay. I tell Charlotte that the authorities are never going to say anything's okay for me, except to live with dreaded people. I don't tell 'em dreaded dad and mom, cuz I already told 'em they're dead. She says, well, it's too bad that all of your family's dead because we could get them to sign a paper and then we could take you with us.

"Where are you going, Charlotte?"

"When Dick graduates in a couple of months now, we're going to move to Florida and live near a University."

"What's a University?"

She says, it's a place where they teach grown ups about things like Nursing and Engineering.

"Oh, I do I have to go? I hate school!"

"No."

Oh. "Well, I want to go, but if I tell you anything about my family, then they won't sign any papers and I won't get to go."

She says, "You won't get to go anyway if we can't get the papers signed. The authorities won't let us take you to Florida with us."

After dinner one night, Charlotte and Dick said they really want to have a serious talk with me. I sat on the couch and I think, Oh boy...I've no idea what they're going to do to me.

Dick says, "You know, lots of mothers can have babies, it's like chickens lay eggs. But they don't take care of 'em, and when they don't take care of 'em, somebody else should take care of 'em. If we could find out who your mom is, or your dad, they could sign some papers. We want to take you — we like you. You could go to Florida with us, but not unless we find out who needs to sign those papers."

I just sat there. I had been living with them a long time now, and I liked my jobs, and they liked me and I loved that applauding and singing. Maybe I should tell 'em.

So I'll tell 'em. Where my dad is out at a lake in a trailer park and he has my lil brother and he screams at me and he gets drunk and pounds on the walls every night and he eats the breakfast and his dinner that I cook, but I have a dreaded brother who comes and does ugly things so I'm leaving, that's why I left, but I'm not going to go back there. My mom lives in Wisconsin and she doesn't like me, but she never liked me. Probably because I tried to kill her by being born, is what she says. They just looked at each other. Charlotte cries. I go upstairs, I think, okay, here I go again. I'm going to have to leave tomorrow, I bet. My mouth. Smartass big mouth.

After awhile Charlotte comes back upstairs to see me. She says, "I'm sorry I cried, but it's sad that people do so many mean things to each other."

I like the way Charlotte talks. I wish I could talk that way. She doesn't let me swear around the kids, but I swear everywhere else. I just want to. It feels good to me. She says I'm going to have to learn to quit it. I don't know if I'm ever going to do that, but I try. She says, she and the authorities are going to get my dad to sign and I said, "You don't know him. He'll pull off your head. He's terrible."

She says, "We'll see."

I said, "I'm not going to go see him. He's not coming here and I'm not going to stay here if he comes here. I'm not going to be around them ever again."

One afternoon Charlotte invited all of her family, her mom and dad and her sister and husband and kids and everything. We're having a celebration! The celebration is about me! The celebration is that my dad did sign the papers, and I do get to go to Florida with 'em! I don't have to go to a University either. We're going right after Christmas. I can hardly wait. They really do want me and I really am going to go, and everybody at the celebration is congratulating me. That's when you think somebody's done something neat and you tell 'em "Congratulations!" Then Charlotte has me sing the song she taught me and then there's all this applause. For goodness' sakes, all these people with the applause! It's great and I decided "Congratulations" is mouth applause. Hand applause — mouth applause — get it?

Florida, Negroes and God

We're packing all the cars. I'm not riding in the one with Charlotte and Dick and Cathy and Ricky. I'm riding with Martha, a friend of theirs. Martha's mom and dad live in Florida so she is going to drive one of Dick's cars down as a favor. I have to go with her, stay with her till we get to Florida. We will leave for Florida one week after Dick and Charlotte do. I think Martha is just going to take me somewhere else. Charlotte says that's not true. But it wouldn't be the first time "not-true" didn't mean anything and it happened anyway. Lots of people say, "Well, that's not true." It is too! It's too true! But they keep saying it's not true, I think it's because then they don't have to know it or something. I don't know.

In Dick's other car is Charlotte and Cathy and Ricky, I hug 'em all and say good-by. They drive away. I just stand there till Martha tells me to get in the car and we go to her house.

It's time now for Martha and me to go to Florida finally! We drive and drive. I see all kinds of land. Different from the land where I live with my animals and my rag house. Some pretty land, some ugly land. Lots of new things. We went into a place called Georgia, she says. Martha says the state of Georgia has pizzas. I had some pizzas at Charlotte's house. I like 'em. I ask her if we can stop and get some. She says we're going to stop pretty soon. We have stopped and eaten on the road. She calls it "eating on the road." We go to restaurants and get food! She pays 'em with money. I ask her what happens if you get food and you don't pay for it, and she said they get really mad. They'll probably make you go in the kitchen and wash dishes. I thought, how easy! I know how to do the dishes.

We stop at another restaurant. Boy, for weird! Everybody here that's not eating has black, black skin! I never saw anything like this! Very black! She says they're called "Negroes." Martha ordered us fried chicken. I love fried chicken. Martha's nice to me. She tells me a lot of things. Like when we pass things, she tells me how they got that way, that a big giant iceberg came and made valleys. Big giant iceberg! I don't know how big it would have to be, but it made valleys, and then after that the water filled it up. She said God did that. She must have a different God than the people where my rag house is. Her God sounds like he does something. I like gods that do something.

This Negro person brings the fried chicken and I grab the Negro's hand and I kissed it. Martha slapped me. She slapped my hand! She said, you must never touch a Negro. I said, "Why?"

She said, "Because we just don't do that."

I said, "I just did that. She was nice to me, look at this chicken, it's wonderful!"

"You don't ever touch a Negro," Martha said. "Don't forget it."

That's the first time Martha's been mad at me. I wonder why you don't touch Negroes. Maybe when I'm not with Martha I can touch 'em. They're really different from me. Very nice to me, too. Anything I ask for they run right over and get it. I don't know why you wouldn't touch a person who's so nice to you.

She ordered a dessert with ice cream. The Negro came this time, I applauded because I thought, if you can't touch 'em, then like Charlotte said, applause is when somebody does something for you that you like. I applauded. Martha made me go sit in the car. No ice cream, no nothing. Martha came out to the car and she said, "I told you. You don't touch Negroes. You don't talk to them except to tell them what to do. You don't applaud in public restaurants. You applaud at theaters."

I told her, "Charlotte applauds me at home."

She said, "Well, never mind. When it comes to Negroes, you simply tell them what you want and nothing more."

I said, "Am I supposed to do those manners things with them? You know, like the thank you's and shit?"

She said, "In the first place, you're not supposed to swear, and in the second place, yes, you can say thank you to Negroes if you want to. You don't have to. They're supposed to do what you tell them."

I ask her why. Why do they have to do what you tell 'em, and you don't even have to be nice to 'em?

Martha says, "You don't have to be mean to them. You just don't touch 'em and you don't talk to 'em except to thank 'em if you want to. First you tell 'em what you want, and then if you feel like thanking them, you can."

Again I ask her, "Martha, why do Negroes have to be treated like that?"

She says "Because God made Negroes, after Cain killed Abel, remember the Bible story where Cain kills Abel?"

"Yes, I remember the Bible story because I'm going to kill my brother too. What has that got to do with it?"

She said, "Well, if you read the story really good, it says, after Cain killed Abel, God cursed him with a dark skin."

Oh, no, I thought. All of these people who are this black color, all of these Negroes, are cursed with a dark skin from God? They have the same God! I just figured it out. They just talk about him different. He's a shit. He's mean and he does stupid things and once in a while, if you're lucky, he makes things like icebergs and lakes and stuff; otherwise, he's just a jerk. I'm not having that kind of God. I'm sticking to my spirit guides. What a mean God! I don't care if I get a black skin after I kill assbite Daryl.

We're driving along and Martha tells me how Jesus died for my sins. I get her to tell me what sins are. "Sins" are the things you do that the Bible tells you not to do. Okay. Sins are the things that we do that the Bible tells us not to do. Jesus died — Jesus is the son of God, and he died so that God wouldn't be mad at all of us for all those sins we do. I ask her, "How come God's so dumb, he makes a whole bunch of people who does things he doesn't want them to do?"

She says to watch my smart mouth. She says, "You need to know more before you start talking like that. You don't know enough about the Bible or our savior Jesus Christ."

I thought, Jesus Christ is right! Jesus Christ! I've been saved by somebody I don't even know, who didn't save me from mom and dad and the assbite boys, but I have to pay for a whole bunch of things that they wrote down that I don't know about. I can't understand — I'm going to sleep! I'm just going to lay back in this car and go to sleep. Who the hell could understand this God thing anyway? God is the father, he sends Jesus to earth, we hang Jesus on the cross, she said. You know what? I had nothing to do with that! I didn't know anything about it. I didn't do it. We hung him on the cross, she says, and he died for our sins. That we don't have to go to hell. I don't get it. I wasn't here! I don't know Jesus. I sure as hell didn't hang him anywhere, and I'd never make people run around with black skin because somebody else did something. That would be like me having to live at home forever. Because they did these bad things, so then my skin starts getting darker and darker and darker till I'm black. Wonder if that's going to happen to me?

I ask Martha, "Do people get black skin after they're bad enough?"

"No," Martha says, "they're born with it."

"I thought God did life and death. He was in charge."

"He is," Martha said.

"Well, why would he do that on purpose, so people can run around and be mad at you because you have black skin. I don't get it. Why?"

"Oh," Martha says, "you lay back and rest. We'll talk about this some more later."

I put my head back to rest. This God these people have is just not good! I mean he does dumber things than my mom does! We're not going to talk about it later because every time Martha says anything, from now on, on this traveling thing we're doing, I'm just going to agree with her. There's no way I'm going to understand this God thing. I think it's just stupid. Anyways, if there really is a God like that, he's mean!

We get out of the car to a place called a "motel." We get to sleep in this motel, and then in the morning we get back up. Every day we do this. We get back up and get in the car and drive again. Motels are pretty neat. I ask her, what happens if you try to sleep in one with no money, and she says they kick you out. Now I get it. You can go into restaurants and eat and if you don't have money, they'll make you do dishes, but you can't sleep in motel rooms without money no matter what you do. Martha and I, when we're traveling on the road, sing church songs together. She says I'm an alto. I ask her if she'd like a sharp slap to the head. She said an alto is a kind of voice. A very high voice is a soprano and a low voice is an alto. A very low voice is a bass. I have an in-between, she says, an alto. I ask her if it's good before I get really mad, and she says it's very good. Now I'm not mad anymore, I have an alto voice. I applaud that. I like it.

Martha says pretty soon we'll be in Florida. That's good, I miss Charlotte, I want to hug her. I miss Ricky and Cathy. I wonder how my lil brother is. I wonder if he misses me like I miss him. I wonder where Mrs. Sawyer is. I wonder if everybody's still there, where they were. Maybe my head made them up too.

We get to Florida. It's so hot! This is January, it's supposed to be snowing. She says it never snows in Florida. Never snows? Who woulda ever thought a place like that would be around? She says in Florida, it's always hot, and it rains a lot. I kinda like this. It means you can go swimming all times of the year. Martha says that's true. I like swimming.

I Am Crazy

We get to Charlotte and Dick's house. I'm so happy to see them. Charlotte and Dick's stuff is coming in a "moving van." It's a big truck that brings all their furniture and everything and I have to help unload it and I can't wait, there's a lot of stuff I miss. Their piano's coming. They live in this beautiful house. I've never been in a house like this. It has these really pretty floors. They're like cement almost, but they're — he calls 'em terrazzo. I like that name, terrazzo. When I get a dog I'm going to name it Terrazzo. Better yet, I should get a horse and name it Terrazzo. Anyway, the floors are terrazzo and they're pretty. They have lots of room and I have my own room again. How did I get so lucky to have my own room. They have a big giant pool and big giant lawns and a big giant house? I'm happy! I like this!

The day the moving van came, Dick was at home and Charlotte called it a three-ring circus. I don't know what that is, I have to talk to her about it later, but everybody was running around unloading stuff and putting it in rooms and saying, "No, that's not the room, put it in this room." That went on all damn morning. We have our couch and we have the piano and we have lots of really neat things. I love 'em. We had 'em before, but I'm just glad to see 'em again. Tonight Dick will be glad because he wanted his own bed. They've been sleeping on the floor on mats.

Cathy and Ricky hug me as usual and we run around and play, and when they make me mad I tell 'em I'm mad and they cry and so I get unmad and they do what I tell 'em most of the time. I like them. They're cute and funny.

I've only been here a few days and already I have things on my legs, big giant bubble-like things. Charlotte says they're probably hives. I've no idea what hives are — the last hive I knew about had bees in it. My brother stepped on one on the ground and I had to drag him out of it because he was just like mom, instead of getting out of it, he just stood there and screamed. I yanked him up and got bit several more times myself so I had to slap him for that. But that's the last hive I knew about. These are on my skin. I ask if there's going to be bees or something in 'em, and she says no, they itch and she's going to take me to the doctor. The doctor says it's probably because I'm allergic to the cat. The cat touches me, and I get skin ulcers.

When Dick got home, Charlotte told him about my cat allergy and Dick said, "Well, I don't know what to tell you because I'm not putting that cat outside. It's been in the family for years and years, and when we left for Florida dad gave it to me and I promised I'd take good care of it. We'll just have to think of something."

Now I stay away from the cat as much as possible and they have medicine to put on the skin sores. I still can breathe good, though. I don't have any trouble. I like breathing good. I hated it when I used to have to sit up all night to try to breathe.

Pretty soon I'll have to go to school, dreaded goddamn school. I hate school.

The skin allergies have gotten very bad. They're all over me. I don't feel very good, and we're going back to the doctor again today. I can't sleep because I itch so much and I can't scratch because it hurts so much and everything is all infected and bleeding and we have to go get it fixed. When we get to the doctor, he checks me over and he gives me a shot. I'm not applauding, or thanking him for that. I hated it. Then he gives Charlotte some medicine for me, and he says, "This medicine will help her sleep."

I have to be in bed for a little while, he says.

Dick told me the other day that I was getting really cute because I'm getting little breasts and pretty soon I'll be a woman. I have to eat right and comb my hair a lot. Pretty soon I'll need a bra, he says. I hate that idea! I'm really mad that I'm getting breasts and I didn't ask for them. I don't want to wear a bra! I don't even want to be a girl. I don't want to be a boy, either. Dick says I'm stuck with being a girl and I should be proud of it. I'm going to be really sexy, he says. I had to ask him to explain sexy, and he got mad and told me to never mind. But first I have to get over these skin allergies. Later when Dick wasn't mad, he told me being sexy is when you look good and men want you. Blaghk!

I get sick to my stomach a little bit, too, and I'm very hot. The doctor says that's because all of these sores are infected now. Not to mention that I grew some fungus. Are you ready for that? Fungus grows on trees here, and so does moss, and I grew some on my toes! In between 'em, icky, yucky, fungus. I hate it. I have to take all this medicine and sleep a lot.

I'm feeling better these days. I don't have anything to do with the damn cat and I guess I'm really a bad girl because when Dick's not home I sling that cat outside. I pick him up with a kitchen dish towel and throw him outside. I have less problems now that I do that. I go get 'em as soon as I know Dick's coming home, or Charlotte's coming home. Besides, Mrs. Sawyer said animals belong outside. Maybe that cat really wants to be outside and nobody lets it.

Now I have to go to school, and I have to actually go, I can't pretend I'm going to school like I used to because I will get Charlotte and Dick in trouble. I don't know why, but every time I go to school, I don't feel good. My stomach hurts, my head hurts, I don't know why. Besides, I think everybody hates me and I don't know why either. The big boys told me that I'm really ugly and have a giant eagle beak and have mean eyes. Maybe everybody can see that. I don't know, I don't feel good at school. I'm going to go, though. I don't want Charlotte and Dick in trouble. I don't want to go back to dreaded dad's house. I'm going to damned school.

There's a bus stop and I stand at it and other kids stand at it and I can't talk. I can't say anything. I don't know why I can't do this. This makes me feel really goofy. I can't go to school, I can't stay home, I can't stand it. At school I don't talk to anybody. I just try to do my schoolwork and go home. At lunch time I stay in the library. I don't know what it is. At school I feel awful. At night I can't go to sleep because I have to go to school in the morning-it just makes me sick. What the hell's the matter with me? Why can't I just go to school...everybody goes to school, why can't I just do it and shut up? Dick and Charlotte talk to me a lot about it. I can't figure it out, they can't figure it out either. But I'm telling you it's awful because I can't sleep at night, then I sleep at school. I'd rather sleep at school, if I could just sit at that damned desk and go to sleep instead of trying to talk to people which I don't want to do.

Charlotte said if I keep not sleeping, she's taking me back to the doctor. And I have to go have all my infections and fungus checked. Charlotte also said I have to play with people who are really nice. People from our neighborhood, from good homes that are good people and I can't swear when I'm with 'em. Every Friday night I have to go to Mindy's house and go out with her and her friends because Charlotte says she's a "good example" for me. I ask her what the hell that is, and she tells me that a good example is someone you should try to be like. I don't want to be like Mindy. She's a big baby. She's nice, but she's afraid of everything. I don't tell Charlotte that, for some reason I don't think she wants to know it. I have to go with Mindy and her friends.

Mindy and her friends get in a thing called a dune-buggy and they have twenty-two pistols and they shoot at the Negroes. There's a special place where the Negroes live and they have icky houses and a lot of 'em don't even have doors and it's stinky-smelling. Reminds me of home. Mindy goes on this dune buggy and we sit on the back and the guys shoot at the houses. I can't believe Charlotte thinks this is what I want to be having for an example. I don't want to shoot at no Negroes. The guys in the dune buggy say that they don't know that they hit any, and I say of course you don't, asshole, that's because it's dark and you're just shooting but we hear everybody hollering. I don't know if we hit them or not. One of the guys hands me a twenty two and he says, "You shoot it"

I said, "I'm not going to."

He says "If you don't shoot this, you can't go out with us."

I said, "Who gives a shit?"

They kick me off the dune buggy and I walk home.

I can't tell Charlotte, though. I don't want to shoot at Negroes. I don't care if God cursed them with a black skin because dumb Cain killed his idiot brother a million years ago. I don't know why Charlotte would think this was good. I'm afraid to ask her anything. One of the mothers called Charlotte today and told her that her son said that I was really a creep and he didn't want me going on his dune buggy anymore. Charlotte was really upset. I didn't know what to say. I can't tell her — I don't know why I don't tell her about shooting at Negroes. But she probably already knows it, that's what she wanted me to learn and I can't do it and I can't tell her I can't do it, for then she'll be disappointed and there'll be no more applause.

When I get sick at school I leave it and I walk around town and I go to shopping center stores. They have one store that says that Negroes drink at this drinking fountain and whites drink at this drinking fountain. Do you know these black people, here in Florida, are called Negroes, they all go to the same bathroom, boys and girls. The whites have a special bathroom for girls and a special bathroom for boys. People shoot at 'em and you can't kiss their hands and you can't applaud 'em. You can only say thank you if you feel like it, and they can only do what they're told. I'd make a real bad Negro. I'd be slapping people a lot.

The doctor says I'm getting worse. Now I have strep throat and my tonsils need to come out. My infections aren't healing up and I'm losing weight and I can't sleep. He gave her some pills to put me to sleep. I have to take 'em every night and see if I get healthy, he said. These pills make me feel screwy. I lay there and everything feels weird, my head is spinning around all by itself without me and I'm not even moving. I dream really weird things try to get me. I feel groggy and sleepy and I don't wake up very good. In the morning I can barely go and do my breakfast chores. I dream things about mom and dad and the big boys and my lil brother and my older sister. I dream about everybody and Mrs. Sawyer. I dreamed I rode one of my deer into the sky. It flew. I used to try to fly off the shed out back. All I managed to do was practically break my neck. I dream and I dream and I dream and the dreams make me sick. Dreams happen to your head when you're asleep, you don't even get to say anything about it. You can't even quit it when you want to. I like dreaming that deer flew, though. I wish I could fly.

Joe says you could fly in your mind. He's right, I can pretend it. Pretending's wonderful. I like pretending. These dreams make me feel bad, though. I keep hearing my dream say mom wants me to help her with her new baby if she has it now. I don't know why she's having a damn baby, she doesn't even like them. Why do I want to help her? She never helps me. Why am I having all these dreams? This pill I take every night makes me do things I don't want to do in my sleep. A lot of times Charlotte comes and wakes me up because she says I'm hollering. I don't remember hollering, but those dreams are horrifying so I'm not surprised. In my dreams, sometimes mom screams at me and tells me she hates me because I look like my dad. Sometimes in my dreams the big boys do all the things that I hate and sometimes in my dreams my rag house is all that's there. My mom's house isn't there anymore, and my lil brother is there and the deer that flies is there, and all my birds and animals and snakes and bugs and frogs, and my dog are there. I guess mom was right. I was born bad, and the big boys are right, I was born bad because sometimes in my dreams I dream that Dick is doing the same mean things to me the big boys did. Why would I dream that? Who the hell ever thought? Dick's nice to me. Besides, Dick said he believes in doing good things, not bad things. I don't know why I dream that.

It's been a couple weeks and Charlotte says we have to go back to the doctor to see if my strep throat is gone. All my sores look better, and I been sleeping because of those pills, so tomorrow we have to go back to the doctor. The doctor says I can go back to school now. I don't like being sick, but I don't like going to school, either. But he says my strep throat is gone and if I can't sleep, I'm supposed to keep taking those pills. I'm going to try sleeping on my own now, though.

When we get home, Charlotte tells Dick I'm a lot better and I do my dinner time chores and I do the baths for Cathy and Ricky. Sometimes I get to tell them stories, too. I sing them songs. They like that. It makes me so happy. Charlotte makes me have some warm milk tonight because she says that might help me sleep since I want to try to sleep without the pills. Dick is out to a meeting, so I go to my room after the warm milk and I go to sleep. I can feel sleep coming to get me. I like sleep coming to get me. This is a sweet Sleep feeling.

Even without the pills I'm having that dream again, that Dick is doing the same kind of weird things of sticking things up inside of me — oooh — the same things my brothers did. Why am I having this dream? I try to wake me up and I move around and sit up. See, I'm just bad inside. I wake up and I'm all by myself and nobody's doing anything to me. I don't know what's wrong with me.

I'm back in school, back in school and trying to like it. I feel so bad, though, even at lunch hours, I don't play with anybody. At my old school at least I used to play with Johnny. I miss him. I don't want to talk to anybody. I don't know why. I stay in school and I do what I'm supposed to do and at night I go home and I play with the girls and I give 'em their baths and I do my dinner time chores and I do stories and I sing songs and I like it. Tonight I'm going to try to sleep without the damn pills again. I hope I sleep without the damn awful dreams.

I'm dreaming again that Dick does those ugly things the big boys do. I wake up. I think I'm awake. I'm laying on my stomach and I believe I'm awake. He really is doing that. This isn't a dream! He has his fingers up inside of me and he has my hand on his thing and he's jacking off and this isn't a dream and I just lay there. I can't believe it. At home I'd get up and throw a fit. But here I just can't believe this. Why would he do this? Am I dreaming? What's wrong here? I don't get this. I don't want to know about this. I don't want to dream this, and if it's not a dream I really don't want this to happen. Dick believes in doing good things. Dick's always nice to me. He says nice things to me about my breasts developing, and I'm going to be sexy someday. Why would I dream this, it doesn't feel like a dream. This is not a dream. I know the difference. I do. Pretty soon Dick stops. I just stay on my stomach. He is doing that. This isn't a dream.

I wake up in the morning too sick to go to school again. I have strep throat again. My throat hurts and I have a fever and Charlotte tells me to go to bed. Again. I lay in bed all day. I'm hot and my throat hurts and I feel terrible. Most of all, I feel terrible that either I'm just awful inside and think up rotten things or Dick is awful inside and looks good outside. Tonight I'm going to try to sleep again without the medicine and see if I have the same dream or if Dick is really doing that. I don't think it's a dream. I mean it, I'm not kidding, I think it's real. How could he be like that? He's a Baptist. He says that he does what the Bible tells him to do. Doesn't the Bible say you're not supposed to put your fingers inside of people unless you ask? I mean, what's that Bible good for? Why does God give people who do nice things black skin so you can be mean to 'em? Let people who have white skin do icky things to people smaller than they are? Why is it bad to be a girl? My brothers always told me girls have to do what boys say. I think God's a boy. He's a shit. When I see him, I'm going to ask him, "All right, are you an assbite just like my brothers or do I not know something? Is there something I don't know that makes all of this okay? Or are you just rotten? I mean, rotten!"

I don't care if women do have to do what men say. I like women better. They don't do weird shit like that. They don't mess with you like that.

I get up from my bed because everybody's not home and I clean those terrazzo floors because it makes me feel better. Terrazzo looks pretty when you get it wet. It's shiny. Has pretty designs. I'm going to have a terrazzo floor when I grow up. I am going to get my own home and my own babies, for sure, when I grow up.

Maybe as soon as this strep throat is gone, I should pack my stuff and go. Like Joe says, though, I'll have to get ready for change. He says that's when you have to do something new. This change will be no more applause from Charlotte for my singing, and no more applause from Cathy and Ricky for my stories and the fun in the bathtub and no more applause from Dick for guessing the answers to questions he asks me. I gotta find out if these are dreams. I can't be mad at Dick if I'm dreaming this stuff.

I got over my sore throat and I went back to school. I try to sleep at night, but I don't sleep very much. I'm not dreaming. Dick is really doing that stuff. He doesn't scream ugly things at me and he doesn't hit me. He just does the other stuff.

I'm going to go away, now. I have to figure out what to do because I don't know where Florida is. I have to figure this out. I check around, ask a lot of questions at school. My teacher says, "Oh, you've decided to join the class!"

I think, No, I've decided to find out where Florida is so I know how to get out of here, but I don't tell her that. I tell her I want to know where Wisconsin is, so she shows me on the map, and I say, "If you were going to go from Florida, which is a long way from Wisconsin, how would you go?"

She shows me. I ask her how you would go to Michigan because I want to see my lil brother one time again. She shows me. I leave and you know what? I don't know what she showed me. I ask her if a person were traveling how would they get to Michigan? She says they would get on a bus that went to Michigan or a plane that went to Michigan or a train that went to Michigan. Now there's an idea! What if I did that?

I stopped going to school. I know that if people found out that Dick and Charlotte would be in trouble but I hope by then I'll be gone. I find out where the trains are and I go ask the man at the ticket counter how much is a train to Michigan. He says, "Where in Michigan?" I tell him Flint because I was born there. He tells me how much. I don't have any money. I think that over awhile. I go to the bus station and they tell me it cost money, too. I don't go to the plane. I don't know where it is.

Charlotte bought me some more clothes today, but I'm not going to take 'em with me. I'm not going to take off those things that she calls "price tags" because she says you can take 'em back if they don't fit. I'm going to go away pretty soon. I ask Charlotte what would happen if I were by myself at this age, and she says, it would be sad, but you would be on your own because you're not really a little girl anymore and you're not quite a woman yet. I ask her "Well, so what about my breasts? I'm making 'em. I am twelve years old."

I want to know when I'm going to be big enough to be on my own. She says, "Luckily, you don't have to worry about it. We're going to take care of you."

I can't say anything. I can't tell her I'm going away. I keep figuring out how I'm going to go and every once in a while Dick does that thing at night. I don't know why he does it. I don't get it.

I found out that you can get on the train or the bus and they check your ticket later, and if you don't have a ticket they throw you off. I'll just keep getting on and they'll just keep throwing me off. Maybe I could get a truck if they throw me off in the right place. Otherwise, I'll just keep getting on buses and trains and I won't have a ticket but I'll be farther than I was. I have my little pictures and letters from Aunt Sara packed again. I'm only taking what I can wear because Charlotte bought me all this stuff and it's mean to take it away from her. She's not going to know why I left and I can't tell her. I don't know why I don't tell her, except I know she won't like it. She'd rather not know, I think. Besides, mom knew. She didn't care. Maybe moms don't — maybe big men don't care if that happens. Why do I hate it so much if it's supposed to happen? I mean it, I hate it, it makes me angry enough, mad enough to kill. When I grow up I'm going to find all the men who do this, all the boys that do this, and I'm going to kill 'em. By then I'll be big enough to shoot that damn twelve gauge. I'm going to get 'em all in one moment, I'm just going to kill 'em.

I wonder if Joe really gave me those spirit guides. Where are they and what are they doing? He never touched me in a mean way, and he wouldn't give me bad things. They must be around but where?

I found out when the buses leave and on Friday I'm going to get on one. Charlotte's going to go to a church meeting tonight and I'm going to be alone with Dick and the girls as usual. When she goes I'm always alone with 'em. I'm going to ask Dick because I can't figure out why he's doing that and if he's not doing that, why would my horrible mind dream that up in my sleep, and make it feel so real?

At night, after I put the girls to bed, I ask Dick, "Do you put your fingers inside of me and use my hand to jack off?"

He says, "I have no idea what you're talking about."

I look right in his face, and you know what? He's lying! He does know what I'm talking about! He swears he doesn't and he has no idea how I came up with that! My brothers lie all the time, too, though. So...on Friday, I'll just take the bus.

It's Friday morning and I pretend I'm going to school, and Charlotte goes wherever she goes, the babies are in nursery school and first grade now. I go home and get my stuff ready and I stand at the front door and I applaud this house. I applaud Charlotte and I applaud Cathy and Ricky. I don't applaud Dick anymore. Another dead family, for me.

Buses and Hamburgers

I go to the bus depot. I'm supposed to get on a bus that says "Savannah Georgia." I wait and I wait, then I find that bus and I get on it. I'm just going to sneak in with other people. I know that when we get to Savannah, they're going to kick me off the bus. I'll have to figure out something there. I have to stop being such a baby, stop being so scared, and stop this damn shaking. Who cares what they do to me anyway.

The bus is pulling out and my heart hurts. It feels bad. I'm not going to cry, though, because everybody's here, looking at me. If they're not looking at me, if I start crying, they will be. Charlotte was going to give me my thirteenth birthday party in a couple of weeks.

The bus leaves and so do I. The bus traveled and traveled and I talked to everybody around me. I told 'em I was going to go home to see mom. I guess I'm going to become a liar because I can't tell the truth anymore, but I was wrong about Savannah, Georgia. They threw me off the bus in Deland, Florida. I started walking down the road and I got a ride on a truck. What a break! I told the truck driver that my mom was sick and I have to go home, and he says, "You're awfully young to be running around by yourself, young lady." I told him I'd be okay if nobody did anything weird to me. He gave me a ride all the way to Chicago, Illinois. That's a weird name, huh.

Anyway, I'm in Chicago. He says, Chicago's really too big to turn me loose in. I think, don't do anything weird. I had enough, I mean it, I'll choke you. I'm tired of this, men bossing me around and doing weird shit to me. I'm going to start killing 'em. I'm going to start figuring out how to do that. But he doesn't mean to do anything weird. He wants to find out how I get to the bus depot so I can go to Flint, Michigan. He gives me some money.

He says, "This is how much the bus ticket cost and a little extra for food."

He doesn't want to do anything weird. He's not even going to touch me. He asks me if he could hug me good-bye. I let him hug me. I hug him back. I thank him. I stand back and I applaud and his truck goes away. I liked him. I'm never going to get this straight. Which one of these men people can you not trust and which ones can you trust? How come women don't know anything? How come they let men do what they do? How come God's a man? Oh, God- God damn it!

This time I get a ticket. I get a ticket to Flint, Michigan and I pay for it so they won't throw me off the bus anymore. I ride and ride and talk to people on the bus. People on buses are fun to talk to. They share things with me. I get hamburgers and french fries at the bus stops. I like hamburgers and french fries. I had a big old thing of french fries and I poured ketchup all over it and I eat it and eat it and eat it and I love it.

I get to Flint, Michigan, and I get off the bus. I have two dollars and fifty cents left. But I don't know where I am. Why did I tell 'em Flint, Michigan if I don't know where I am?

I sleep in the bus depot. A man says I can't stay here. I say I'm waiting for my dad.

He says, "Where does your dad live?"

I say, "Here, in Flint, Michigan, where I was born, is where he lives."

I tell him what my last name is and he looks up names in the phone book. He calls 'em and asks 'em if they have a daughter or they know a dad named Fred with my same name. Nobody does till he calls the one place called Lloyd. The man's name is Lloyd and he says he knows my dad, and they'll come down and get me. I wait at the bus depot and a man and woman called Lloyd and Lil come and get me. Lloyd is my dad's brother. Uncle Lloyd and Aunt Lil is what I'm supposed to call them. They say my dad is really mad at me. They get me to their house but I don't stay. As soon as night comes, I leave.

I have to go to a bus and go back to Duluth, Minnesota where Aunt Sara is. I can't see my little brother till I figure this thing out. I can't see my dad and have more weird things happen to me. I find out where the buses are to Duluth, Minnesota. You have to get on three different ones here. I can do it. I get on the buses and they throw me off and I get on and they throw me off and now I go into places to get something to eat and I order and I eat and then I tell them, "I guess I better wash some dishes."

They get really mad, but they let me wash the dishes and clean the floors and I just keep doing that. Pretty soon I'll be in Duluth, Minnesota.

I get to Duluth. I'm so tired. I call Aunt Sara's. I know how to use a phone, she taught me how to call places for her. I call her and Jodie answers the phone. Aunt Sara is dead, she says. She died in her sleep. Jodie says she'll come and get me. Aunt Sara is dead? I put the phone back where you're supposed to put it and I cry my eyes out. This time I get it! You cry when your heart hurts!

I start walking around. I guess I'm not going to wait for Jodie. I'm just going to go away. I'm going to go see mom to see if she has that baby. Maybe she'll give it to me. I ask and ask and find out I have to get on a bus that says "Superior Wisconsin." I wait until I see a bus that says it. I get on. I'm going to get yelled at again, I bet. But I get on anyway. We go across the bridge over Lake Superior. I like bridges. Now we're in Superior and the bus stops and the bus driver wants to see my ticket and I tell him I don't have one. He calls me all kinds of dumb things. I don't listen. I just get off the bus.

I go across the street where they have a hamburger and coca-cola sign. I order hamburger and french fries. I eat them. Then I say, "Welp, time for me to do the dishes."

They threw me out. They called me a rotten no-good thief. I don't know why they were saying that. I didn't steal anything. I'm going to walk, though. I don't want to get yelled at anymore today. I start to walk for home. I take the highway towards Mrs. Sawyer's. I start walking. Maybe a truck will come. They never yell at me.

I walk and walk and walk. It's getting late in the day and I'm so tired. I'm almost at the edge of town. That makes me walk faster, that makes me happy. Pretty soon I'll be in the country where Mrs. Sawyer lives and I can see mom and see if she wants to give me that baby because she doesn't like kids anyway. She told me that when I was born, I wrecked her whole body. She says that her teeth went bad and her hair went bad and her health went bad. She says I damn near killed her. I mean it, I didn't mean to hurt her. I was too little to know about it, even. Just like the Jesus things I'm supposed to feel bad about. She says she was so sick from having me that when she had my brother that's why he's sickly too. I guess I just was bad all the time.

No Man, No Babies

I walk and walk and who do I see- Mr. Sawyer coming home from work. He picks me up! He puts me in his car, he hugs me hello! He tells me Mrs. Sawyer will be so glad to see me, she's been worried about me!

Worried about me! Mrs. Sawyer has been worried and the kids missed me and Mr. Sawyer is glad I'm safe. I ask him if he puts his fingers inside his girls and jacks off, and he says, "No. Not ever. That's a bad thing."

I say, "Men do that. Why don't you?"

He says, "Bad men do that."

When I asked the question, I thought he might throw me out of the car, but I'm ready to take my chances. He says, "Why don't you come home with us and we'll forget about the mean things people do, and Mrs. Sawyer will be so glad to see you."

I'll be glad to see her, too. I ask him if he thinks mom will give me the baby because she doesn't like kids, and he says, "She didn't have it. She had a miscarriage. But now she's pregnant again with a different baby. I don't think she'll give you the baby. Maybe she'll let you play with it." I think that sounds like fun. But I have to get my own home and my own babies that no one can mess with.

I lay back in the seat and pull my head back, and think, "We're on our way to Mrs. Sawyer and her kids and I like 'em."

I want to teach him about that applause thing. Mr. Sawyer says, "Well, this time we'll have to make sure the authorities don't find out about you so we can keep you. You're just like a daughter to us."

I ask him what a daughter is, and he says when you're a mom and dad and you have a girl it's a daughter, and when you have a boy it's a son. I'm a daughter! I lay my head back again and I just want to forget everything. I just want to remember my rag house and Mrs. Sawyer and the kids and my deer and birds and my fish and frogs and my dog. I just want to rest. I go to sleep.

Mr. Sawyer wakes me up because we're at home, we're at Mrs. Sawyer's house. He says, "Walk behind me now and we'll surprise her."

We get to the door and he opens it and he says, "Well, dear, I brought you a surprise."

She's getting something out of the oven and she says, "What is it?"

Mrs. Sawyer's like that. She never gets very excited — she's just kinda the same all the time. He says, "Well, you're going to have to look up if you're going to see the surprise."

She looked up and he stepped aside and she squealed! That's the first time I ever saw her do that! She grabbed me and hugged me and hugged me so hard I couldn't believe. I loved it! The kids are coming from everywhere, screaming and hugging. That's what this room was about for awhile, just some squealing and hugging. I like this! I'm going to stay here till I die!

We get the table ready and I set it like I'm supposed to and I help bring everything in. Mrs. Sawyer made venison. I don't like it that the deer get killed. Mr. Sawyer says none of 'em should be killed unless you're going to eat 'em. Joe told me that, too. You're never supposed to kill anything unless you want to use all of it. When I kill those assbite boys I'm not going to eat 'em or make use of 'em. The wolves can have them. The truth is, though, I like the taste of venison, I think to the deer spirit, in my heart like Joe told me, and I feel better. We're eating that venison and we're talking about all the things that have been going on and the fact that mom's going to have a baby. Everybody knows that it's Tom's, and I think, Tom? How could he have a baby? Mrs. Sawyer says, "You always have to have a man to have a baby."

That's disgusting to me. I didn't know that. I thought women could just have babies when they just decide to. What horrible news! You have to have a man? Oh, no, I'm never going to have any babies, either!

I get up from the table and I start hollering at the top of my lungs that I hate goddamn men and I'm not going to get to have babies because I hate 'em! I just don't know what's happening to me. But I'm yelling and screaming and Mrs. Sawyer is trying to tell me to get upstairs and be quiet! She puts me in the bed and tells me to calm down. She puts her hand on my head and strokes my hair. I don't know why, I just feel awful. Again! I even think of hitting Mrs. Sawyer! I want to hurt something, have a fight. I jump out of bed and go outside. I run and run! I want everybody dead. I hate the way everything is so fucked up with rotten men, rotten minds like mine, rotten imagination like mine! Why do I give a good goddam. Why don't I just die or shut up! I keep running until I can't run anymore. I go back in the house and Mrs. Sawyer gets me some milk. She doesn't say anything, she just sits with me while I try to breathe and drink the milk. I don't tell her the things my imaginations are thinking, I just want all the assbite boys dead. I want everybody to leave me alone.

I sit a long time. I can go to bed now, Mrs. Sawyer says. I'm glad, I feel so tired. Sleep's going to come and get me. I like it when sleep comes and gets me. I'm going to think of a way, in my sleep, maybe, but I'm going to think of a way to have my babies with no damn man at all. It's important that I have babies. I fuckin' will figure out something.

I'll Have Mom's Baby

I wake up because everybody else is waking up. I wake up thinking I will have to go get mom's baby because she won't want it. Then I won't have to have a man.

This house is noisy! Everybody's running around getting dressed and getting breakfast and getting everything and I get up and my head hurts really bad. I go downstairs and I tell Mrs. Sawyer that something's hurting me in the eyes, and she gives me two white pills, and I eat them. I just chewed them up. She laughed really hard, she says, "You're supposed to swallow 'em with water."

Then I drink some water because they really don't taste very good. She says they're aspirin. Aspirin? Well, bite my ass, I never heard of them.

I do like I'm supposed to and get the bowls and plates and everything on the table and I help get breakfast ready. I have to do my work or I can't be anywhere. Nobody wants a lazy person, Mrs. Sawyer says. I'm never going to be lazy. I have breakfast, we talk about anything but babies and men.

Mr. Sawyer says, "Someday you're going to feel differently."

He also says, "But you're always going to be a handful, young lady."

I ask him why he called me a young lady, and he says, "Pretty soon, pretty soon, you're going to be a teenager. Not very long now. You're developing and it's good."

I thought, Oh, no. Is he going to do — and he looked at me and he says, "No one should touch you unless you want them to. When that happens, you'll get married "

I thought, yes, that's right! I tell him, "I'm going to tell people you told me that. They touch me and I'm going to tell 'em, you said they can't."

He says, "You do that. Anybody touches you, you come to me. "

What a deal! I can come to him! I say, "You bet. That's what I'll do from now on."

Mrs. Sawyer has lots of things to do. The kids go to school and Mr. Sawyer goes to work on the railroad and Mrs. Sawyer has to bake bread and make food and feed all the rabbits and the chickens and collect all the eggs and take care of everything else. Fix the clothes, iron the clothes, mountains of clothes. I help. I help all day. She says I'm a hard worker and she's glad to have me.

She says, "School's going to be over pretty soon, so we just won't put you in school this time. Maybe nobody will know that you're here."

I say, "What if the kids tell somebody?"

She says, "I told them if they say one word, I'm going to cut out their tongues."

It'll be a few weeks before school is over, so I kinda have to lay low, she says.

I say, "What about going down to see mom and see if she wants to give me that baby?"

Mrs. Sawyer sits me down, pours me some coffee, and says, "She's not going to give you that baby, so get that idea out of your head."

I tell her she hates kids, she told me that. Mrs. Sawyer says, "This time it's different, you'll see. She's not going to give you that baby. Maybe she'll let you take care of it or play with it or something. That's going to have to be enough because I'm telling you, she's not going to give it to you."

Then Mrs. Sawyer says, "Everybody is talking about her, more than ever"

I just say, "Oh, hah, everybody's always been talking about her. It's all they do, and they never help her and they're never nice to her. Sometimes I think that's one of the reasons she's so mad at me all the time. Because I'm not nice to her either."

Mrs. Sawyer says she thinks that might be true. But she also says, "You know, I tried to be nice to your mom and visit her and everything, but she's just not very nice and she doesn't want to be friends, so I quit trying."

That was true, I thought about that. Mrs. Sawyer was always nice to mom, and mom wasn't friendly. She wasn't mean, she just wasn't anything. Mrs. Sawyer and Mr. Sawyer quit going over there. I know what mom does, but not why she does it. Mom always bitches about everything and she won't do anything new, she just keeps whining about dad and us kids not doing what she wants.

Gettin' a Home

Nighttime at Sawyer's, after we finish the dinner dishes, is always the same. I don't know what they do when I'm not here, but when I'm here we go outside and we look at the stars and we chase each other around and we sing songs. I sing "Old Shep Was a Dog" and Susie cries. She's the littlest and she always cries when I sing that song, and I sing it all the way through all the verses. Sometimes Jenny, who's the oldest girl, cries too. I don't know why that makes me feel good, but I know they're crying because the song is sad not because they're sad at me.

I sing hymns from the church and I sing songs from the radio and Jimmy — he's the oldest boy, and he can't sing very good, but he can't talk very good either. Like when he says the word "ketchup" he says "gut-lup." I ask him, "What the hell was that word, huh?" — Well, when he sings songs, if I make him go really slow, he sings the words right, and when he talks, he doesn't talk right, so we go over and over the songs and I teach 'em to him and he sings 'em, but his voice stays the same. All the sounds when he sings are the same. Almost sounds like he's talking. But he gets all the words right. That really surprises me. All the words when he sings are right, and all the words when he talks are really ass-backwards!

Buck, he's the youngest boy. I love Buck because he and I play to-gether. We always get to play and sing songs and pile up on each other on the bed and go to sleep and get cranky because everybody's laying on everybody, and then we have to all go to our right beds, and besides all of that, I have to go sleep on a clean sheet because Susie and Jenny have every damn dog on the neighborhood sleeping on their bed. I used to like that until I couldn't breathe with 'em all on the bed. Now I sleep on a sheet on the couch and then I wake up and I feel better. I even write songs with Jimmy. I make up songs of our own because it makes me happy when he says the words all right. He likes me when we do that, I can tell. We build all sorts of things to live in and to hide in and to do "Cowboys and Indians" and Jenny and Susie and I and Buck play together a lot. Jimmy, for some reason, doesn't play with us very much. Sometimes he has temper tantrums and hits himself a lot and pulls his own hair. I think that's really nuts, but he does it. I don't know why a person would hit themselves, when there are all kinds of grown-ups to hit ya. Mr. Sawyer hits Jimmy sometimes and I wonder why that's not enough hitting for him. I like all of them. I'm always hugging all of 'em. They hug me, that makes me happy.

School is out and everybody gets to run around and play and not have to go to school and we get to plant and fix up the garden all the time. All summer long we get to do canning. We put food in jars and save it and you get to eat it in the winter. First it's the strawberries, and then it's the beans and peas and corn and — oh, it's just endless. We put the jars in the basement. The last couple of weeks I made closets to fit in the house by using old boards. I wash them all off so they don't have any dirt on them and I nail them all together and I fix them and finally Mrs. Sawyer has closets to hang things instead of having to fold everything. I like that! I make closets in everybody's room.

I'm going to call mom and go down and see about getting that baby. I guess I really think it's true she's not going to give it to me. But it's worth a try. What the hell. Who knows what she's ever going to do.

I walked down the road. I checked to see if my rag house is there. It's all fallen down. It's all flat on the ground now. I don't know — but I didn't care. I'm not going to build it again, either. I don't know why I don't care about my rag house anymore. Anyway, I went to see mom. I didn't call her first. We talk about the baby and she says flat out I can't goddamn have the baby and I can either shut my mouth about it or I can go right back up to Mrs. Sawyer's. I'm going to shut my mouth about it. She's just going to have that baby, she says, any minute now. I stay a long time because I think she might have it. She doesn't. She doesn't know what to name it. I keep telling her the name of this song, that Peggy Sue song, that I sing all the time and sometimes they call mom Peggy — a nickname for her — so she says she's going to name that baby what I say. I almost faint. She's going to do something I suggested. What a surprise. Or maybe she's losing her mind while she's having the baby. She actually took an idea from me! I'm going to have to remember this day for the rest of my life! Mom had a minute of listening to me.

Lots of days I go see mom and she needs lots of help so I do lots of work and then I stay at Mrs. Sawyer's all the rest of the time. Mrs. Sawyer's says I'm a hard worker and that everybody likes a hard worker. I'm just happy, I like this. My mom isn't screaming at me. I don't have to live with her and she can't wreck anything. See, my little brother is still in Michigan with my dad. Dreaded dad. I don't care if I ever see dad again, but I do care if I see my little brother. I started sending him little notes and pictures, but he never sends any back. I wonder, mom says she heard from him, he's okay. Everything seems so different these days.

Well, mom had the baby. It's a girl. I was right. I told her it was going to be a girl and we should name it Peggy Sue and she did. She did that. She's home and she holds it and hugs it and I don't know why, but I get really mad. I play with the baby and I like her, she's really cute. But it makes me mad when my mom talks about the baby — my mom calls her "a little doll." Boy. She calls me a little hell-yen. She calls that baby a little doll. That baby is a little doll, though. Maybe I was a mean baby, and that's why she didn't call me a little doll. I don't know. Anyway, I hold that baby a lot. My mom says it helps her get things done.

Aw, Jesus Christ. One of those wonderful church people, one of those wonderful marvelous Christians, told Miss Grubb, trusty icky horrifying authority, that I was at Mrs. Sawyer's again, and here is Miss Grubb dragging her fat body up to the goddamn door at Mrs. Sawyer's. You know, if you didn't have to go to jail and stay there and not get out, I'd shoot her right where she waddles. Jesus. Jesus, shit, I hate this. I stand outside of the window, I think I'm going to hear something, but I don't hear anything for a few minutes. Pretty soon the goddamn window goes up. Aha! Mrs. Sawyer wants me hear this! That's why she's doing that. Miss Grubb and Mrs. Sawyer are having coffee. Miss Grubb says I can't stay here because Mrs. Sawyer can't be a foster home because she has too many kids. I can't stay. Miss Grubb already checked with my mom, and my mom said she wouldn't keep me no matter what. She has a new baby and she doesn't want me. Besides, my mom said she can't afford to keep me. Can't afford to keep me! I hear Mrs. Sawyer say, over and over, "We don't want any money. We just want her."

I feel so good when I hear her say that. She keeps saying it and Miss Grubb keeps saying, "That can't happen, that's not legal."

Legal! What the hell is legal!

I hear Mrs. Sawyer tell Miss Grubb how hard I work and how good I am for the kids and how well I take care of everything and what a good girl I am. She told her I was a good girl! Mrs. Sawyer keeps telling her that she doesn't want my money and she doesn't care if she gets any of the things for foster homing, she just wants to keep me and she doesn't want any other foster kids, just me. She only wants me! Goddam rotten miserable hideous old authority Miss Grubb says no. Mrs. Sawyer says, "Well, I guess we have nothing more to talk about."

Miss Grubb says, "Yes we do. We need to know when we can come and pick up this girl and take her to a foster home."

Mrs. Sawyer is crying. She's crying and telling her to get out and that nothing she's going to say is going to make any difference. Mrs. Sawyer says,

"Miss Grubb, you're just going to do any mean thing you want, so just do it and get it over with."

Miss Grubb waddles her fat body back to her rotten car and drives away.

Mrs. Sawyer comes outside and sits on the porch and says, "So you heard, huh."

I thank her for leaving the window open. I just stand there, after I thank her. I know I'm going to be leaving again. Mrs. Sawyer asks me, "Will you stay in a foster home if they'll let you visit us? You know, you could stay most of the time at a foster home and visit us. At least we could see you sometimes."

I just stand there. I think, "All right. I could try that."

I could visit with Mrs. Sawyer and I could see my mom and the new baby I named and maybe I could do that. I could try that. I tell Mrs. Sawyer all right, goddammit, all right, fine, I'll try that. Mrs. Sawyer goes back in the house. She says she has to make bread but I don't believe her. She's going to make bread, all right. But first she's going to go in the house and be really mad by herself like she always does when she's mad.

At dinner Mrs. Sawyer tells Mr. Sawyer all of the stuff that horrible Miss Grubb said, and Mr. Sawyer looks at me and says that he's really sorry, that I was like a daughter to him and he wants to be sure I know. They don't care about getting any money, and the only reason that I wasn't going to live with them forever was because the authorities won't let me. I tell him I know that, and I'm going to try really hard to do the goddamn foster homes so I can visit 'em, and if they don't let me visit 'em, then I'm not going to stay in any foster homes either.

Now I'm at the Wallenses'. Damn dumb foster home. I work in the barn — they have a dairy farm. Everybody around here has a damn dairy farm, that's good old Wisconsin for you. Anyway, the Wallenses have one other kid. The check comes for me every month and they don't hassle me. Their other kid is named Marilyn and we don't have much to do with each other. She's a little older than I am and every time I even think about doing something I'm not supposed to, she tells me that her mom says that if I don't behave myself, I have to go away. I behave myself. I just do my chores and go to school. I hide behind the school a lot and I go down to the pond and play and when it freezes over I'm going to skate on it. I get in trouble for not being in the classes, in the classroom, or even at the gym when I'm supposed to be doing PE. I don't care. They can't send me away for hating school, I found out. I get to hate it just like I want to.

I get to see Mrs. Sawyer once in a while and I get to see my mom and the baby I named once in a while. That baby is getting bigger and bigger, and crawling around, and she has hair and teeth now, and she can bite. If you're dumb enough to stick your finger in her mouth, she'll eat it. She's also really sweet, I love her. She hugs me when I pick her up! She seems glad to see me. At the Wallenses I just do what I can. You know what I found out yesterday, though. I was listening to Marilyn and Mrs. Wallens talking and they were talking about the new clothes that she gets when my check comes. I flew into the house and asked them, "Oh, hello, yoo-hoo, oh dumb people, what about if it's my check, how come I'm not getting any clothes?"

Marilyn and Mrs. Wallens both told me to shut up. I figured it out. Money comes that's supposed to be for me, and Marilyn has been getting clothes and stuff from the money, and that's why I don't get anything. I tell Mrs. Sawyer about it, and Mrs. Sawyer says she was really sorry, but some people just aren't very honest. Mrs. Wallens and Marilyn tell me that if I don't keep my mouth shut, behave myself, I have to go to a different foster home. Well, I have a big surprise for their sorry asses, you know, I packed up all my stuff because Miss Grubb is supposed to make one of those home visits where she comes and skulks around and looks at shit, and so I packed up all my stuff and when Miss Grubb came, I told her that they were spending the money on Marilyn and none for me and that I wasn't staying here and I took my box and threw it in the car and sat there. What do you think of that? Miss Grubb wanted me to get back out of the car and I told her not on a goddamn bet and on top of it all if I get out of this car I'll simply run away. She took me back uptown, put me in the children's home for a few nights so I could sit there and look stupid until she gets me another foster home. Then they move me out to Larson's. That's a lucky break because the Larsons live closer to Mrs. Sawyer, so I like this.

At the Larson's there's two boys, a girl, and Mr. and Mrs. Larson. The two boys are really much older, they're older like my brothers are, and they don't talk to me and they don't touch me, which I think is a lucky break, and the girl is a lot younger than I am. I play with her and I give her a bath and I dress her and I take care of her sometimes. I help around the house and I do chores in the barn like I'm supposed to.

I've only been here a month or so but it seems okay with me. We just passed damn Christmas, and I tried to find my mom a Christmas present at the dump, but the snow was way too far over everything to find something good. Mrs. Sawyer crocheted something and I gave it to my mom, and guess what, my mom thanked me. The crocheted thing lays on a table and then you put something on top of it. The word they use for this is "doily." What a word! Doily! Everybody thinks up chortle words for things. I made her a card, too, and I made one for my little brother and sent it to him in Michigan. I miss him.

I don't sing very much anymore unless I'm in the barn doing my chores. It never makes me as happy as singing at the gravel pit. The sound isn't so good here.

Well, I'll be dipped in shit. Mr. Larson has been watching me do my chores for days now. Every once in a while I catch him skulking around the corners of the barn. You know, I know what's going to happen. I can just tell. All I have to do is wait and kill him, right? I hope he doesn't touch me, but I can just tell he's going to. Every night at dinner, at the Larson's, everybody holds hands to say a dinner prayer and I have to hold his hand, so maybe he just likes me, maybe I'm wrong. I just don't feel very good, though. I haven't had this feeling for a long time. Maybe it's my imagination again. I thought I'd stopped those.

Nope. Not my imagination. He walked up behind me and put his hands between my legs from behind and he says, "I've been watching you watch me, girl."

This man is out of his fucking mind. I have not only not been watching him, but I've been catching him watching me, and he turns me around and he tries...I'm not going to stand for this. I back up and grab the pitchfork and run at him. I nicked him in the arm and the last prong of the fork stuck him. He's hollering at the top of his lungs. He hauled off and hit me one. I don't care. I fucking don't care. I'm never going to care again. Anybody who touches me I'm simply going to kill 'em. He hits me, I fall down, grab the pitchfork and run at him again. This time he took off out of the barn and I took off right after him and he's hollering for everybody and his older sons come out and grab me and take away the pitchfork and they drag me in the house and they call Miss Grubb and they pack up my stuff and they throw me in Miss Grubb's car when she gets there. Mr. Larson has a pitchfork hole in his arm. Too bad it wasn't through his goddamn stomach, which was what I was aiming for. I tried to tell Miss Grubb on the way up to the city what he did, and she told me to shut up.

I've been thinking about this shutting up for a long time. Why I don't do it is beyond me. Nobody listens or cares anyway. When it comes to the authorities, they make up their minds and then that's what's true. All because they say so.

I'm in the children's home for awhile again. The home mother tells everybody I'm dangerous now - that I stabbed my foster father with a pitchfork. They don't say anything about what he did. I guess it isn't important. I think about it. He didn't stab me or anything. I did stab him. I guess I'm just getting worse. Meaner. Maybe I'm going to be as mean as those assbite big boys. They probably are just like what I'm going to be like.

The house mother tells me that it's going to be hard for me to get a foster home after stabbing Mr. Larson. I try to tell her what happened and she tells me to shut up. She doesn't want to hear any more of my horrible stories. I don't know what's wrong with me, and I sure as hell don't know what's wrong with rotten-foster-home-men. I hate 'em. I hate everybody. I hate myself.

It's been awhile, and they found another foster home for me. Their name is Weber. I'm going to go stay with 'em. If I do anything wrong, then I go to reform school because I'm too old now to do anything wrong anymore. I turned thirteen a couple of months ago. That's what the authority, Miss Grubb says that I'm too old to do anything wrong without going to reform school now. I better behave myself. I don't care if I go to reform school. I don't care where I go anymore. I don't think I care about much of anything. I don't even care when they don't let me go see Mrs. Sawyer or my mom now. I'm going to go stay at the Weber's, it's going to be my new foster home, a place where I have to behave or I go to reform school. Miss Grubb says most bad kids go to reform school, and I tell her, "Oh yeah? I know a whole bunch of bad people that aren't in reform school. They live at my old house, I grew up with them. They're bad, some foster people are bad, how come they're not in reform school?" She never answers me and I really don't give a shit, I just want to tell her that.

At the Weber's, I have a bunch of chores to do. I don't feel the same anymore. I don't sing. I don't go find things. I don't go pick berries, I don't think about doing anything, I just do my chores and I go to sleep. I eat and wash the dishes and I go to sleep, and I get up and I go to school and I sit there and I don't do anything and I go home and do my chores and I go to sleep. I don't like anything anymore.

Mr. and Mrs. Weber have a whole bunch of kids but they're all grown up so they only come to visit on the weekends. They have babies of their own, so I can play with 'em. Everyone watches me real close because I might be dangerous. I watch me too so I don't hurt the babies. I just get so mad I have to just go outside.

I went and saw my mom and she asked me to do some work, and I don't know why but I ask her if I can come and live with her again. I could take care of the baby. She tells me not to be such a dimwit, of course I can't live with her. She can't have me there. So I get mad. I get really mad. I'm just standing there, getting very mad. I almost feel too tired to be mad. I ask my mom again, "Can't I come stay with you so they can't keep sending me anywhere and nothing else can happen to me?"

She says, "You know you're a pain in the ass. You have always been a pain in the ass. Shut up about coming here, you can't stay here. You know, Tom won't let you. Tom doesn't want you here."

My mom wants to know why I can't just be satisfied with things the way they are. I don't know the answer to that!

I got so mad that I grabbed her by her shirt and I screamed at her, "Do you know what it's like to have everybody pawing you and messin' with your body and making you feel terrible? Do you know what that's like, mom? Do you know what it's like having people jumping up and down on you and getting you in trouble for it? Do you really know what that's like, how awful that is?"

She hissed like a snake, "Yes, I do know."

I let go of her shirt. It was snowing outside and I didn't care. I just put on my coat. She knows. Then I screamed, "Did it happen to you?"

She screamed, "Yes."

I left.

I stomped down the road toward Mrs. Sawyer's thinking, You stupid bitch! You always knew and did nothing about it!

I was supposed to wait for the Webers to pick me up, take me back to the damned foster home, but I just walk down the road anyway. A car comes up behind me and it's my uncle Lucas. I knew him a long time ago but I haven't seen him for years. My cousin told me that he used to mess with her, too. She said he called it a "secret teaching." He stops and asks me if I want a ride, and I get in the car and I cry. I hate it when I cry. Someday I'm going to learn how not to cry at all. He pulls me over and puts my head down on his lap and he drives. I quit crying. He asks what's wrong and I stupidly tell him. He says he's so sorry and wishes he could have taught me himself. You know, I hear that dumb son of a bitch unzip his zipper right by my head. I hear it and I feel it. I sit up and hit him as hard as I can and he stops the car and I get out.

I walk to Mrs. Sawyer's. I don't tell her about Uncle Lucas. I don't say a word. I'm not going to say a word anymore about any of it. The Webers come and pick me up because Mrs. Sawyer called 'em so we won't get in any trouble and I get in the truck and ride home with 'em and get in bed. I don't care about anything. This life doesn't mean much to me, even though I'm getting bigger, it doesn't change anything. Nothing seems to change. Maybe reform school would be a better place for me. If it's like the children's home, there aren't any men except the janitor. Maybe that would be better for me. A bunch of kids and no men. Maybe I wouldn't get in any more trouble. I can't believe my mother knows all about this. I can't believe that all that happened to her and she let it happen to me. Why? How come she's not mad about it? How come when all of it started happening to me she didn't get upset?

It's morning. Big deal. The start of another wonderful day. I can hardly wait. I still can't believe my mother knew all this. I thought she was just dumb all this goddamn time. She had a lot of brothers. She told me that a long time ago. She knows all about getting jumped up and down on, she knows all about being made fun of and embarrassed and all this sickening stuff, she really does know about it. I don't know why she didn't just tell me, "Oh it happens to everybody."

I wonder if it does. It certainly happens to lots of us. Some girls at the children's homes say it happened to them too. But they're smart enough to keep it a secret. Why is it such a big deal to me? She knew all about this, she had brothers who did this too, and she just left it like that. You know when it comes to what men do, she always acts like she can't do anything about it. I don't understand this. I don't understand this at all. I thought I'd be a lot madder this morning, but I'm not, I just feel like there's no fixing it, so never mind. She doesn't care about it. I also figured out today it isn't me she wants around when I come down there. I'm just a lot of help. I help with her and help with the baby and help with the chores so it isn't me, it's just the work I can do for her. She was always like that. She's still like that.

It's been a few days since I had the fight with mom. I was surprised that I grabbed her by her shirt. I wasn't surprised that I screamed at her. I wasn't surprised that she screamed at me. The whole idea that she knows all about this stuff and never does anything to change it, that did surprise me. You know, I think that's the biggest surprise I got in my whole life. Anyway, Tom had mom call the Sawyers and the Webers and I'm never supposed to go there again. I'm not supposed to go there again because I'm too upsetting to her. Ha ha. I'm too upsetting to her. I love it.

The Webers decided that I have to stay in my room when I'm not doing my chores and I'm not going to school as a punishment for not respecting my mother. I have nothing to say to that. I don't care that I'm in my room. The Webers aren't talking to me very much now. I go to Mrs. Sawyer's on Sunday to feel better. I don't feel any better. I don't know why I can't even play with the kids. I don't have anything to say. I still like coffee. I guess this was what I was supposed to learn a long time ago, maybe I should just shut up. The story that's going around is that I beat up on mom. That's just like the story that goes around about Mr. Larson, that I stabbed him with a pitchfork for no good reason. I did not, and I did not beat up on mom, I didn't even hit her. I don't know why I didn't hit her, but I didn't even think of beating up on her. Now Miss Grubb is going to come out and talk to me. Maybe they'll put me in the reform school. I don't think I care what the hell they do with me anymore.

Mr. and Mrs. Weber sit me down at the table and ask me if I care what happens to my life. I tell them it doesn't do any good for me to care what happens to my life. Mrs. Weber says, "Girl, what has made you so bitter?"

I ask her to tell me what bitter is because Mrs. Sawyer is always saying, "Don't be bitter, buddy." I always think she's saying, "Cheer up." Mrs. Weber says it's when you get so that nothing means anything to you and you're just mad all the time inside. I start to tell her, nitwit that I am, I actually started to tell Mrs. Weber the stuff that's happened that might make me bitter. I stopped and I thought, I'm not going to do this ever again. I'm just not going to do it. I'm not going to tell anybody any of this ever again. I wish I lived someplace where nobody knew about me, or my family, and nobody would call me dangerous and nobody would call me a liar and nobody would say that my imaginations are terrible. Mr. and Mrs. Weber talk to me for a long time. I don't really know why, but I don't listen to anything they say. I just sit there, thinking in my head, I wish I were somewhere else where no one knew me. After awhile they go to bed and I go to bed. I'm in bed thinking, I could go somewhere where nobody knows me. I could go out west. I'm old enough now. I developed breasts and I look old enough, I could just go out west, say my family's dead, and do some sort of pioneer thing. Work somewhere, do something, and nobody knows me out there. I could do it.

These days I just do my work, go to school, and do whatever I feel like. I sit in the damned desks now because I don't feel like talking or arguing or anything. I try to get as much information as I can on "out west" and I get all the books on that I can read. Then I read 'em. I don't see mom and the baby I named. I don't even go see Mrs. Sawyer much anymore. I almost like just working. You know, I just want to just do something and keep doing it. I only say exactly what I have to say to answer questions and I never say anything more than that now. I hear the teacher at school talk about how all of a sudden I just don't talk any more than I absolutely have to. Mrs. Sawyer says she's worried about me, so I go over there even less because I don't want to talk about it any more. Mr. and Mrs. Weber say that they can't keep me after the end of the school year because they're going to go on a big vacation to Florida. Florida is a place I'm not going to again, but they didn't ask me to go anyway. They're going to put me in a different foster home for the next year. I figure all I have to do is exactly what I'm told and answer exactly what I'm asked. When I'm in my room I can dream about how I'm going to go "out west" and nobody will know me. Maybe I'll like that. Maybe I won't be bitter and mad and dangerous anymore.

In my room I try to figure out what kinda jobs I could do "out west" and I don't know, except I know how to do farm work. I wander up to Superior a few times and I take enough money for coffee. I sit and watch the waitress at the bus depot. I finally made it to the train depot. They have a waitress at the counter there, too.

Now I spend my Saturdays there, instead of going to mom's or Mrs. Sawyer's, I watch the waitresses at the depots, I watch how they serve coffee, and I watch how they put the cup on the saucer, pour in the coffee, put it in front of the customer and get a spoon, and the milk and sugar. That looks easy enough. They get the pastries out, they put that in front of the customer, if the customer wants it. They call 'em "customers." Then they talk to 'em if they feel like it. When they order food, that seems a little harder because the way they yell it to the cook doesn't sound like food. They say, "Two eggs over." Which means that the white stuff isn't runny, and "two eggs sunny side." Means that you don't ever turn them over and the white stuff stays runny. I don't know why anybody likes that, but they do. Or it's "Two eggs over, bacon and rye." I found out rye is the kind of bread they make the toast with.

You say things the way the cook wants you to. Then the cook puts it all on a plate and you put the plate in front of the customer. I keep watching it, thinking, "I could do this." They have to wash a lot of things, I watch them scrub up all the glasses for the water. When a customer comes in the first thing they get is water. When they order the hamburgers, if they want it really done, it's called "well" and if it's kind of done, with the middle not quite done, it's "medium," and if it's really not going to be done, then it's called "rare." They do that with steak too. If you don't want something on it, they always says to "hold it." That cracked me up at first. I thought, is somebody back there holding all of these onions or what? But when you don't want onions on something, then as the waitress you say, "Hold the onions." That way it doesn't get on your food. That sounds easy enough to me.

One of the waitresses at the train depot asked me if I was looking for a job and I say, "Yeah, I've been thinking about it."

She gave me what she called an "application" and I filled it all out. Then I took it home because I was afraid to give it to her. On this application they ask you a lot of questions that I don't know yet how to answer, like where's my parents, you know, where do I live, stuff like that. I'm going to have to figure this application thing out before I go out west. I found out from the waitresses that you get a thing called "tips" and "tips" are what the people give you when they liked what you did — instead of applause they give you tips. They leave you money, and then that's how you live. The customers give you tips and the guy you work for gives you some money. I could do this. I bet I could.

Every Saturday the Webers think I'm seeing Mrs. Sawyer but I'm really at Superior watching and talking to these waitress people. They're nice to me, and I always leave 'em a dime tip. Sometimes I don't get to have any coffee because if I leave the tip I don't have enough money for the coffee. Once I sat and watched and when I left I left the tip. Next time I was just sitting watching and the waitress said that my coffee was free. I thought that was really funny, I leave 'em a tip and I get free coffee.

I ask 'em a lot of questions about jobs. They tell me somebody my age (they think I'm sixteen) can be a motel maid and I could be a counter girl like they are. I don't tell 'em I'm thirteen, I just let them think that I'm sixteen. I could do dishes in a restaurant. I know about that, anyway, I used to do that when I was getting food and not paying for it. I'd do the dishes if they didn't throw me out and yell at me. I could be counter girl, a motel maid, and a dishwasher. With all of 'em I could make enough money to have a room of my own someplace and eat because when you work at a restaurant you get a free meal while you're there. I guess a restaurant's the best idea for me. The best part of all of this is I wouldn't have anybody who knew me, or knew about my imaginations or knew I was dangerous. Plus I'd never have to go to school. I could just be a counter girl forever. I like that idea. I wouldn't get to see Mrs. Sawyer and the kids and I wouldn't get to see mom's baby Peggy Sue, but I don't care anymore about them. I wouldn't have to see Miss Grubb either. Maybe I wouldn't have to see an authority ever again.

The teacher at school sat me down, wasted a recess talking to me because I'm not talking at all. The Webers came to the school and talked with me and the teacher and the principal about the fact that I'm not talking at all. I just don't want to talk anymore. The only time I talk is if the waitress is telling me something, or asking me questions. Everybody was bothered before that I talked, and now they're bothered that I don't. What a dumb-assed world! I don't talk about not talking either. I don't know why everybody's bothered by it. Before, I know, everybody wanted me to shut up. For months now I haven't said anything that I didn't absolutely have to say. You'd think they'd be happy. They're not.

School's going to be out pretty quick and I'm going to live with some people named Jensen. They have a dairy farm with a bunch of horses on it. If I do good work, maybe I could ride some horses. I'm always riding horses anyway. I just go get on people's horses and ride 'em around bareback. But I'd like it if I could go at 'em and not worry about getting caught. I don't say anything because what I'm going to do at Jensen's is just get on the horses and ride 'em and if I get yelled at I'll get off.

At Jensen's I can't go anywhere on Saturdays anymore, I have to work. But it's summertime and there's a lot of hard work on dairy farms — everything from hay to manure spreading. I just work and I ride the horses when I want to. They don't seem to mind at all. They have a daughter and a son but I don't talk to them either. I've noticed I don't have as many problems if I don't say anything. It's just easier. If somebody touches me now, I'm not going to say anything, I'm just going to stab 'em like I did before with the pitchfork and I'll go to reform school. But I don't have to talk about it anymore.

Riding the horses is more fun than ever before. I have a saddle and I get to ride 'em with permission because I worked hard so I don't have to worry about getting caught. I can ride 'em around and not hide in the woods and get knocked off. I've been knocked off of more horses trying to ride 'em in the woods. After I ride 'em I brush 'em down and I pet 'em and they like me and I like them. That's what I do these days, I work really hard so I can ride the horses. The Jensens talk to each other about things — everything, anything. They ask me questions. I either say I don't know, or I say yes, or I say no. They ask me to tell 'em about something and I say I don't remember. Those are the things I say. It gets me out of trying to tell anybody anything.

When I'm doing gardens and I'm shoveling shit and when I'm bringing in hay and when I'm picking apples, whatever — I notice I'm getting stronger and stronger. I like that. One of the Jensen kids said I have as many muscles as a boy. Who cares? I like helping when a cow is going to have a calf and I like it they had a horse who was in foal. I want to have a baby. I'm going to, too. But first I have to get a good job.

It's Christmastime. I always disappear at the holidays. I go and stay in somebody's barn or something. I do that with all the holidays. I did that with Webers too. After that fight with my mom I make sure I don't talk very much to anybody and I stay gone. Everybody always wants to know where I am but I don't tell 'em. I just don't say anything. This not saying anything works. I have figured out there's nothing you can do if a person doesn't talk to you, except hit 'em. Christmastime goes away and I go to school and do my chores and go to school and do my chores. I've decided when spring comes I'm going out west where nobody knows me. Get a good job and have my own babies. That's what I'm going to do.

The Jensens have decided that since I never talk anymore and it's almost Easter, that I should go to church for Easter. I'm not doing that. Maybe I should go out west sooner than I thought. I get my stuff ready. I take what's really mine and I have two small boxes. I go up to the train depot and I have coffee with Lucy, the counter girl, and I ask her which train goes out west and she tells me. I have to wait a couple of days somewhere. I go out and look over a train and figure out how I'm going to get on it. I didn't tell Lucy that's what I'm going to do. I figured out if you don't say anything, nobody can stop you. I packed all my stuff and left Jensens. Pretty soon the authorities will be skulking around so I need to get on a train and go someplace. I already know from Mr. Sawyer telling me about his job on the Great Northern that they have cars that they empty out. They're called boxcars and if they empty 'em out, nobody goes in 'em, the boxcars get taken someplace, and they get filled up again. He used to talk about how bums would sleep in those cars and they had to run 'em off every morning. I might be one of those bums. I'm going to leave in one of those empty boxcars that's going out west.

Out West

Lucy thinks I'm out of my mind. I think I'm out of my mind, I always thought I was out of my mind. She says that if I come in at the right times, early in the morning during the rush hour, she can feed me for the next couple days at the counter where she works. At night, she says, I'm on my own. She asked me to stay at her house. I'm afraid she'll call the authorities.

Tomorrow morning that train's going to leave. Last night I slept in the boxcar. I liked it. Lucy gave me an old blanket. It was kinda cold. But it was all right. I'm going to be able to do this. Lucy laughs, she thinks I'm a riot. She calls me "a riot." She says I'm the funniest person she ever met. When I get her laughing, then I start laughing. Lucy has great big white teeth and brown eyes. When she laughs, she laughs all over her body. She tells me that they'll probably be really mad if they catch me in that boxcar and I tell her that it won't be anything new to have people mad at me. She says I can keep the blanket and take it with me so I can keep warm on the train. She says she's worried about me. She doesn't know if I'm going to be okay. I keep asking her what she thinks could happen. I laugh a lot when she tells me that some man might try to do something to me. I think that's really funny. Do what to me? What could they do besides kill me? I don't tell her why I think it's funny, but I sure laugh a lot. She says somebody could steal something, and I say, "Lucy, you saw my stuff. I mean, what are they going to steal? My shirt? My old shoes? What, Lucy? My pictures? The songs I write? What the hell are they going to steal?"

She laughs. She says "I just don't want anybody to hurt you."

That's really nice of her. Tomorrow morning, I'm going to get in that boxcar and hope the damn train takes off. Lucy says sometimes they change their minds and they don't use the right boxcar and I'd just be sitting there. Would that frost my ass or what? I'd be furious! But I'm going to take my chances and hopefully tomorrow the damn thing will leave and I'll finally go out west.

Lucy's about to get off shift for the afternoon and she has to go home and take care of her kids. She says I can come over and take a bath, but I'm just too afraid the damned authorities will get me. So I don't. But she let me wash up really good in the bathroom at the restaurant, and that'll just have to do for now. I go out and walk around and walk around and walk around. I get tired and I go to my boxcar. I hope this trip is a good one. I didn't tell anybody good-bye here because I don't want them to have to lie to the authorities or tell 'em where I'm going. I have to grow up now. Lucy says I'm going to have to really grow up. She told me I should act like I'm sixteen and I should tell everybody I'm sixteen. Since I'm almost five foot, and I'm developed, I could pass for sixteen. She says, besides, you act older. She tells me I act older than my age so I'm just going to tell everybody I'm sixteen.

I get in the boxcar and I push the door shut as much as I can and I go back up in my corner and I go to sleep. In the morning the sun isn't even up. The boxcars are rattling. What the hell? What in the hell is going on? I can't get up and look because if they're taking off and they see me look out that door I'm not going anywhere, right? I just wait and wait and somebody comes by and slams the boxcar shut. That really scares me. I do not like that door shut. I don't know what the hell I thought they were going to do, just leave it open? Anyway, the door slammed shut and a whole bunch of clanging is going on. This is kind of exciting, but I wish I could see out. I should've gotten in one of those cars she calls cattle cars. They have openings in the sides. But they also have cows in 'em. Just what I need, a nice bath in cowshit for a couple of days while I'm going out west. My boxcar is so dark you can't see anything. This isn't okay. I don't like this. I want the door open. I'll wait until the train is actually going and then I'll see if I can open it.

There's a lot of clanging and banging and yelling and the train starts to move. I can open the pouch of cookies that Lucy gave me yesterday for breakfast. I kept 'em in my pocket and they're all scrunched to hell but it's better than nothing. As the train moves, the boxcar rattles and rattles and rattles. I didn't know they rattled like this. Who in the hell would want to ride in this rattling from head to toe boxcar? It's going to be hard to sleep because when I lay down or I put my head back it just rattles me silly. I wonder if I crawl up to the middle of the car and lay down flat if I'd rattle as much, so I did that, and it worked.

The train goes for quite a while. I finally get up enough nerve to go and see if I can get the door open. I pull and yank and carry on and I start yelling and kicking it and screaming. Having a fit isn't going to get this door open, but it sure feels better. I start cussing out the door and pushing on it, and it opened. The trick to train car doors is swearing, I decided. The more you swear at it, the more apt it is to open up.

I can see outside. It's snowing. My blanket almost blew out so I put it back in the corner. When we start to stop, I'll try to shut the door again and hope the hell I can do it. I sing songs at the top of my lungs because nobody can hear me over this train rattling. I read some of the papers I have with me and I think about things. I think about mom, and the baby and my little brother. I think about mom knowing what it's like to have assbite boys doing rotten things to you. I guess I just don't get it. I don't even feel as mad as I usually feel. I don't understand why she'd let that happen if she already knows about it. But I noticed everybody lets that happen. I sit in the damn boxcar and I watch this wonderful snow and trees go by and I don't get why anybody would let this happen.

If I ever have a daughter and anybody touches her, I'm going to kill 'em right where they stand. All she has to do is tell me and I'll kill 'em. I don't even have to see it. I will believe her and get on with killing whoever did it.

I don't know why this is okay with everybody. If it's okay with everybody, why is it a secret? Why doesn't anybody like to talk about it? Or hear about it? I mean, if it's supposed to just happen, you know, why does everybody have a goddamn fit when you say anything about it? I don't understand that. I don't believe that anything that awful is okay, anyway, but these other people think it's okay, including my mom, including Miss Grubb, including the wife of Mr. Larson. Why don't those people say, "Well, it's time for you to get hit and jumped up and down on!" Why don't they just say that, get it the hell over with?

The women are as rotten as the men. They all just let it happen. The men like it and the women just bitch about it. Flaming assholes, all of them.

Where I'm going, nobody knows me, and I don't ever have to talk about it again, but I can't help but think about it. I like it that for a long time I haven't talked to anybody about anything, really, except for the things I talk about with Lucy, about this train, but I like not talking about my family. I like the idea that they're all dead. That makes me feel safer. Then they can't do anything to me. I like the idea of being sixteen. At sixteen you get to work and you get to have cars and you get to drive and you get to do all sorts of things.

Three days now. I hate this rattletrain. I want out of here! We're in a big town. The station thing says "Billings." This is Billings, Montana. I never heard of it. Lucy gave me a dollar so I go to the counter. I'm so cold from that boxcar. It really rattled me silly and froze me to death. It's not as easy as getting on a bus without a ticket. I take the dollar and I go to the lunch counter at the station and I tell 'em I'm looking for a job as a counter girl. That's what they call it, a counter girl. The woman says, "You're in luck."

I'm in luck! I get to be a counter girl! She says, "Not here, though. We don't need a counter girl at this station, but at the bus station they need a counter girl."

She says, "You better wash up and dust off your clothes, young lady, you look like hell. Get over to the bus station before somebody else gets that job."

She says, "I'll write you a note."

I say, "Why are you going to write me a note?"

She says, "I saw you get off the train, you know, I saw that. You don't have to keep a secret from me, but you won't be able to get a counter girl job at the bus depot unless somebody in town says its okay and so I'll say it's okay on paper."

I go in the bathroom and try to get all cleaned up and I wash even my ears. I can still feel that train rattling. I rattle out and I ask the woman at the counter if she has a brush for my hair because I don't have one. She hands me one and I go rattling back in and rattle brush my hair really hard. I need to look really clean, she said. Really clean. I scrub and scrub my hands and I shake off all my rattled clothes, put 'em all back on, and I go rattling back out, and she says, "That's much better. Much better."

She writes me a note and tells me to give it to Dottie at the bus depot counter. She tells me how to get there, I just have to walk. I thank her and I take off with my note. As I'm rattle walking to the bus depot, I figure I'm going to have to sleep in those train cars because I don't have anywhere else to sleep. There ain't going to be no more boxcar rattle rides for me. Even when the damn train would stop and I jumped off to pee — I just kept the hell rattling.

A Room and a Counter Girl

I get down to the Greyhound bus depot counter and I ask for Dottie and this woman — she looks like she's not very happy. She comes towards me and says, "What do you want?"

I show her the note and she says, "You ever been a counter girl before?"

I say, "Only for a few days, and that was in Superior, Wisconsin."

She says, "What the hell are you doing out here?"

I say, "Well, my parents are dead and I just thought I'd try it out west."

She laughed. She says, "That's a new one."

I just sat there. I thought, well, yeah, that's a new one all right. Actually, it's not a new one, I've tried this one before and it worked just fine.

She says, "Okay, I'll try you out for a couple of days. Where are you staying?"

I say, "I don't know yet, I just got in on the train."

She says, laughing, "Yeah. In on the train."

I feel like laughing too, I think she knows damn well that I didn't come in on the train on the coach car, right? She doesn't say anything, though, she just thinks that's funny. Her eyes light up when she smiles. She has dark hair and dark eyes and they light up when she smiles. She says she'll try me for a couple of days.

She tells me to go down a coupla blocks and there's a rooming house. She says she'll give me a note and they'll let me stay by the night until I see if I can do this counter girl work. I say, "Well, why would they let me...what is...stay...doing what?"

She says, "Look. The way you do this is you go down there and you tell them — you take this note and tell them that you're going to be the counter girl here with me and that when you get paid then you'll pay them for the room."

I say, "What room?"

She just looks at me like, are you stupid or what? She says, "You have to rent a room, you have to stay somewhere, or do you know somebody here in town?"

I say, "Aw — Nope — I have to get a room."

She says, "Okay, you can rent it by the week, but at first they'll rent it to you day by day."

I'm a little confused still. She just takes a deep breath and she says, "Okay, one more time. You go down, you rent the room, and everyday that you work here you take all your tips and you give it to them and they let you sleep in a room there. It's your own room, it even has a lock, you get to have the key."

I say, "Well — is there no family? There's nobody to — that I have to — "

She says, "You're on your own. Your room is your own business. You can do whatever you want in it, as long as you behave yourself, and you can't drink and you can't have guys in there."

I think, what the hell would I be doing with a guy in there?

"Anyway, you can rent this room," Dottie says. "You can rent it every day and if you work out and you get to be the counter girl, and you're good at it, then you can rent the room week by week."

I say, "Do I get to just keep the same room?"

Dottie keeps looking at me, like are you a nutty or what? "Yes, as long as you pay for the room, it's yours. They change the sheets every week, and you have a bathroom to use, but you have to share it with everybody else." Then she says, "Mr. and Mrs. Row own the rooming house and they live downstairs and they rent out all the bedrooms upstairs. What I want you to do is take this" and she gives me an apron and she says, "Do you have a skirt?"

I think, a skirt? I don't wear skirts. I don't say it, though.

She says, "Well, I can tell you don't have a skirt. Oh, let me see." Then she says, "I'll tell you what. You just go back, take a bath, get settled in your room, and come back here and I'll have some clothes for you to wear because you can't wear those Levis and that white shirt in here. That white shirt is filthy, anyway. Now get going."

I follow the directions Dottie gave me. There's a big sign that says, "Row's Rooming House" and then underneath the sign it says "Weekly or Monthly Room and Board." I wonder what board means. Just so it doesn't mean any rattling I don't care. I knock on the door and this woman answered it. I show her the note Dottie gave me and she looks up from the note and says, "How old are you?"

"Sixteen."

She says, "When were you sixteen?"

I say, "November."

Pretty quick of me, huh? She just looks at me funny. She says, "Okay. You have to bring your tips home every day and then if you work out then we'll rent you the room week by week."

I say, "Okay."

She shows me the room and then she shows me the bathroom. She says, "When you're finished taking a bath, you have to hurry up and clean out the tub. Nobody likes a dirty tub. Clean up after yourself, we give you fresh linens and fresh towels every week."

What a deal! I think it is a great idea.

She leaves me and now I have the trusty key to this trusty room. It's mine now. I put my stuff in it and my two little boxes of things. I have drawers and I have a bed and I lay down on the bed and guess what? No rattling. I like this, this feels great. It has a bedspread on it, even, and it has pillows, and it's upstairs so I can see out the windows and see all over the place, all kinds of houses and streets, I like this. I have a closet of my own, too. Well, I better hurry up and take a bath, get cleaned up and get back down to be that counter girl.

I take a bath and scrub and scrub. I really want to do this good thing. Nobody here knows me, nobody's asking me any questions, I really like this. I get all cleaned up and I go back down to the Greyhound Bus Station to the counter girl job. Dottie shows me what to do. She says, "You're not going to work much today. Here's the clothes I want you to use for tomorrow. My daughter brought 'em down."

Her daughter's older than I am, she says, and she hopes her clothes fit. I have to wear a white blouse and a skirt and this apron. I have to wear a hairnet. I don't like the hairnet.

"But," she says, "you can't work here without it. Your fingernails have to be absolutely clean, and so do your hands and face."

I can do it. She shows me how to serve coffee but I already knew how to do that, I watched enough. So I just keep listening. Then she has me do an order to see if I can call it in right. You know, like a burger with fries, hold the onions. That kind of thing. I can do that. I do that easy.

She says, "You get one meal when you're working and then you have to eat somewhere else the rest of the time."

I think that's fine. I'm going to work what they call a split shift, that's two hours in the morning for the breakfast rush, that's when most people eat breakfast, two hours at lunch time, eleven to one, when most people eat lunch, and two hours at night, from four to six when most people come in on the buses and have dinner.

I pick a lunch time to have my one meal, so after I get off of work around one, I get to eat a giant hamburger and fries and a milkshake. I get my burger, dip it in ketchup and I get my fries and my milkshake. I like that. I work everyday and in between the times when I'm not working I run around. I'm free to go and just look at anything I want, and I learn all about things like the post office, the stores. I also found out they have a thing called the movie theater and it runs day and night around the clock. You pay for one movie and you can stay and watch it as many times as you want. They have a movie called "Spartacus." What do you think of that word? Anyways, it's about a man who wants to be free so I'm going to go see that movie and I'm going to stay for as many times as I want. Every day I go to work and every night I have to wash out that white blouse and then I have to iron it because every day it has to be very clean. People don't like to eat food from you, Dottie says, without you being very clean. Dottie brought me some things called "curlers." You put 'em in, wrap your hair around 'em, and they make your hair curlier! I do it. I didn't do it right the first few times, so she shows me how to do it. I get it right. Now I have curly hair. It's okay, I think, and I don't ask anybody else what they think because if they don't like it then I'll have to be mad. I don't want to be mad. Everyday I take the tips that I make and I give 'em to the lady at the rooming house. Next week, if I work all week, I only pay for just a week. From then on, every week on Friday, I pay for that week.

"Spartacus" what a movie! This man was a slave and he beat up on everybody and he had a wife and they were both just beautiful. I loved that movie! First he was a slave and he fought and he fought and he fought and he fought everybody and he won! At the end of the movie his wife had this little boy and she holds up the little boy to Spartacus who didn't win in a way because his ass is on the cross, you know, like Jesus. Anyway, she holds up his little boy and she says, "See, a boy born free." Which was what Spartacus wanted...if he couldn't be free, he wanted everybody else to be free. That's pretty neat. If that Jesus guy was like that, that's pretty neat too. He just shouldn't have blamed me for it, I think. I didn't put Spartacus on the cross, either. I don't hear Spartacus stories going around blaming me, either.

I saw the "Spartacus" movie two times, then I fell asleep. There's people who sleep in that movie house all night. If I ever run out of a place to sleep in the city, I can hide out there instead of haylofts and other people's barns. You can also sleep on the benches at the bus depots, but the authorities, if you're really young, get you. They don't get you if you stay at the movie, I don't think. I slept through the movie and I almost missed my damn work this morning. It was close. I didn't wash out my blouse. Dottie gave me hell, but she wasn't too mad. Just don't let it happen again, she told me, so I won't.

I can't get that movie "Spartacus" off of my mind. All those people are pretending, but they pretend so well I believe 'em! I think that's really great. I have never seen a movie before. It's the same kind of magic as making music. I'd like to know a man like Spartacus who thinks of something besides his silly crotch, but who also really fights for things. That's pretty hard to find, I bet.

I've been working as a counter girl for a while now, and I pay my room rent every week and I go to movies. I figured out a way to eat when I'm not working. I bought these giant jars of apple butter — I love apple butter! — and peanut butter and bread and I keep them in the closet in my room because you can't cook in your rooms. If you pay for room and board, it costs more than I can make. I just pay for the room and no board — board, by the way, means you get to eat there too. That's funny. I laugh a lot over that. "Please pass the Board. May I have another helping of Board? Would you like some gravy on your Board? A slice of Board please. Yoo Hoo, some Board and hold the onions." Anyway it costs more money for that Board and I don't make that much. Besides, I want to go to the movies. "Spartacus" is a wonderful movie. Any movies that come, I'm going to see 'em. They change movies almost every month.

The guy at the movie theater is really nice but I don't get very close to him and I don't talk to him very much. He gets really friendly with me, but I think that I don't trust him. I think he might do some of that weird stuff. I talk to him a little bit and get out of his way. I feel so good about my perfect room and everything in it. I have clothes of my own that I keep looking good and I come in my room — I feel grown up. I feel like I can work hard and do what I want and I feel like I don't have to take any more shit from anybody.

Good Old Man

I met this old man. He comes to the bus depot counter, you know, and he's really old. His name is Henry. Henry's wife died a lot of years ago, he says, and he still misses her, and he talks to me about things. Sometimes he just goes on and on and on and on - makes me nuts — but I listen to him. He's lonely, he says, and he gets tears in his eyes, and I feel sorry for that. He must have really loved his wife, kinda like Mr. and Mrs. Sawyer. He comes into the counter every day at breakfast time and every day I give him coffee and a donut and I talk to him in between customers. He tells me I'm a real sharp girl. I like the way that sounds. At least he didn't tell me I'm cute or sexy. Otherwise I'd have to quit talking to him. Henry brings me things sometimes, and Dottie says it's okay if I take the stuff, just to be careful. I am! I told you, I ain't taking any more shit.

Henry brings me things his wife used to wear, and he brings me little knickknacks, he calls 'em. They're like little statues and stuff. They're cute. He brought me a real pretty plate when I told him I have apple butter and peanut butter sandwiches for my other meals. He thought I should have 'em on a pretty plate. I got all choked up. I thought that was so good of him. I hope he doesn't do anything to me so I have to hit him.

Henry asked me if I had my driver's license, and I told him no, and he says, "Well, you're sixteen, you should have your driver's license, you could drive one of my old cars." He asked me if I wanted to see his old cars, and I thought, yeah, right. I come up to see your old cars, you do weird shit. I told him I'd like to see his old cars, but I'd like to see 'em here at the bus depot, not go see 'em at his place. He smiled and says, "I won't hurt you, little girl." I say, "I don't care, I'm not going to let anybody hurt me, I'd just rather see 'em here." The next day, he brought one! It's a Packard. He let me sit behind the wheel. I told him I drove trucks and tractors before because I have. On the farms you have to be able to drive things a little bit. He says it's not the same as driving on the highway. He says he'll teach me how to drive and I say, okay, Henry, I'll tell you something. You know, then I change my mind. I don't tell Henry anything. I remember not to say anything again. Pretty smart of me, huh? I just tell Henry, "Aw, I don't know if I want to learn to drive yet." A coupla weeks later I thought, I just really do want to drive!

I take Henry up on his offer. We get in his car and he drives out uptown so that we don't run into anything, he says, and I think, boy for dumb, why would I run into anything? Then he gets me behind the wheel and he tells me how to start the car and how to steer it and how to go really slow and which gear is what, and I think, oh boy, I don't know if I'm going to learn this or not. I put it in what he calls first gear, I get it in the damned first gear, I step on the gas, we leap forward, we don't go anywhere after that because the motor stopped.

I tell Henry, "Boy, you have a dumb car."

He laughs, he says, "Yes, and a dumb driver."

I think that's pretty funny, I laugh too. Inch by inch I learn how to step on the gas and let up on the clutch. That makes it keep going.

Every afternoon I go and practice driving that Packard of Henry's. Henry hugged me one time and he rubbed my chest and I grabbed his arm and I said, "If you ever touch my body again, I'm going to hit you dead in the face."

You know what he did? He apologized. Henry apologized for touching me! He did! He promised he'd never do it again. I'm going to believe that. If he touches me, I'll break his face, but up till then, if he never touches me, then okay.

Henry keeps teaching me how to drive and I keep driving. I want you to know something. If you think you're so damned smart, you know how to drive, just do what I did. I put it in first, then I put it in second, and I stomped on the gas, and we went right off the road and into the ditch. We had to go get this guy and this truck to haul us out. I felt so dumb. I don't think I felt that dumb for a long, long time. I don't want to feel that dumb again, either. Henry tells me, "You know, if you kill me of a heart attack running into ditches, I'm not going to be able to finish teaching you to drive."

I don't know why Henry wasn't very mad. We didn't wreck the car or anything, we just landed in the damn ditch. Dumb me! Dottie says Henry has a crush on me. I tell Dottie, "I don't care. Henry's old enough to be my grandfather. Anyway, I don't want any men."

Dottie says, "Girl, you have to have men sometime."

I don't say anything. I remember not to say anything. I just think, "I do not, I am not, I'm not going to do it."

Fired

A man comes in to look over the restaurant. He's an inspector. He has a big Stetson on. That's a special kind of hat. A really pretty gray, soft-looking hat. He has a suit to match it, it's really pretty, but he's really fat, so it probably would be prettier on somebody thinner. I've been working here almost three months, and he's never been here before. He's just inspecting the place. It has to be clean enough and everything, some kind of state laws. Guess what, he's an authority. I stay away from him as much as I can. I just answer any question he asks me any way I think he wants them answered. I don't say anymore than that. He's been inspecting all goddamn day. He runs around, he even looks under everything, inside of everything, around everything, what a pain in the ass! Dottie calls him a pain in the ass, too. I love that! Dottie says when he goes out to do something in his car, Dottie says, "I never knew a pain in the ass could wear a Stetson."

I laugh about that all goddamn hour. That's pretty funny. "A pain in the ass can wear a head and a pain in the ass can wear a Stetson and a pain in the ass can talk." I have fun in my head for hours. The fact is, I still laugh about that, and he's not even around anymore.

I have to tell you the bad news, though - Dottie had to fire me. I was handing him the man in the Stetson a cup of coffee, he was going to take it over to a table. He's standing at the counter, I'm handing him his coffee, and he says, "I want you meet me at my car after work because I'm sure you could use a little money."

By this time he has his hand on the other side of the plate, and I say, "What do you mean?"

He says, "Come on, girl. You give me a little loving, I give you a little money."

I slap that man's head. His Stetson, cup, saucer, everything goes in every direction. Dottie asks me what happened. The man is screaming at the top of his lungs, and I say he said something really rotten, and I slapped him, and Dottie says, "I'm so sorry, you can't work here. Nobody works here who hits the customers."

She says, "Besides, this guy is really important. He's the one who says whether we get to keep serving people or whether we have to close the counter."

I'm fired. I go home to my boarding house. I'm really fired. I don't work at the counter anymore. I shouldn't have hit him. I should have just said, "No thank you." Next time I'll say "No thank you." I go back down to the bus depot to tell Dottie that I'd say no thank you next time, I won't hit anybody else. Dottie is really sad. She says, "You jut can't work here anymore. If I let you work here, he'll close the place down."

I ask her if he said that, and she said no, but she knows him. She says he says things like that to everybody. I think, Yeah, well, everybody should slap him too.

I don't tell Dottie that. I just say, "Well, I'll have to get a different job. I won't hit anybody again, Dottie, I got it."

I don't know what I'm going to do, though. I have to look around for a job, starting tomorrow. Dottie says I can keep the skirt and white blouse, so I'll just get 'em clean and look for jobs.

Jack

I'm looking for jobs and I don't find any. I go back to the counter to see Dottie around lunch time. Henry is there. Henry is really sad. He says his son is in Wyoming and he's sick and so Henry is going to drive down to see him. He asks me if I wanted to go with him. I tell 'em yes. I figure since I don't have any money and I don't have a job, I might as well go somewhere. We go back to the rooming house, I make things square with them, put all my stuff in Henry's Packard, and we go to Wyoming.

After we get into Wyoming, Henry says there's a place called Yellowstone National Park, and there's a place called Tetons National Park. I ask him what the hell a Teton is, he says it's mountains, it's an Indian word for breast. I think, "Maybe I belong in an Indian mountain place. Maybe that would be neat." First we go to a place called Lander, Wyoming, and there's a Sinks Canyon place, like a park, only it's huge and it has mountains, giant rocks, and it's called a Sinks Canyon because there's a river there and it disappears (sinks) into the ground. You can climb down in it aways, but the passage gets too narrow to follow it all the way.

Henry and I are having what he calls a picnic. We're just sitting on a rock eating is what we're doing. This guy drives up and he's in a truck and it has a sign on the side of it — Forest Ranger. He's a good looking guy. I like the way he looks. His hair is so wavy. He's super tall. He has on a uniform and he has blue blue eyes. He has a deep voice, a Gary Cooper deep voice like in that "High Noon" movie. He talks to us about all sorts of things about the area and he talks about searching for Indian arrowheads up at Sweetwater. He tells us the story, even better than Henry did, about how the river disappears into the canyon, that's why they call it Sinks Canyon. He shows me right where it goes down and you can't see it anymore. He tells me that he has to go pick out coyote dens and get rid of the babies. I hate that. I tell him, "What do you do with them?"

He says, "Well, they just expect me to get rid of 'em and so I do."

I say, "Do you kill 'em?"

He says, "Naw, I don't kill 'em."

I tell him it was a damned good thing. He looks at Henry and says, "She's sharp!"

"Smart as a whip!" Henry says.

These guys are pretty nice to me. I like 'em. The guy's name is Jack, and Jack asks me what we're all doing out there and we say we're just visiting. Then Henry tells him about his son and asks him where he lives because he wants to see him. I decided I'm going to stay in the Sinks Canyon and I ask if that's possible. Henry says, "Yeah."

He gave me a big old bag that we had of food and he gave me some blankets to sit on so I can just be there for the day.

Henry and the ranger leave at the same time. It's a beautiful place. There are giant pine trees. I put my bedroll blanket thing down in the middle of the pines and sit on it. Then I climb some hills and I wander around and I watch everything. It feels good to be back outside. I sing songs and all of a sudden I look up — Jack is standing there. "Jack, what are you doing?"

"Well, I thought I'd come back and bring you these."

He has some flowers. Wild flowers.

Jack says, "These flowers remind me of you."

They remind him of me? I thank him. He looks right in my eyes. He gets down on his haunches and he tells me, "That was a really pretty song you were singing. I wish you'd finish it."

I'm too embarrassed, or something, I can't sing a note. He asks me if I have a boyfriend, and I say no, I don't, and he asks me if Henry is any relation to me and I say no, I just met Henry in Billings, Montana at the bus counter where I was working. The ranger says, "So how old are you?"

I say, "Sixteen."

He looks at me and he says, "Well, you're a real pretty sixteen."

I say, "Yeah, and if you touch me, you're not going to be a pretty ranger. I'll hit ya."

He stands up and he says, "I wasn't going to touch you."

I stand up and say, "It's a goddamn good thing. Nobody is messing with me ever again. You got that?"

He says, "Yes. Yes. I have no intention of messing with you."

I say, "Fine then."

I sit back down and he gets back down on his haunches and he starts telling me all kinds of things about Wyoming and the animals. He talks to me about a lot of things. I really like that. I like him. He keeps looking right in my eyes. I can't explain exactly how it feels, but it feels good, deep, down inside of me really good, but different from anything I ever felt before. It's close to when I used to kiss Butch in that tree by the lake in Michigan. Something like that.

Henry comes back and we all go into town and we have dinner at a cafe. Henry says he has to go out to his son's ranch and stay with him, and I say, "I'm going to stay in town, and get a room and get a job."

Jack tells me he can help me get a job and a room. Henry looks at me and he says, "You be careful, girl."

Jack says, "You know Henry, she already let me know exactly what I can do and what I can't do. I don't think you have to worry about her."

Henry says he'll visit me whenever he can, he'll come into town. I think that's really nice of him. He says maybe we can finish some of our driving lessons. I hug Henry good-bye, I kiss him on his cheek and he hugs me really hard.

He says, "You're a sharp girl, you just stay that way."

"I will," I promise him.

Jack says, "There's a job you can have, I don't know if you'd want it."

He points up on the hill and there's a huge bunch of buildings.

He says, "It's called the Wyoming State Training School. All of the mentally retarded people in Wyoming go there. Then they hire people that help take care of 'em. I have a friend who works up there, and maybe we could get you a job up there, and it pays good money."

We get a room and Jack signs for it because I don't have any money, but we don't have to pay any money till after I get my job. This time we sign for room and board. I think, "What am I going to do if I don't get a job?" Jack gets me up that hill and in to see Dr. Jamison. I'm going to work there. I'll be taking care of mentally retarded people. They have shifts there. You work from six in the morning till two in the afternoon, or from two in the afternoon till ten, or you work from ten at night till six in the morning. Dr. Jamison said since I'm single and I don't have any children to worry about, he'd like me to work from two in the afternoon till ten at night. I told him I'd work anytime.

Nurse's Aide

On my new job, you have to wear a white nurse's uniform and you have to wear white shoes and nylons, but you don't have to wear a hairnet. That's one good thing. They're going to get me a paper that says I'm working there, and then I take it downtown and I get my uniform and shoes and nylons and then I pay for it all when I get paid for working. That's all right with me. They gave me a tour of the grounds. A tour of the grounds mean that they take you to every building and show you all of these people they call patients. These are the retarded people. Boy, I have never seen anything like this in my life! These people look funny. Some of 'em don't talk, some of 'em make these grunting, weird, icky noises, some of 'em are all twisted — their bodies are all twisted up, they're wrecked! They can't help themselves. My job's going to be to feed 'em and get 'em dressed and bathe 'em, kind of like taking care of all the babies that I've already taken care of but they're big people and little people and they don't have any brains. They can do very little. Some of 'em have more brains than others, but they can do very little, so I have to do whatever it is they can't do, for them. I don't mind that.

One of 'em hugged me! A wrecked person hugged me! They call it a "Mongoloid." He has a giant tongue and he flaps it back and forth and back and forth and he hugged me. I laughed a lot and by the look on everybody's faces, I thought maybe I shouldn't laugh anymore. I guess they don't think this stuff is funny. I better watch it with that laughing.

They take me from one unit to another and I see old retarded people and I see little tiny baby retarded people and I see people that have giant heads. They call these people "hydrocephalic." It means that they have water in their head. Their heads are huge! I never saw anything like that in my whole life. They can't hardly hold their own heads up, so they have to lay down all the time. I can't figure out why anybody is leaving 'em like this. I ask Dr. Jamison, "How come you don't fix these people?"

He says, "Well, it's really complex, but we can't fix 'em. There's no way to give 'em brains they don't already have, and there's no way to fix their bodies. We just take as good a care of 'em as we can."

That hurt my heart! I couldn't believe that. God, He let shit like this happen, look at this mess! People messing with me is better then this kinda mess. They were born wrecked! I'm going to take good care of 'em but I'm afraid of them making me sick. I ask Dr. Jamison if I can catch any of this, and he just says no. He thinks that's kinda funny, and he chuckles a little. I don't think it's funny. I don't want to catch any of this retardation. I'm crazy enough without any help.

I ask him if they know anything. Can I talk to 'em?

He says, "There a couple of 'em you can talk to here and there. Don't be surprised, though, when they just don't know anything. Your job is going to be to keep 'em clean and keep 'em fed and keep 'em dressed and give 'em their medicines. That's your job. You have to help clean all of the units, like, you know, do the floors and the sinks and everything, so you're going to have your hands full, young lady."

He says, "You do a good job, though, and you can work here and you can make plenty of money. This is the best paying job for lots of people in the whole area."

I have to take this thing they call "Nurse's Aide Training." They give you a certificate after you finish it. I want a certificate! I like the idea — that's exciting to me! I get to have a certificate! It's a piece of paper, he says, that proves that I did the training. I could do the training. I can even drive a car. I didn't tell him that, though. I didn't want him to ask me where my driver's license was because I already lied telling him that I'm sixteen when I'm not.

What worries me is that this is going to be a sad job. These people are really broken. Some of 'em are blind, some of 'em are blind and they can't hear, some of 'em have no nose. I saw some kids with no nose at all. They have trouble eating, Dr. Jamison says, you have to feed 'em really carefully. I'm going to be sad, these poor little things. Some of 'em are mean, too, he says. Some of 'em will bite you, you can't let them bite you, it causes a horrible infection. Some of 'em scratch you and hit you and you have to be really firm with 'em. You can't let 'em get away with anything. Otherwise you can't do a good job. I told him, "Oh, ha, I'm not going to let anybody on this earth get away with anything." He laughed.

I can't figure out why they can't fix these people. I mean, there's a lot of wrecked people. He says that there are hospitals like this in every state. I can hardly believe what he's saying. I ask him a couple of times if that's really true, but he looks a little annoyed, so I quit asking him, but you know what? Figure this — figure this! In every state there's ten of these places with eight hundred of these ruined people that nobody can fix. We have a lot of states. I have to add that up. I can't do it in my head. I hope he doesn't find out I'm not sixteen yet because I want to keep this job, but I don't want to be too sad. I'm already sad when I'm looking at them. Some of 'em throw things at you. They threw things at me, we were just walking through. I don't know what I'm going to do about that. I have to remember to be careful, don't be dangerous, like stabbing Mr. Larson with a pitchfork and slapping that goddamn Stetson. I'm still not sorry. I know I should be, but I'm not. I'm sorry that I didn't get to work with Dottie anymore, but that man needed slapping and I slapped him and I'm glad.

He tells me I have the job, and I go back to my rooming house. Jack drives me back down. Jack waited in the truck the whole time that I did the applications and the rounds of the grounds and all that talking. Pretty nice of him, huh? He asks me if he can buy me a dinner. He wants to buy me a whole dinner? I told him yes, and he says, "Okay, I'll drop you off at the rooming house, you get all prettied up" — prettied up? Jack, you're a strange man. Anyway, he wants me to get all prettied up and then he'll come and pick me up and take me to dinner. I go in the boarding house and I take a bath and I put on clean clothes — a new clean white shirt. The kind I like best, they're men shirts, they're just white shirts with tails, and my Levis. That's what I wear. That's as pretty as I get. I get all dressed up in that and he comes and picks me up. He's really dressed up. He smells great. I feel like licking him. What a not-me weird thought!

He takes me to dinner and he sits and talks to me. He asks me when my birthdate was, and I tell him it's in November and it's on the 27th and I don't say the year because I have to go figure that out again so I can be sixteen. I do that every time I make out an application, and I never can remember what the hell year it is. Anyway, I don't tell 'em I was born in 1944 and that I'm only going to be fifteen in November. He says I'm a Sagittarius. I tell him I'd like to know what the hell that is, and he says, "When you were born the stars and the moon and the sun and everything were in a certain special place just for you and if you're born at certain times of the year, you're called certain things." He says he's an Aquarius. He says I'm a Sagittarius. He says he had a book I could read on it. Oh, I want to read that book! What an exciting idea! Stars and sun and moon and everything just in a special spot! He says Sagittarians are really go-getters and they always tell the truth. (That lets me out because I lie when I want to.) I just sit there. I don't know what to say. He says, "Well, I probably shouldn't talk a lot about this until you read the book and then we could talk about it because then we'll both know."

I tell him, "I like that idea."

Then he asks me where I came from and I say, "Jack, I don't want to talk about anything like that. I don't ever want to talk about it."

He says, "You seem so feisty about anybody touching you, I figure somebody must of hit ya or something."

I say, "I'm going to tell you, Jack, somebody did a lot of something. They hit me a lot and everything. I'm never going to talk about it again."

He says, "Okay."

He called me "Tumbleweed." He said I remind him of a tumbleweed out on the prairie, they really just go and go and go, wherever the wind blows 'em. Good idea, I say.

He says that tumbleweeds are beautiful and sturdy. I guess that's an okay thing. I don't know if I want to be a weed. I've seen the tumbleweeds, though. They do just go and go. I don't know how he knows that I do that. But he knows.

I get my uniform for work and my shoes and my nylons. Jack says I look really pretty. He calls me an angel in white. Just like in the movies, that's how he talks! He makes me feel funny. Sort of kind of warm. Especially when he looks right in my eyes and talks to me.

I start work tomorrow and I'm really scared. I don't know if I'm going to get too sad with these broken people, but I'm going to go to work. Jack asks me if I want to go for a walk. I say yes, and we go for a walk around town. A couple of times he holds my hand — he takes hold of my hand and just lets go. I like holding his hand. I love the way he sounds. I could listen to the sound of his voice forever. I just feel so weird around him. Kind of a pretty, tumbleweed weird. He tells me I'm a really caring person so I won't have any trouble on my job. He says be careful not to get really mad, or I'll end up fired again. 'Cause I told him about slapping the stupid fat Stetson man. He thought the story was funny, but he says, "That'll get you fired every time."

We talk about his job and he talks about how he helps animals that are broken and he goes and gets the coyote pups. He says he has a secret to tell me about those coyote pups but he can't tell me yet. He asks me if on my first day off if I want to go see what he does with the coyote pups. I say, "Not if you're going to kill 'em."

He says, "I'm not going to kill 'em. Do you want to go with me?"

I say yes. We're walking around and he's holding my hand and telling me that he's always here in Wyoming from April to September every year. I don't know why, but I really felt awful. I ask him, "Where are you the rest of the time?"

He says, "Well, the kind of job I have, I have to be at a different place. Different parks. Every year from April to September I'll be here."

Well, okay. I can just wait before September and April and just work. He chuckles. He has a wonderful, low, really deep laugh. He chuckles and he says, "Are you saying you'll wait for me?"

I say, "Of course!"

He says, "You know, you don't have any idea what you're really saying. You don't know how much I already care about you."

I say, "I do too. You don't do anything mean to me. You must like me."

He walks me back to my rooming house and he kisses my hands, both of 'em. He lifts 'em both up at the same time and kisses 'em. I feel really weird. Wobbly, almost. I go inside and shut the door and wobbly me right up to my room. I get into bed and I think about him a lot. I love his hair and his eyes, his wavy hair and his blue eyes and his white-teeth smile, "High Noon" voice. I love the way he walks, but he has really long legs, so it's hard to keep up with him. He says he's six foot four. Six foot four! What a big person! Wonder what it would be like to ride on his shoulders! He brought me flowers.

It's my first day on the job and I'm on the ward. It has a lot of little kids, but they're all broken, and they don't have minds, and they can't learn, and they're never going to be okay. They're going to live forever like this. It makes me so sad. I try to feed 'em like I'm told to. They have silver trays and in each little section of the tray they have food, but you know what? This food looks like soup! Green soup is peas, orange soup is carrots or sweet potatoes, even the mashed potatoes are watery! They tell me that that's because these wrecked people can't swallow very good, they can't put chunks of anything in their mouth. I think about being wrecked, and I think I'm so glad I'm not wrecked.

We have a nurse named Mrs. Jones, she's mean, I don't like her already — but I'm not going to hit her and I don't want to get fired. Mrs. Jones told me these people don't know they're not okay. I can't figure out how you'd be this wrecked and not know it! Some of them have arms that are all curled up and their legs are bent so they walk funny and their arms stay in these curled up positions and they come at you making these "Raargh" "Ewwwah" sounds. It's awful! Crazy sounds. They can't talk. I don't believe for a minute they don't know they can't walk right, talk right or hold their arms right or undo their fingers. Their fingers are bent permanently! I don't believe these people can't know this. Who wouldn't know they're that wrecked?

I just keep trying to feed 'em and I wash 'em all up. They don't eat very well, it's really frustrating to try to feed them because they can't swallow. A couple of 'em, I fed 'em, they ate it all and then they threw it right back up. I wasn't happy with that! I didn't like to clean it up but I also found out that when people throw up, I do too. Then I get to clean me up and then I get to clean them up. What a goddamn mess this has been all day, and my white uniform isn't white anymore.

Sally

They have this one little baby, they say she's a Mongoloid, all of her fingers are the same size. She has great big lips and a great big tongue, and she looks comical. Her eyes are little but slanted. She hugs me. I mean, she's really affectionate like a lot of these little Mongoloid children. When they hug me, I hug 'em for all I'm worth. But some of 'em I can't stand it if they even look like they're going to touch me. They're drooling and slobbering and ewww...their eyes are crossed, their hands are crossed, their legs are crossed, I mean, their whole life has been crossed and double-crossed. I hate it. I don't want 'em touching me, either, it makes me nuts. I wonder if they know that I feel like that. I can't help it. I feed 'em the breakfast stuff and I feed 'em the lunch stuff, then I'm supposed to go eat. Guess what? I can't eat. I go to the cafeteria. Nothing is going down this throat today.

I go back to the ward and little Sally, the Mongoloid, is always hugging me. Just runs over to me. She's a sweetie. I drag her around on my leg while I'm trying to clean out all the tubs and sinks and stuff. Mrs. Jones comes in and tells me to put the little rat down. I've heard that word rat before. I hate that. I turn around to Mrs. Jones and then I think, You shut up, Louise. You shut the hell up. It's never going to be okay with me to hear nasty old nurses call little tiny people rats. I don't like her. It's only one day, I'm already wanting to hit her a lot. I'm not going to do it, don't worry.

I put Sally down because I don't want Mrs. Jones getting mad. I've seen her today, she must've slapped ten kids if she slapped one. She runs around the damn ward, I'd swear that's how she gets her exercise, running around slapping wrecked people. Dumb bitch. I absolutely can't stand her. She's the nurse so she only gives 'em their medication, she doesn't have to clean up after them or feed them. She's only good for slapping, bossing, and medication. She's going to teach me to do the medications so then she'll be worth even less. To give medications you have to take this thing, it's almost like a pea shooter, you know, and you put it down in their throat because otherwise they'll chew it or spit it out. You shoot the pill down their throats with this little plunger. What an idea, huh? Some of the medications are liquid, so you have tilt their heads back, hold their nose, pour it down their throat and they have to swallow. I didn't know that trick. I should of tried that on the assbite boys, stick rat poison down their throat and hold their noses. Even though, Sally is a little teeny wrecked up Mongoloid, she has more love than all those rotten boys, who aren't wrecked, put together. This is a strange life. I'm never going to figure it out.

I have to work five days in a row, then I get a day off, and on the day off I'm going to go with Jack to see what he really does with those coyote pups. I didn't see him today after work and I miss him. I already miss him.

Boy, every day at this place, with retarded wrecked-up people, is bizarre. Some of 'em have what they call epilepsy and they have a thing called seizures, and some of 'em are small seizures and some of 'em are really grand seizures. Their seizures are terrifying. They flip over on the floor and practically break their own necks and then they twist and jerk, and the poor things can't help it, either. Mrs. Jones stands there with her foot on their chest. I bet you're not supposed to do that. She tells me to keep my mouth shut about anything I see on this ward or I'll be in real trouble. I know that she said that because she's doing something wrong. Otherwise, why the hell would she say that to me? After these five days I start the nurse's aide training. Maybe they'll teach me how to do this right. I don't want to stand with my foot on a poor person's chest, who's already banging their own head and beating themselves up! You have to put a thing in their mouth so they don't swallow their tongue, Mrs. Jones says. She couldn't find the thing. One of 'em bit their tongue so hard it bled all over the place. I can't wait for the training. I want to know how to do this right.

If I had my way, I'd knock Mrs. Jones on her ass and stand with my foot on her throat. Fact is, I might stand with my foot on her throat, only a second before I started jumping up and down. Goddamn, she's mean! Of course, I hate it. I might find out when I get in the nurse's training that you're supposed to be mean. I'm going to figure out a way to just look mean and not really be mean. I don't like this.

Part Three

The Teenager

Laughing, Singing and Loving

It's my day off and I get to go with Jack and see what he does with the damned coyote pups. We drive out in his truck. He has all kinds of stuff in it and he has a bunch of cages in the back. I ask him, "Do you put 'em in the cages?"

He says, "Yes, and you're not supposed to guess, you're just supposed to watch this."

We get out to the prairie place where he's supposed to pick up the pups. I ask him how come we have to do anything with the damn pups, and he says that there gets to be too many of 'em, and they eat the people's live-stock, so he either has to kill 'em or take 'em out to the mountains and drop 'em off, so he takes 'em out to the mountains and drops 'em off. Pretty smart man, I think. I ask Jack what makes him smell so good, and he chuckles that wonderful, low chuckle of his, and he says, "Old Spice." It's a kind of perfume for men. It really smells good. I tell him I feel like licking him. He laughs out loud. I love it. I made him laugh! I like making him laugh. I like talking to him, listening to him, and making him laugh.

We get to the first hole that he says coyote pups are in. He shines a flashlight down there and I can see their eyes. We put gloves on and he reaches in first. He sticks a stick in there first to see if the mom was in there because moms, when you're dragging off their babies, can get pretty mad. I sure as hell would. He sticks his hand down there with his gloves on and he picks out a coyote pup that's chewing on his glove and he puts it in one of the cages. Now it's my turn, and I reach in and I pick one out. I want to keep it.

Jack says, "You can't keep that."

I say, "Oh yeah, you say so, but I can do anything I want. I'm keeping this coyote pup."

Jack takes it out of my hands and puts it in the cage and he says, "You're not keeping any of these coyote pups. Do you want to get me in trouble?"

I really have to think about that because I really don't know that I care if he gets in trouble, I want that goddamn coyote pup, I said. We take the rest of the pups out of the hole then we drive to the next one. This is quite a ways away. We have fourteen pups by the time we're through picking out all those holes. I still want that one with that really teeny white thing on its ear. I might have it. He's not the damn boss of everything, you know.

We start driving up into the mountains and Jack starts singing this song and it's called "Sands of Gold."

Then he sings this song called "Four Walls." I recognize those, they're all Jim Reeves songs! I sing with him. We sing really good together. Oh, I couldn't get happier. We're singing and driving and singing and driving. I love this! He smells good and he looks good and he sings good and we're singing and driving. We didn't kill the coyote pups.

We get up in the mountains. He says we can't leave 'em all in one damned spot, and I say, "Yeah, because you're leaving that one with the white tip on its ear with me because it's mine."

"Louise, you're impossible," he says. "You can't keep these coyote pups, it's against the law to have 'em for pets."

I say, "Do I look like I care about the law? I hate the law, I hate authorities, and I'm keeping that pup!"

He says, "You're not keeping that pup, if I have to hog-tie you."

Hog-tie me! I say, "Jack, you mean that? Are you going to hog-tie me if I keep that pup?"

He says, "One, you're not keeping that pup, and two, I'm going to hog-tie you if I have to, girl, you're not keeping that pup, you get it out of your head."

"Boss me around, you asshole, I'm really mad now, Jack. I want that pup and I don't see any reason I can't have it."

"Where're you going to put it, Louise? Where are you going to put that pup?"

"Never mind, Jack, okay, I don't have a place to put it. I just want it."

Jack hugs me. My head only reaches to the middle of his chest when we're both standing up. It feels so good. He's petting my hair like you do with dogs. I love it, I just stand there. I never felt like that in my whole life. I just stand there and smell him and he's talking in his wonderful voice telling me that coyote pups do not want to be anywhere but out in the wild and it's really sweet that I love that pup, but I can't take it back and make it miserable.

I tell him, "I know, I'm sorry I yelled at you. I'm not going to keep that damn pup."

He just hugs me for a while more. Why do I like this? This feels so strange.

We put the pups in different locations and he shows 'em how to get in another hole, only there's no mom in this one.

I say, "How come we don't take the mom?"

He says, "I have to go back and get the moms by myself because they're dangerous and sometimes I really do have to shoot 'em."

"Why?"

"Because if they're not gone, Louise, I lose my job."

"You mean — Jack, you have to shoot them or they fire you?"

"Yeah, because it's my job to thin out the coyote population."

"Do you hate it when you have to shoot 'em?"

"Yes."

Jack's eyes look sad when he says that. I believe him. I don't believe he's a mean man and I don't believe he likes killing anything. He hunts, though, he told me. He's also a guide for fishers and hunters when he's not working as a ranger. That means he takes people and shows 'em how to kill things. Well, he even comes back for a special thing called a "one shot antelope hunt."

Famous stars come to that. Like Roy Rogers. Well, guess what? I hate Roy Rogers! I think he's stupid. He talks goofy. I don't like it. Jack laughs.

He says, "You know, you either like or don't like everything."

I think about that for awhile. It's true. I either like things, or I don't like them. That's right. I wonder if that's okay.

We drive back from giving up the pups to the mountains and we sing some more Jim Reeves songs. I don't ever remember feeling like this. I just want it never to end. He takes me back to the rooming house, kisses both of my hands again, it tickles me. It's sweet. He says he has to hurry up and get back out there and find the females of those dens, get them up in the mountains, or else he's in trouble and so are the babies. He leaves and I go back in my rooming house and now every time I'm not with him I write songs about him and for him. I wonder what he's going to say when he finds out about that.

Tomorrow starts my nurse's aide training so I can learn to do this job right. I betcha that Mrs. Jones doesn't know what she's doing. I can't wait to get started.

I start a song for Jack, and the first line is "Let me put my arms around your neck." And I just start laughing. Around his neck, my ass! I'd have to stand on top of his truck to do that. I don't know why I think that's so funny, but I laugh until I go to sleep. Things are getting better. I knew out west would be better.

Help, help, help! Nurse's aide training has books! Shit! It's just like school! I didn't know this was going to happen, I hate this! I have to read all these books and do the workbooks, take the tests. I thought they meant teaching me how to nurse people. I don't want to do books. I sit in this classroom thinking, Why did I do this. Why didn't I think of this! Just books and more books. Oh, I never pass anything in my whole life. This'll be awful. I'll fail the goddamn thing and then I'll get fired for that instead of for hitting Miss Jones. I think I'll hurry up and hit her so I can have the pleasure before I get fired for not passing this book class. Books! Why is everything books? I read all the books about Nancy Drew, but they don't give me a test on them.

They start talking to us about the training and what's in each chapter and what we have to do. Oh, happiness! After we're through with these idiot books, then we do the actual hands-on training which is where we really do the work. I'm saved! All I have to do is get through the goddamn books. I don't know if I can do that. They don't know that for years I haven't been to school. I read a lot, though. I can read. Maybe I can get this anyway. I have to make it, I want this job. I want to help those wrecked-up little people. Just like Jack does the coyote pups. I'm going to be good. Do something good. Maybe I could do these books. They show all the parts of the body. That's pretty interesting. I didn't know all that stuff had names to it. I know about arms and legs, right? I know about eyes and ears, but I mean inside your body. Everything in there has a name and everybody knows about it. It must be from cutting everybody open. What a sick idea.

Nurse's training is only three hours a day for this whole week. I have the wildest urge to just throw the books straight in the goddamn air and run screaming from the room, I'm not kidding. Hurry up and run over and smack Jones before I get fired. I better not do that. Besides, Jack will be disappointed. He got me this job. He really helped. I can't disappoint Jack, I'm not going to do that. Okay okay, I will memorize this stuff in the books, I'll write it down in the workbook. After this class I have to go to work, too. Then at night, or in the morning, each day I have to figure out what all the stuff means and write it down. I have to write it down in the workbook, then they're going to give me a test at the end of the week. There's three other people in the class, they're all much older than I am. They probably know a lot more about school. I read a lot, I write a lot of songs. I have already written almost a hundred songs. I don't like school. After this class I asked the instructor if there's any more after this week of training, and she tells me no. One week of school, I could live. Okay, okay. School's over, I take all my stuff, and I go to the ward where Mrs. Jones is skulking the fuck around. Oh, she's icky. She has very dark hair and very dark eyes and she's very skinny and mean-looking. No lips. Somebody else has her lips someplace because she sure as hell doesn't have 'em. Of course, it's really no big deal because nobody on earth would kiss her anyway.

I get to the ward and she tells me what's been going on and who's sick and who's not sick and what special things we have to do and I tell her that I went to the nurse's aide training and that I'm glad I get to do this, and she says, "Yeah, well, when you get through just remember, I'm the one who's going to tell you what you're really going to do."

I say, "Don't I have to do what's in the nurse's training?"

She says, "You have to do what I tell you to do, as long as you're on this ward. What you really have to do is stop being so kissy-face with Sally. She's going to think that you're really going to be here forever, and you might not be, and then she'll be disappointed, and she'll really feel bad, so you just leave her alone."

I ask Mrs. Jones, "What the hell am I going to do when Sally leaps on me and hugs me — I'm not going to throw her on the floor or anything."

Mrs. Jones says, "Just don't be too affectionate with any of these kids. They start counting on hugging you and stuff."

I say, "I think it's good that they hug me. I like it."

She says, "Well, none of the other people hug 'em like you do, so stop it. They'll get used to it and then we'll all have to hug 'em."

I go out on the ward to start doing my job. I've done a couple of day shifts, a couple of afternoon shifts, and one graveyard shift and I never knew all those people don't like hugging. I wonder why they don't even hug 'em. Pretty strange. How the hell could a hug hurt. Maybe that's all these wrecked people know, to feel good is just a hug. That's all I ever see 'em do. They sure as shit don't play with each other or talk to each other. They don't do anything most of the day, except sit, mess themselves, cry, and bang their heads on the wall. They sit in their cribs and on the floor and bang their heads.

They have great big huge lumps on their heads. Mrs. Jones calls 'em head-bangers. All the different types of wrecked people have different names. Mongoloids and head-bangers and epileptics — they call 'em fit throwers, that makes me nuts, so I call 'em epileptics. I had trouble with that word at first, but I got it. Maybe the only good feelings they get to have are hugs. I don't want to get fired so I'm just going to do what this old bitch tells me to do. I don't have to like it and I'm going to sneak as many hugs to Sally as I can. Mrs. Jones says Sally has a very bad heart, but she says a lot of Mongoloids have bad hearts, you know. A big shock could kill 'em. I have no intentions of running around shocking these poor little people.

I get home from work and I only have two more days to this week. I'm doing the nurse's aide thing just fine. All you have to do is read and be able to say what you know about what you read. I can do that. Jack comes by. He says on my day off do I want to go and look for Indian arrowheads up on the Sweetwater. Sweetwater is a place, it's a big, just a big place, and it has a river that has good water for drinking, that's why they call it Sweetwater. I say yes, I want to go.

We go up on the Sweetwater and I find some Indian arrowheads, so does he. Jack and I walk for miles. Miles! We walk all day. He has a canteen with him and we drink water. I pick out a lot of pretty rocks, too, and little chips he says are pieces of arrowheads, you know like when they're making the actual arrowhead, these are chipped off pieces. I keep all of it. I still write my mom notes and I still send my little brother pictures. I could try sending them little arrowheads. Some pretty rocks, maybe, at Christmastime. I wonder how they are. I'm glad I'm not there anymore. I'm kinda mixed up about where it all is. I asked Jack if he could show me because he has these maps, could he show me where I am from Wisconsin? When I say Wisconsin he looks really funny. He says, "I go to Wisconsin sometimes."

He asks me where I lived, and I tell him, and then I think I shouldn't have told him but I already did it. He shows me on the map, he comes from a place close to where I came from. I never heard of him.

We collect a lot of stuff and we get back to the truck and he asks me if I'd like to have dinner at Sinks Canyon in the trees. I laugh, I think, Okay. We're going to have dinner in the trees. Right. We're going to eat pine nuts, is that it? I know, we're going to have scrambled rock soup or something, and I tell him all the kinds of food we can have, like pine needle stew and we could have bagged bark and he laughs and laughs, and I say, "Yes, I'll have dinner there, and I'm not eating any rocks, though. My little brother doesn't eat 'em, and I don't eat 'em either."

We drive from the Sweetwater down to the Sinks Canyon, it's a long way, and we sing some more songs together. He says sometimes he sings at Bud and Blackie's and if we practice together, maybe I could sing with him sometime. Bud and Blackie's is a bar. He says since I'm only sixteen — ha ha, he doesn't know I'm not sixteen yet - I wouldn't be able to go over to the bar, I could just stay on the little tiny stage with him. I think my heart is going to stop. I actually get to be on a stage with a real audience, real people. I can't believe it. I can't even talk. He keeps asking me if I'm upset, but it takes me a long time to be able to say how much I like that idea.

We get to Sinks Canyon and he takes a thing out of the back of his truck and he clears a place under the pines so it was all just dirt and he put around some rocks, and he makes a fire and he gets this food, two steaks, he has two steaks in that thing, sitting on top of a thing of ice. Two steaks and some tomatoes. He cooks up those steaks and he cut up those tomatoes. It was gorgeous. It looks delicious. Then he has a thing called gin and tonic. One of 'em is booze, he says, and one of 'em is a mix. He mixes 'em together and he says, "Here, try this."

It doesn't taste very good. He's drinking his, and I'm sitting watching the fire, and I'm so happy. I can't tell him that I don't like this, I'm not going to drink it because maybe it's part of his dinner and he'd be insulted. I drink it.

Suddenly I think, Welp, time to go over and hug him around his neck like I wanted to in my songs. I get right up from that rock and gin and tonic my way right over to his neck and I hug him and I hug him and I hug him. He kisses my neck. He isn't mad. I like it. Then he kisses my ear. I feel like I'm floating. He kisses me all over my face. He says, "The moon will be completely up in a few minutes." I look up and there's the moon. I say, "How did you know it was going to be a full moon?"

He says he had a calendar that tells him when there's going to be a full moon. I say, "Jack, every time there's a full moon, let's come and eat here!"

He says okay. He still has his arms around me and I still have my arms around him. We're just there. He kisses my forehead a bunch of times. I just hold on to him. He turns me around so that my back is against his chest and both of his hands are on my arms and my arms are across my chest. I love that position. We just watch things and listen to things.

He kisses my hair. He likes my hair, he says. He likes the way it smells. He says he likes the gold in it when the sun shines on it. I don't have gold hair, I told him. I have a kind of brown, auburn like thing, and he says, "You have some gold in it and you have some brown in it and you have some red in it. It's just beautiful."

He says, "You know, sometimes your eyes are green, especially if you're mad, and sometimes they're brown."

I say, "Yeah, they call 'em hazel eyes like my dreaded dad."

He says, "He might be your dreaded dad, but he must have pretty eyes. You have pretty eyes."

I ask him if he'd mind not lying to me, and he says, "I promise, Tumbleweed, I'm never going to lie to you. I just want to love you."

I'm just going to sit right here and love him until that moon goes away. He gets a bedroll out of his truck after awhile and he puts a little more wood on the fire and we both lay down on the bedroll and he puts a blanket over me. Some over him. I sleep with my back to him, with him hugging me just like when we were sitting. I never thought I'd do this and like this. Just so long as he doesn't do any leaping and bounding up and down on me then I won't have to smack him one. What a beautiful, beautiful night this is. A bunch of songs run through my head. I listen to him breathe, he's sound asleep. I just lay there. I love his breathing.

I wake up off and on in the night and just look up, look around and listen to him breathe and I go back to sleep. In the morning we get up and he puts the bedroll away and we go and wash our faces and our hands in the creek, dust ourselves off and get in the truck and go into town. He has to go to work and so do I, but I don't have to work till afternoon, so he drops me off at my boarding house and I go up and I take my bath and I get my clothes ready and I just hope I get to see him again on my next day off. I go to work and I do all my chores, clean up all those little wrecked people and hug Sally as many times as I can get away with. After work I'm walking back down the hill toward the boarding house and Jack drives up and asks me if I want a ride. I'm surprised to see him.

Jack says he wants to talk about the books he wanted me to read. I tell Jack I read Nancy Drew, I read Life magazine, but because I can't afford to buy it I just read it right in the store, and I read Jack London. He hands me a book. It's about how man didn't come from the way Christians talk about, that they came evolved, he says, from cells, little microscopic beings, they came to be humans. I like that idea! That gets rid of that misery that we were created and fucked up in the Garden of Eden: we were just set up for a mess in the first place.

I ask Jack if he's going to give me a test on all this, and he laughs and he says, "Tumbleweed, you're so silly. No, I'm not going to give you a test on all of this, but I'd like it if we could talk about some of the same things."

I say, "I thought we did talk about the same things."

He say, "No, I mean, new things. I'm really interested in Darwin's theory of evolution and I want to be able to talk to you about it."

Nobody ever wants to talk to me about anything. I'll read it. I ask him, "What if I don't understand it?"

He takes both of my hands like he always does and kisses 'em and tells me I'll understand it, don't worry.

I take the book and he walks me up the door of the boarding house and I ask him, "Can you sleep here like you slept at Sinks Canyon?"

He says, "No. Anybody knew that, they would be really upset, that's a bad thing to most people."

"Oh, piss on most people, Jack, I don't care what the hell they think."

He says, "You will. Right now, we're not going to get anybody mad at us. Nobody's going to like it if they know that we slept at Sinks Canyon. You better not talk about that."

Okay, I won't, I won't already.

Jack asks me if on my next day off if we can go and do something together. He says there's a place called Dubois a little ways from here, it would take us all day to go up there and back, but he'd like to show it to me. I say, "Of course. I'd go anywhere if we could be together, Jack."

Then he hugs me and I go inside and go to bed.

Jack picks me up on my day off. I tell him about Mrs. Jones and how mean she is to the kids and how many times she hits 'em, and they're just little wrecked kids and I hate her. I'm going to slap her senseless one of these days. He says, "Well, better be right after you get a different job."

I tell him, "I know, I know, I don't want to get fired, but I hate what she does with those little people."

I tell him about Sally, and how affectionate she is, and he says, yeah, he knows, he had heard that little Mongoloids are very affectionate. We talk about them having a bad heart and we talk about me getting an A in my nurse's aide class and I have my certificate and he says Congratulations and he gives me a little necklace. He had it ready for me, I know he did. It's red and it has a star on it and you slip it around your neck and it has too little rhinestone things on the ends of it, so it's like a red ribbon with a star of rhinestones and two little rhinestone bottoms.

He says, "If you move it up a little bit it looks like a shooting star, huh?"

"Yeah, yeah, Jack, it does. Thank you."

We go to this place he calls Dubois, we sing in the truck on the way up, and when we get to Dubois, this really teeny town has about four buildings. He says it's been there since Wyoming's been there. The people are really nice and they know him and we go to eat at the little cafe and the guy who owns the little cafe comes out and sits and talks to him for awhile. I listen to Jack's voice, I don't really listen to what he says when he's talking to other people. I just like the sound of his voice.

When the owner gets up to walk away, he says, "Don't you think you're kinda robbing the cradle there, Jack?"

He keeps on going. Jack looks a little upset.

I say, "What the hell is robbing the cradle, anyway?"

Jack says, "Well, I'm a lot older than you are. What they mean by robbing the cradle is that somebody old picks somebody very young."

I say, "Who the hell cares about that? How old are you?"

He says, "Well, if you're sixteen, I'm twenty two years older than you."

Twenty two years older than me? That's a long time! That's older than my mom.

"Jack, I don't care. It's all right with me. If it doesn't bother you, it's not going to bother me. I'm not a baby."

Jack just says, "Thank you, Tumbleweed. You just make me feel good, that's all."

Jack brought another book with him, on astrology. That's where all the stars and moon and sun are in a special place when you're born. We talk about that for a long time. He brought me some old other Life magazines that he's already read. He wants me to read a lot, I can tell. That's okay with me. We walk around this little tiny town and we look at rocks and gems and Indian arrowheads and stuff like that. We just walk and talk. I feel completely safe with Jack. I think he knows that. He tells me he's never felt better in his whole life. As Mrs. Sawyer would say, "This is a wonderful thing." Next time

I have a day off, Jack says we're going to go to the Grand Tetons. I'm going to like that. I'm going to like going anywhere with Jack.

The sun is starting to go down and we stop on a hill on our way back to Lander from Dubois. We just stand outside and my back is against his chest and his arms are around me. We just watch it, it's wonderful colors in the sky. He kisses my hair. He squeezes me once in a while. I never knew this could ever happen.

All summer long I work at the Wyoming State Hospital with the wrecked up babies and I do my best. Every day I feel good because I do my best and every day I'm sad that so many people are so wrecked up. I'm glad I can do something that makes 'em feel better. Every day off I have I go with Jack. We just run around. He shows me everything he knows. He says he wants me to know about everything.

Gin and Tonics and Making Love

Jack has some friends called Bauer, and they have a big ranch, and in the fall there's going to be a round-up and he wants me to go with him because after round-up he goes away for the winter. I don't want him to go anywhere, and if he goes anywhere, I want to go, and he said I can't. I'll be stuck waiting for him. I'll do it. I just don't like that. I want to sing with him and stand with him and look at things with him and talk about things like Darwin and Jack London and astrology and the articles in Life magazine. Now I read the paper every chance I get so I can talk to him about things.

We go out to the Bauer's Ranch and Mr. and Mrs. Bauer are real nice to me, but Mrs. Bauer takes me aside at one point and she says, "You know, you're a little young to be running around with him. I understand he's been married before and has a lot of kids."

I tell her she's full of shit, which doesn't go over very well. He never told me he had any kids. He didn't talk to me about a divorce or anything.

We ride back from the Bauer's Ranch and there's a cabin right by a stream, a really cute little cabin, it has two horses. That's for the Bauer's ranch hand but he's away.

Jack says, "Let's stop and look it over. I've always loved this place. It's really pretty."

We stop. He goes to open the barn door thing, it's a big wide board across it, and there's a rattlesnake sleeping on it. I slap it. I didn't know it could bite me and kill me. It doesn't bite me, it gets the hell off that board and gets mad and leaves, and Jack about has a stroke. He's screaming, "What the hell is the matter with you? That snake — that's a rattlesnake! Those bite you, you can die!"

I just stand there, I'd heard a lot about rattlesnakes, I didn't ever see one before. I feel like I'm going to faint.

We sit down for awhile and he tells me how to handle rattlesnakes when I run across 'em. I keep laughing and he keeps asking me why I'm laughing, and I say, "Jack, I just slapped that one off its little board, and it didn't do anything!"

He says, "You're impossible! Impossible."

We go in and look at the little house. It has a fireplace and in the fire-place is a place to hang up pots, just like they show in the books of really old, old Western stuff. It's so pretty. Jack turns around and he puts his arms around me. This time it feels different. I can feel him shaking. He puts his arms around me even harder, and he lifts me off the floor, and he kisses me. On the lips. Just keeps kissing me. I love kissing. I loved kissing Butch but I really love kissing Jack. I can feel those kisses all the way to the bottom of my feet. Jack keeps kissing me and telling me he loves me and he's never going to be the same since he met me. I just keep kissing him back. He's sweating and shaking, and he keeps holding me and hugging me and picking me up and kissing me. He asks me if I will stay with him tonight. He's looking right in my eyes. We've been together so many weeks now, he looks at me like that a lot, but never this intense. I think he's looking straight through me. He means something new and I know it. I tell him, "Jack, I spend all the nights I can with you."

He says, "I want to make love with you. I want us to take off all our clothes. I want our bodies together. I want to kiss you everywhere. I've never felt like this, Louise. Tumbleweed Louise, stay with me tonight. Stay right here in this cabin with me."

I feel hot and I feel like I've never felt before, but I can also feel the frantic franticness roaring to the top of me. This is where I get jumped up and down on, I just don't know if I can do it. I've never done that with someone I cared about. Maybe it'll be okay. Maybe I won't get mad. He's still holding me and kissing my neck and my hair and my head and my face and my eyes, and I say, "Okay, Jack, I'll try. I'll stay with you here tonight. I'll take off all my clothes, and I'll try."

Jack is kissing me all over and asking me, "Have you made love to a man before? Did he hurt you?"

I can't tell him what really happened, so I say, "Yes."

He keeps promising, "I won't hurt you. I'll be as careful, I'll love you as well as I can."

I can't believe that I'm going to do this.

He stops kissing me after awhile, and we go out and get all the stuff we need out of the truck. We light a fire and he makes soup and we make some coffee and we hang around and he brings me a gin and tonic. We have a "toast," he calls it, that's where you hope for something and put your glasses together, drink some of the stuff, and hope it all comes true. Like birthday cake candles.? I want that hope to come true.

He takes off his shirt. I know I'm supposed to take off my shirt. I just stand there, I can't do it. I can't even think. I can barely breathe. I like his skin, he holds me really close, my head on his chest. He's so tall. When he puts his arm out straight, I can stand under it almost. He starts to unbutton my shirt, and he keeps saying all kinds of wonderful things. He keeps telling me he loves me. He keeps telling me he loves every part of me, my hair and my eyes, my neck. Before I even understand what he's doing, my shirt and my bra are off. Then he just holds me. We just stand there, skin to skin. My breasts like that. I never did this before, this feels good! He picks me up and takes me over and lays me on the bed and he undid my pants, took off my shoes and socks and took off my pants. He starts to lay down on top of me. I can feel a fit coming. The biggest fit of my life but I barely have the energy to move. I turn on my side and try to get off the bed. He keeps saying, "Honey, where are you going, come here."

Finally I'm standing up. I don't know what happened, exactly, but he has his arms around my waist and I'm yelling and crying and hitting him. Just kicking and hitting and screaming and crying. He just keeps hold of me. He keeps saying, "We don't have to do anything, darling, it's okay. It's all right, we don't have to do anything. Please, just lay down with me. I won't take my pants off. Just lay down."

I'm exhausted. I'm sorry. I feel bad that I can't just do this. I really love him so why can't I just do it? We lie down and I fall asleep. I wake up and I'm covered up and he's up, putting wood on the fire and having a drink of gin and tonic. I sit up and he brings me over some warm coffee and I drink a little, and then he offers me a little drink of gin and tonic. He sits on the floor by the bed, telling me he'll never hurt me, he doesn't want me until I want him. His face is so clear. He means what he's saying, and I know it.

I drink the gin and tonic and he drinks his. He sings a song to me, "Let the rest of the world go by." The words are "We'll build a sweet little nest, somewhere out in the west, somewhere beneath the clear blue sky, and we'll find perfect peace, where joys will never cease, and let the rest of the world go by." Then he's on his knees over me on the bed and he kisses me and kisses me and kisses me. He kisses my breasts. I can't believe how good that feels. He kisses 'em and he kisses 'em with his mouth open and with his mouth closed and he kisses 'em all over, both breasts. He stands up and he unbuckles his belt and unzips his pants. I move the blanket, so he just lays down on top of my naked self. With his naked self. I just want me to do this without scream- ing. I love him. I want him to be happy. He kisses me all over and he keeps saying the same thing, "I've never felt like this. I've never wanted to kiss any- body all over."

He kisses my legs and he kisses my feet and he kisses me everywhere. Everywhere. Then he's laying on top of me, but he's on his elbows, keeping from squashing me, he says.

He says, "Now I'm going to go inside of you. Please, honey, remember I'm not going to hurt you."

Inside of me? I didn't think of that. Very very slowly, he goes inside of me. Then he lays down on top of me, completely. Holds me really tight, and keeps telling me he loves me and keeps kissing my face, and then he starts to move. I think, this isn't what my brothers did. This isn't ugly, and this isn't the same. He keeps moving. It feels good. A little bit uncomfortable. It feels good. Maybe this is how it happens if you do this and you really like it. He keeps moving and moving. All of a sudden he's moving really fast. He's sweating, he's absolutely soaking wet. I don't know what to do. I just lay there. At one point he reaches down and puts my legs up like he wanted me to put 'em around him, so I do. He really kinda feels like a bucking bronco. This is a wild thing. I don't know if this is how it's supposed to be or not. I wonder about this. He keeps moving really fast and then he stops. He's exhausted and soaking wet and I'm soaking wet by now. He's like dead weight on top of me. I put my arms around him and I can feel him fall out of me. I don't remember anything else, except his breathing.

I wake up in the morning and the fire is already going, and the coffee is already smelling. Jack walks back in the cabin.

"Where have you been?" I ask, and he comes over and he scoops me up, blanket and all, and he takes me out on the porch, sets me in a chair, and he says, "I love you."

I tell him I love him too. I feel like I'm just dreaming. I don't understand any of this, and for the first time in my whole life, I think, who cares about understanding it. He brings me coffee and eggs and bacon. I'm wrapped in my blanket on the porch watching the horses play down by the stream. I ask him if we can just live here forever, and he says he wishes we could, but we can't. I ask him if he'll take me with him when he leaves after the round-up and he says he can't take me. His eyes are wet. He doesn't cry, but I think he wants to. He serves me more coffee and he kisses me and kisses me and kisses me everywhere. I never had so many kisses in my whole life. I feel so different.

We go back to town in the afternoon because I have to go back to work. Jack talks to me about going on the round-up with him in a couple of weeks and he also says that he's going to leave and go to his other job for the winter pretty soon. Be about four weeks, he says. He won't be back until the end of next April. Jack tells me he loves me and when I get older he's going to marry me. He says for now we have to keep it all a secret. I ask him, why is it a secret? He says, "Because everything isn't ready for us to tell everybody yet. Just promise me, Tumbleweed, you'll keep it a secret" so I say yes I will. I don't really get why we have to do that, but what do I care? Who gives a good goddamn if it's a secret or not?

Horrifying Mrs. Jones

I go to work and I don't know why, but all afternoon I keep thinking, why does it have to be a secret? All afternoon I don't have an answer for that. These wrecked-up people make me feel better. I think I'm lucky. At least I can walk around and I can do what I want to do. I don't have to have Mrs. Jones take care of me, either. I mean it, I'm just lucky. My spirit guides must like me some because the worst possible thing could be you can't move or you can't think about anything. I don't like it that Jack's going to be gone pretty soon, and he's going to be gone all winter, too. I don't know what to do about that. I don't know what I'm going to do on my days off. Lucky me, though, I can move around and I can think of something to do. My wrecked-up people at the hospital can't.

I take good care of them. Sometimes I get so mad I want to hit 'em, and I just have to stand there, just stand there and not hit 'em. I have to just think, Okay. Don't hit 'em, don't hit 'em, don't hit 'em. I don't hit 'em. I feel bad that I even want to hit 'em. They couldn't even hit me back if I did clobber 'em one, but they sure piss me off sometimes. They drool on me like old dogs do. Spitting, slobbering, drool on me. Makes me nuts. When they do that, then I always want to smack 'em one but I don't do it. Mrs. Jones does. She slaps their faces. Pinches 'em. Pulls the back of their neck hairs. You know, I should take all the slapping I want to do and start on her sorry ass. She makes me crazy. She can think and eat and walk around and everything, and she hits these people who can't even hit you back! Not a fair fight, I'm telling you, it's not a fair fight. Like Jack says, I need to do my job and do a good job and never mind damn Mrs. Jones.

The Round-up

Jack says on the days off I have left, except for the weekend of the round-up, that he's going to help me drive his truck so I can get my driver's license. He doesn't know I'm not sixteen yet. He thinks I can just go get a driver's license. I have to wait until after November, until I'm sixteen. I can't tell him because he already thinks I'm sixteen! I have to remember not to drive in the goddamn ditch with his truck. I wonder what's happening with Henry these days. Henry went to see his son because he was sick and I haven't heard a word from him.

This time on my day off we go back up to the Bauer's Ranch. They're teaching me how to ride a horse for the round-up. This horse is bizarre! I sit on the goddamn thing and it takes off, and it runs like the wind and then it does a right turn or a left turn. You have to hang on tight and I didn't. I'm still in the air and that horse is gone, and then I'm flat on my ass on the ground. I think this isn't one bit funny. Mr. and Mrs. Bauer and Jack are having a laughing fit. I mean, this horse can turn on a dime!

"You need to learn how to hang on, Louise, or you're going to be on your ass a lot," Jack says.

I think, "How'd you like me to give you a hit in the nose? You could have told me that horse does that."

He says, "You have to be real careful how you touch those reins and everything" and I start yelling at him, "You asshole! You knew that was going to happen, you knew that horse was going to take off, and you knew he was going to turn and you didn't even bother telling me it's a special kind of horse. It's called a cutting horse, thanks a goddamn lot, you jackass!"

Mr. and Mrs. Bauer are real quiet and Jack stomps off, and I stomp off right after him.

"I don't know who the hell you think you are, doll boy, but don't be putting me on horses when you know what they're going to do and you don't tell me. What kind of person does stuff like that? I wouldn't do that to you."

I'm screaming and yelling and he's just stomping his way to the corral. I'm stomping right after him. I'm going to get an answer to this, or the fight's on!

"You might be tall — I'll climb up on this fence and whop you one, I'm not kidding! Why didn't you tell me what the horse was going to do?"

He gets to the corral and he starts to open the fence and I just grab him by the arm. "Goddamn it, Jack, you answer me, why didn't you tell me?"

He turns around and looks down at me and he says, "I don't know."

I say, "Well, it was just fucked, you hear me?"

He says, "You shouldn't talk like that."

I say, "Yeah, and you shouldn't put me on horses you know are going to knock me on my ass!"

I stomp off.

Mr. and Mrs. Bauer are back in the farmhouse by this time. So what, I think. I'm going to stomp right over to that goddamn horse and this time I'm not falling off! Well, I want you to know, this time turns into several times. I think my body is broken. I get it, though. I figure out how to use my legs to stay on the goddamned cutting horse for more than a minute. I'm mad at Jack, too. Jack says we should go back early tonight, and I say, "I'm not going back early. I'm staying right here and tomorrow I'm going to get up and do that horse again. I'm not going to the round-up and make a goddamned fool of myself, Jack, and you had no business putting me on that horse knowing it was going to buck me off or turn right and drop me or anything."

He says, "How long are you going to be mad about that?"

I tell him, "Just as goddamned long as I feel like it! You're not in charge of who's going to be mad for how long."

I stomp outside. Awhile later I'm just standing there watching the horses and Jack comes out and he says, "I'm really sorry, honey, I shouldn't have put you on the horse and not told you about it."

"That's right," I says. "That's goddamn right."

"Can we go back early tonight?"

"No, I'm staying and I'm going to have that horse ridden so well that when I get to the round-up I'm not going to land on my ass."

Jack looks really upset. I ask him what was the matter. He says, "I thought we could stay at the cabin that we stayed at before."

I don't know why that makes me mad. I see red, I'm so mad. "You know sometimes, Jack, you're just fucking sneaky. First you put me on the horse and don't tell me it's going to do that and I land on my ass, and then you tell me you want to go back early and you don't tell me why until you have to. That's just sneaky. I don't like that, and I'm not going back early tonight."

Jack is pretty quiet most of the night. We don't sleep together, either, and I figure that out after I get in goddamned bed. No wonder he wanted to go down to that cabin! He's afraid to let Mr. and Mrs. Bauer know we sleep together! Make love, like Jack calls it. I don't like this! There's something sneaky about this, it makes me really mad! I don't say anything, though, and the next morning I get up and I have breakfast and I help with the dishes and I go outside and get the hell back on that horse. I don't fall off once, not once! I have it! I can do it! Now I won't make a fool of myself at the round-up. The round-up's only in one more week. I asked for an extra day off. I get to be off Saturday and Sunday, and I get to do the whole two days at the round-up.

I worked all week and now we're leaving for way out in the hills where they do the round-up. Do you know at the round-up they put a brand on the horses! They also castrate a whole bunch of the male cows and horses because they don't want 'em breeding. They don't castrate the women. Jack laughed when I asked him whether they castrate the women horses. It's a different kind of thing you have to do. I thought, good! I like it better that the male horses and cows get castrated. I don't know why, but I think that's pretty good. For once something happens to them instead of the females. I like that idea. Jack doesn't think that's funny. He's real quiet after I say that, so I guess I won't say it again. For whatever reason he doesn't like that.

I have so much fun at the round up. I'm on my cutting horse, and I help chase down little tiny calves, and I help chase down little tiny horses, and I put a noose around their neck with another guy and we hang on to 'em and the guys run over and they lay 'em down and they stick a branding iron on 'em. It makes 'em holler a lot. It doesn't look very good but they have to do it, otherwise somebody can either steal your horses and cows, or nobody will even know whose they are. I keep helping, I just keep herding things around and chasing the horses and cows. I love this, this is a fun thing! When I grow up, I'm going to have a ranch. I have to grow up a whole lot more, they cost a lot of money. I'll just keep my job and I'll get a ranch when I get older.

The Gin and Tonic Trick

It's the weekend before Jack leaves. He asks me if we can go stay at the cabin. Just be by ourselves, and I told him yes. We go to the cabin and we make dinner and we have a fire and we sing and we gin and tonic and we talk. We gin and tonic some more. I drank so much gin and tonic I hardly remember making love. Jack says that's okay, so I guess that's okay.

I ask him why he has to go away. Why can't he get a job here, and we can just be together forever? He says he can't do it, that's the way his job is. He says, in this life, you have to do what your boss tells you to do. I keep thinking, I don't know if I can do that in my whole life. I can do it for awhile, but pretty soon Mrs. Jones is going to piss me off, and I know it, she's mean to those wrecked-up babies and it makes me mad. Jack says, then you won't have any money and you'll be in trouble. I think about that. I know he's right. Maybe there's a way to get money and not have a boss who's a creep. Jack says, yeah, lots of times you can change jobs, but you always have to have a job. Jack shows me on a calendar when he's coming back. It's a long time. All winter he'll be gone. He asks me if I'd wait for him. I don't know what wait for him means, so he explains, that I don't do any making love with anybody else but him. I say, "Aw Jack, that's easy. No kidding. I don't want to, anyway."

He hugs me and kisses me and thanks me. That makes him really happy.

The weekend before Jack actually left we went to Sinks Canyon and we spent the whole day and we make love twice. I'm worried. Once we do it without gin and tonic. After few minutes I'm so mad but I don't quit this time and I don't scream and yell. I just think, well, okay, I'll just wait. I just wait. Jack is upset. He says, "What's wrong?"

I tell him, "I don't know, I really don't know."

The second time we make love that day is after we had steaks and tomatoes and gin and tonic again. A good idea is for me to drink enough gin and tonic so that I feel good about making love, so I just keep drinking. It is good? I don't remember much of that making love the second time, and I'm glad. I don't know what the hell I'm doing. I don't understand it but at least I'm not screaming mad.

The next day, before I go to work, Jack talks to me and tells me he loves me and hugs me and kisses me a lot and says he'll see me in April. He drives away. I miss Jack. I go to work and I just miss Jack, that's all. I don't know what I'm going to do now, but work.

Spaghetti and Brett

I work all week and I miss Jack and I hate Mrs. Jones and I love my little wrecked-up people, except the ones that drool on me. I found out that the restaurant called Gionini's on Main Street has a spaghetti dinner every Wednesday night for really cheap. I decided I'm going to go and have that spaghetti dinner every damn Wednesday from now on. I ask Mrs. Jones to change my days off so I can have Wednesday off and have that spaghetti dinner, and she tells me I'm out of my mind, and that I can't do that. Forget it, then, you old bitch! I didn't ask you that so you could tell me I'm out of my mind. I don't want the damn Wednesday off. Just never mind it.

When my day off came on Saturday, I go down to Gionini's and I see what they're going to give people on Saturdays. They have spaghetti on Saturday, too. You can have spaghetti at Gionini's any time you want! I didn't know that. It's just not as cheap. It's a dollar more. I don't care, you know, you can get the spaghetti and the bread and the salad. I sat at the counter and had spaghetti, then I just walked up and down the main street. I don't know why I never did this before. I guess because I spent all my time off with Jack. I still miss him.

I went to the drugstore. They have a soda fountain in there where you can drink pop and have ice cream floats. What a place! I don't have enough money right now, though, so I just go in and have a coke. They tell me they don't have a coke, they have root beer. I'm having root beer. Fine. I'm sitting next to this kid. He really is good-looking. He has black hair and blue eyes. I never saw that before. I told him, I thought he was really pretty, and he says, "Pretty, like a girl?"

I say, "No! Um — you look good."

He says, "Thank you. That's called handsome."

"Okay, you're handsome. Jesus Christ."

I told him it's really neat to have black hair and blue eyes. I never saw that before and I really think it looks good. Very handsome. He says his name is Brett. I tell him mine's Louise.

Brett goes to school here. I ask him what he goes to school for. I say, "You look big enough to go to work."

He says, "I don't have to go to work. My parents want me to get a good education so I can get a good job."

I tell him, "I don't have a good education and I have a good job."

I tell him about working with the wrecked-up people and he says he'd hate a job like that. He wants to fix cars when he gets older and have a big house and have a big car of his own. I tell him, "Fine with me. I don't care."

He asks me what I do when I'm not working, and I tell him, "Well, I used to have a friend but he left and he's not coming back till April."

Then Brett asks me if I want to go chase down jackrabbits. I say, "Chase down jackrabbits? I'm not fast enough to catch a jackrabbit. I'll bet you're not fast enough either, Brett. Whoever heard of that?"

Brett laughs. He says, "I mean, chase down a jackrabbit with a car. We go out on the prairie — my friend Shorty and I — and we chase 'em down and shoot 'em."

"Why do you shoot 'em, Brett? To eat 'em? I thought jackrabbits taste awful."

He says, "Naw, we just shoot 'em because there're too many jackrabbits."

I thought of Jack and the coyote pups and I say, "You know, I don't like killing animals. There's a couple of people I'd like to kill, but I never did meet an animal I wanted to kill yet."

Brett says, "Boy, you're weird. You're strange, girl."

Then he says, "I'll tell you what. How about you run around with me and Shorty on your day off and we won't shoot any jackrabbits when you're around."

I say, "It's a deal."

Then I tell him, "Today is my day off. Saturday's my day off all the time."

He says, "Well, come on, let's go."

We take off and we go in his red and white Ford, a really pretty car. I like that car. It belongs to his daddy. We take off and go get this guy named Shorty. I know why he got his name, he's smaller than I am.

We pile in the red and white Ford and we go out to the prairie. We go down this dirt road and there was more jackrabbits than I've ever seen in my life. They're coming from everywhere. We even hit a couple of 'em with the car, without even wanting to! The guys were shooting out the windows, but they don't shoot any jackrabbits that I see. Then we come to a place where there's a big, big wide flat place and a little stream, and Brett opens the trunk and they have beer and chips and he turns on his radio in the car. We keep the doors open and we dance around and we laugh and we drink beer. This beer is better than that gin and tonic! We get back in the car and go back to town. I go to the rooming house. Brett tells me before he goes home, "Next Saturday we can go run around."

I tell him, "All right! Good idea!"

"In a couple of months I'm going to get my driver's license," I tell Brett, and he says, "Yeah, but you won't be able to get a car because they don't sell cars to girls."

"What? They don't sell cars to girls?"

"Yeah, you have to have a guy sign for you."

"Sign for me? What the hell does that mean. Brett, you don't know what you're talking about. When I'm sixteen, I'm getting a driver's license, and I'm getting a goddamn car. That's that."

Mrs. Jones Killed Sally

I'm back at work, and Mrs. Jones is just as icky as she always is. My little wrecked-up Sally isn't feeling good. It's on the chart that she threw up her breakfast. It's night, and I'm trying to feed her dinner. She can't eat, she doesn't feel good, so I don't make her eat. I give her a drink and start to clean her up. Mrs. Jones comes in, shoves me aside and she says, "When we tell these kids to eat, if they don't eat, you hold their nose. Put the food in their mouth and they have to swallow."

I'm just madder than hell. I think, Sally's too sick to eat, you goddamn stupid woman.

Mrs. Jones takes over and she feeds Sally everything. Sally swallows it. It makes me sick. I go and feed one of the other kids. Boy, I hate Mrs. Jones.

A few minutes later I look over and Mrs. Jones is yanking Sally out of her chair. We have to tie the kids to the chairs because they fall over if you don't. They grab the spoons or they do something weird so we always tie 'em with what looks like diapers but they're just rags. You tie the kids down and then you feed 'em, which I guess is okay because otherwise they'd never get anything in their mouth. Mrs. Jones yanks Sally out of there and she throws up. All over Mrs. Jones. I think, good enough for you, you stupid bitch. Mrs. Jones is so mad, she picks up Sally and throws her towards the floor, grabs her by the arm before she hits the floor and drags her — now she's on her butt, and she's dragging her toward the room where we hose 'em off or we wash 'em in the tub. It really scares me and I follow her in. I don't know why, I'm really scared. She throws Sally in the tub and Sally bangs her head and then Mrs. Jones turns on the water, only the cold water and hoses Sally off. Sally goes down flat in the tub. Sally twitches and twitches and twitches and turns purple and I go and try to take the hose away from Mrs. Jones and she turns off the water and shoves me out of the way. Sally's dead. She's really dead! She isn't breathing! I run over to get the phone and Mrs. Jones grabs me and she says, "I'll make the call, go back and feed the kids. Go back and feed the kids!"

How am I going to feed the kids? Sally's in the tub! I go get Sally. I hold Sally. I try to push on her stomach. Sally, you just need to breathe, goddammit! Mrs. Jones is a nasty bitch and you don't need to die! Sally doesn't breathe. Sally doesn't do anything.

The people come over from the office and after about a half hour, the doctor comes. Sally's really dead. They take Sally away. I'm screaming at the top of my lungs at the doctor. "She killed her! She killed Sally! She put her in the tub and turned on the cold water on her and the Mongoloids have a bad heart and that's how she killed Sally! I mean it, she really killed her!"

Mrs. Jones is standing there looking at me like she's going to kill me. The doctor is saying that he'll check into this tomorrow. I'm going to kill Mrs. Jones. I start taking care of the rest of the babies because they have to go to bed and have their medicine. I think about the way I'm going to kill Mrs. Jones. I don't know how I'm going to actually do it, but she needs to die. Sally didn't do anything to anybody. She threw up because she was sick.

Mrs. Jones is out there on the goddamned phone. I don't know who she's talking to but she's not doing any work as usual. She better do her last talking because when this shift is over I'm going to take her head right off her goddamn body. I get all the kids quieted down and in bed and give them their medicine and I go out and start to do the charts. I hardly can think, I just want to kill her. I keep thinking I don't want to go to jail. All of a sudden the supervisor of the whole place shows up. Mrs. Jones tells him she wants me fired. She says I don't take good care of the kids and I'm just bad for the whole place and I'm not good at my job. I'm yelling the whole time it's not true. I take a swing at Mrs. Jones and miss. The supervisor grabs me and tells me to get my stuff and go home, I'm fired. I get outside and I think, I'm not going anywhere. I'm going to stand right here and kill that bitch when she comes out here. The supervisor walks up to me and he says, "I told you, get off the property. Go home."

I say, "Do you know what happened? Do you know she killed Sally with cold water after Sally threw up and she made her eat everything and she knew she was already throwing up? Do you know about that?"

The supervisor says, "It's not going to do any good for you to try to blame Mrs. Jones when you're not doing your job."

I say, "You son of a bitch, I didn't touch Sally, she killed her, I'm telling you, and I did my job fine for a long time now and everybody knows it. It isn't that I don't do my job, it's that Mrs. Jones wants me gone because I saw her do that to Sally."

The supervisor says, "All right, I'll tell you what. Tomorrow morning you come up here at nine o'clock and we'll have a meeting with Dr. Jamison."

I tell him, "I'm staying out here because when that bitch comes outside, I'm going to take her head off her body." He says, "Come on, get in my car, I'll take you home. You aren't going to do anything until you find out what the supervisor's going to do tomorrow morning. What Dr. Jamison's going to say tomorrow morning. Now get in the car."

He drives me back to the rooming house. I can't understand how in the hell I'm fired when she killed Sally. I want to go right back up there and kill her, I'm not kidding. I didn't know people killed babies, and still get to be the boss of the place. What kind of goddamned thing is this? You know, every time I turn around, there's something uglier than the last thing. This is awful!

I can't sleep. I write and I write and I write songs and I sing and the guy across the hall comes and knocks on my door and tells me to shut up, he can't sleep, and I tell him to fuck himself someplace, but I shut up, I'm not mad at him, really. I write songs about Sally and I sing 'em really soft. I miss my little brother. I don't know why people pick on people littler than they are. I don't understand any of this, and how come nobody's mad? I want everybody to be mad! I want the whole world to be mad when this happens, that's what I want!

Morning comes and I get ready for the damn meeting up there. Boy, they better do something about her, I'm not kidding. There's going to be real trouble if they don't. Jack told me, you piss off your boss, and you don't have a job. I don't care. I didn't have a job before, and I got one, I'll just get another one, after I kill Mrs. Jones or somebody does something about her. I don't want to go to jail.

I go up the hill and I go to Dr. Jamison's office. Dr. Jamison and the supervisor and horrifying Mrs. Jones are there. I ask Dr. Jamison what the fuck she's doing here, and he says to settle down, sit down, we're going to have a talk. I sit down and he says, "I'd like very much for you not to swear for the rest of this meeting."

I say, "Fine. I won't swear. Mrs. Jones killed Sally, she turned cold water on her after she threw up. She made her eat all that food and Sally's been sick and that's why she threw up and she threw up on Mrs. Jones. "

Dr. Jamison says, "Mrs. Jones says the opposite story."

"What opposite story?"

Dr. Jamison says, "Mrs. Jones says that you slapped Sally around and you threw her in the tub and you turned cold water on her."

I just sit there. I can't even move. I can't believe this. I did not! I didn't do any of this. How am I going to tell these people. This is just like home! Everybody just makes up their mind and that makes it true, right? I stand up — but I just stand there, I can't talk.

Dr. Jamison says he felt kinda fatherly toward me the whole time I worked here, and I think, Just what I need is a father, I had one of those, the goddamned thing tried to kill me. I tell him that and he just sits there and I say, "Dr. Jamison, why would I kill Sally? Why? Besides, everybody who has ever worked with Mrs. Jones told me before I started working with her how awful she was to the kids. Why don't you check around? What the hell's the problem here? You know, how come if I killed Sally, I don't just goddamned go away so you don't put me in jail?"

He asks me again to stop swearing. I'll try, but boy, this isn't going to be easy. I feel like cussing a blue streak.

Dr. Jamison says to Mrs. Jones that she can go. Mrs. Jones says she doesn't want to, she wants to hear what I have to say, and Dr. Jamison says, "We'll take this up later, I want to talk to Louise by herself."

I think, Oh, great, and then they tell me I'm really fired, he's going to keep me here till the cops come. Mrs. Jones leaves the office and I ask him, "Are you just going to talk to me till the cops get here and arrest me for killing Sally and I didn't even do it?"

Dr. Jamison says, "No, what I'm going to do is put you on a different ward."

Put me on a different ward? "What do you mean?"

He says, "I'm not going to fire you. I have heard bad reports about Mrs. Jones and I'm going to check into this. Until I find out what really happened, both of you are going to stay working here because I don't know what happened and I'm not going to make a decision on that until I do find out."

Dr. Jamison tells me, "You know, we were going to give you an award in January for being our best new employee."

I say, "Dr. Jamison, I don't give a good goddamn what you do with me in January. I don't care about an award. I told you, she killed Sally. I want something done about her, she's mean to those kids. That's bad enough, but killing 'em isn't what we're supposed to be doing either! If killing Sally's okay, Dr. Jamison, then killing Mrs. Jones is even better."

Dr. Jamison says, "Louise, you just don't understand. None of us like this. We don't know what happened. We don't know which one of you to believe."

I say, "You should believe me because I'm the one telling the truth."

He says, "You know, that might be true. But we don't know that. We weren't there."

"Okay, Dr. Jamison, you weren't there, I get it. How are you going to find out what happened, I was the only other person there, and the wrecked-up babies were there but they can't tell you anything."

Dr. Jamison says, "I want you to let me handle this, I'm going to give you a different ward to work on and different people to work with and I want you to let me investigate this and find out what happened."

I tell him okay, but I don't know how you're going to find out when she was the only one that was there besides me, and she's lying. He says, "You can't work here if you don't promise that you'll let me find out what happened." So I goddamned promise because I have to have a job. Besides, I want to take care of the wrecked-up babies.

I want to blow Mrs. Jones's ass right off her body. I should get Brett and Shorty to shoot her like they do jackrabbits. He says the new ward I'm going to be on is called geriatrics. It means really old people. Great. I heard about that ward. Everybody dreads it like the plague and I get to be on it. When I had the tour in the beginning of this job, and I was taking nurse's aide training, I went through that ward once and it smelled so bad, I thought I was going to throw up. I don't know what I'm going to do about that. Dr. Jamison says I have two days off, and then I go to work on the geriatric ward. Okay. Fine then. I ask him if they're going to have a funeral for Sally and he says, "We don't have funerals up here."

That's kinda good, though, because I think if Mrs. Jones came to Sally's funeral, she would get out of her casket and go throw up on her again.

I go home and I call Brett and I tell him that I have two days off and he says, "Well, I'll ask my dad if I can borrow the car and then we'll go see something fun and we'll do something fun if I can get hold of Shorty."

Brett's dad says he could have the car in the evening after dinnertime and so we get to go run around and drink beer and listen to the radio with the doors open, but we ain't going to shoot any jackrabbits. We're not bringing the guns because I asked Brett, this time, just this time, can we just not do that, can we just like each other and don't shoot at anything. Go see something different besides the jackrabbits. Brett said that was okay.

Brett's nice to me. I'm going to be nice to him, too. Shorty's funny, and he's nice to me, so I'm going to be nice to him. I'm going to take the stash of money and take him to spaghetti at Gionini's, that's what I'm going to do. I only have enough money for two dinners, though, so we're just going to have to share. We get together in the evening and go to Gionini's and I ask the woman at the counter if we can have just an extra plate because I only have enough money for two spaghetti dinners and I want my friends to eat with me, and she says, "I'll do this just this once, I ain't ever doing it again." I don't care because I'm ain't doing this again either.

Brett and Shorty and I eat a spaghetti dinner and we all shared with Shorty and we all had a good time.

We get in Brett's car and we go running around. We go everywhere. We stop and see some people I never even met and I like 'em and then we run around some more. We laugh and laugh. We laugh so hard, we run off the road into the ditch. We get out, it isn't the kind of run-off-the-road-into-the-ditch that's too bad to even get out of, but Shorty says, "You better watch it, your dad's going to see scratches on this car and you ain't ever going to use it again."

We take the car back to town and we wash it off at Shorty dad's shop. It looks pretty good, though, and the next night, we do the same thing. I don't sleep very good. I keep seeing Sally, twitching and turning purple. I hate Mrs. Jones. I miss Sally.

I start back to work today on the geriatric ward. Mrs. Jones is still taking care of the babies. She has somebody else working with her. I hope they catch her doing a rotten thing. Why can't I just go shoot her ass like I want to, what's the matter with me? I thought about shooting a lot of people I never do it. Goddamn chicken shit, just like my mom says.

On the geriatric ward, everybody is dying. Little by little, they're dying, and the smell is awful. The head nurse has to put Vicks under my nose so I won't smell it. They have a jar of Vicks in the office for that very reason, so I put Vicks under my nose. It does make it better. You have to swab out all these horrible sores. You pour stuff in one sore and it comes out the other sore. They're called staph infections. You can't touch 'em because you'll get it yourself. This ward makes me nervous. Geriatrics means you're old. I'm not going to get old, I decided today. I know, I know, I know. I've only been here one day and I might change my mind, but I don't think so. I ain't never going to get old. I'm never going to be on a geriatrics ward, and I'm never going to be unable to move. Just the thought of it makes me unhappy. If I think that I'm going to get that old, I'm going to shoot myself.

There's a lady who lays in her bed and she keeps saying, "Mama, get these men off of me."

I know what she means. I know what she's talking about. Everybody else just says she's crazy.

I ask 'em, I say, "Don't you know what she's talking about?"

They say, "You're too young to be worried about that, just do your job."

I just do my job. They don't make the geriatrics people eat. They don't do anything very much to 'em. We sit in the office most of the time, and just talk about nothing because they're just dying and we're just letting 'em. This is really bad, I'm probably getting worse by the day, I keep thinking they should die too. I don't want to kill 'em, but they should die, their lives are bad! They lay in bed and they have bed sores and they can't swallow and they can barely breathe and they're dying. You can smell them dying. I don't like this, but like Jack says, I have to have a job and I can't be running around the world making bosses mad.

My Pals and Revenge

I told Brett and Shorty about what Mrs. Jones did and how mad I am. We took red paint from Shorty dad's shop and we wrote on both sides of her black car while she was working, "Mrs. Jones killed Sally." We did that. I didn't do it alone, but I did that. I've never done anything to anybody's stuff before, except I had to take food from people's root cellars. I painted that on her car, I meant it. She got a new paint job after that and we painted it on her car again, in white paint. Every time she paints that car Brett says, "We could just paint it on there again."

The third time we painted it on the windshield so she couldn't drive, and we painted it in black paint on her windshield, in red paint on both sides of her car and let the air out of her tires. She called me into Dr. Jamison's office because she said I was the one painting her car. Nobody saw it. Nobody saw you kill Sally, and nobody saw me paint that on your car, you old bitch. Somebody is going to be watching her car, Dr. Jamison said, so I guess I won't paint it on there again because they'll catch me and then they can prove it. I painted it on my uniform and they sent me home from work.

Dr. Jamison called me in his office after they sent me home for painting "Mrs. Jones killed Sally" on my uniform. He said that I can't work there if I'm going to act like that. That made me so mad, I couldn't even talk, and I think Dr. Jamison thought I agreed with him, but I couldn't say anything. I left his office and it was lunch time on the hill, everybody has a certain lunch time, we all go in different shifts, but we do the same thing for dinner on my shift. I went into the lunchroom and stood there and yelled as loud as I could, "Mrs. Jones killed Sally, and that's that." I left.

Dr. Jamison never said a word to me about it, and a couple of days later a few people complained about Mrs. Jones that had never said anything before, and Mrs. Jones got fired. She doesn't work here anymore. I feel a lot better. It's not quite what I had in mind — I had in mind shooting her a lot, but Dr. Jamison said you go to jail for that. You know what's worse than not being able to move? It's to have a cage like jail, like those coyote pups do when we put 'em in those wire things, I don't want to do that.

I ask Dr. Jamison if I can go back and take care of the babies and he says no, he's going to put me on a different unit, from Geriatrics. Geriatrics is making me sick. He says, until November I have to work on Geriatrics till he can replace me. I tell him okay.

On my day off Brett and Shorty and I run around and run around and run around. We go places — I get to see a lot of this country, it's so beautiful! Mostly we spend it on the prairie terrorizing the jackrabbits. We don't shoot 'em — they don't bring guns anymore, I don't know why. We have a lot of fun and we go visit people and sometimes we take 'em with us and we run around the prairie. On the prairie there aren't any roads, you don't have to follow roads. We ran around every which way. Brett drove his car — zoom! boom, we're across a ravine. One side of his car is sitting on one side of the ravine, and the other side is sitting — where? The wheels aren't even touching the ground, and when you look down, it's several feet down and if this car falls we're dead. It scares us half to death. Shorty almost had a heart attack and I almost had a screaming fit, and Brett just keeps saying, "My dad is going to kill me."

We try to figure out how to get out of this, but it's pitch black outside, so Brett says, "We just have to sit here until morning, till we can see what we're doing."

I don't want to do that. I don't like that! I don't know what they're going to do, and it's dark out and if they think they're going to touch me, I'm going to have to knock their heads in, then I won't have any friends anymore. We sleep, we really do, and nobody does anything stupid to me, and I didn't do anything stupid to them. It's an awful sleep, though — Shorty gets to sleep laying down, he's so small, he fits in the back seat. Brett stretches out a little and I can lean on him and we fall asleep. He doesn't do anything stupid. I like the way he smells, too. I like leaning on his chest. I like chests, I think.

It's morning, and we gotta figure out a way to get out of this car. This isn't funny. Brett says he and I should just sit still and Shorty should go out the back door, go up on top of the roof and go over the trunk. Shorty says right after he wets his pants he'll do just that. He opens the door and he pees out the door. That's what's good about a penis, you can point that thing someplace and not have to wet your pants. I, on the other hand, can't do that. I'm thinking, okay, hurry up, Shorty because I'm going to wet my pants if we don't get out of this car!

Shorty climbs out, goes up on the roof, and the car starts creaking and wobbling. I'm not a happy person here. I do not want to fall into this ravine in this car wetting my pants. I start to panic and Brett grabs me by the arm and tells me, "Hold still or we're going to end up toppled over on the bottom. Just hold still."

I'm holding still. Shorty is up, he did it. Brett says, "Okay. Shorty's now standing on the ground behind us."

I want to be standing on the ground behind us. Brett says, "You and I need to sit in the middle of the front seat." We scrunch together in the middle of the front seat, and he says, "Now crawl over the back seat and go out the same way Shorty did."

I do that. I damn near die of fright. I crawl up on the roof and I go over the trunk, and now I'm standing behind that car happy as hell. Brett's starts to climb over the car, and up comes a tow truck with Brett's dad in it. Mad hopping goddamn mad. Brett just gets up on the roof of the car and he's heading for the trunk so he can get where we're standing. He sees his dad, he freezes in his tracks, and I'm still peeing, and yelling, "Brett, the car's moving, get the hell off of it!"

He's so scared, he can't move at all. Okay, fine, then, here we go.

Brett's dad says, "For Christ's sake, son, get off that car!" and Brett scrambles over the trunk and the car starts to sink. I pull up my pants. It doesn't really sink all the way, it just moves some and Brett's daddy and his friend come up and put a thing on the back of the car, and they start pulling it, and they tow it out of there with the tow truck. Brett's dad drives off without us, saying, "You assholes can just walk back home."

It takes us almost all day to get back to town.

While we're walking' back to town, I think to myself, "I'm going to get my own car and then nobody can drag off and make me walk all goddamned day." I tell that to Brett and Shorty, and Brett says, "That's a good idea because after this mess, dad's not going to let us use his car."

When we get back to town I go to my rooming house and Brett and Shorty go home, I reckon they went home. A little while later Brett comes to the rooming house. It's getting dark and he and his dad got in a fight. His dad must think we enjoyed sitting over that ravine, scared to death all night, so his punishment is he doesn't get the car for a long time. He got in a fight, though, and Brett's really upset. Brett asks me if he can stay with me. Stay with me? Okay, Brett, but you can't be doing any of that jumping up and down on me. He looks at me like he doesn't know what I'm talking about. I ask him, "You mean, just stay overnight and sleep, nothing else?"

Brett says yes and I tell him okay. We eat a bunch of my bread and apple butter and then we get in the bed and we snuggle up, warm, like I used to do at the Sawyer's with the kids. We go to sleep. I'd like to have a friend to sleep with forever. Brett says you can't do that because people who sleep together, if they're girls and boys, sooner or later they have sex. Sex. Making love. Jumping up and down. Is it always like that? Brett says "Yep," his dad told him that. His mom told him that too. I asked him can we just be friends and no jumping up and down and no sex and no making love? Brett says he could try. We made a pact that we'll try that whenever we feel like it, and when Brett can't do it, then we won't sleep together. I tell him besides I promised Jack that I wouldn't do that with anybody but him. I'd like it if I never had to do it with anybody ever. I wonder if I did this with Brett, if I drank enough of beer, if it'd be okay with me like it is with Jack, but I already promised Jack so I'm not going to do it.

Brett says men can't help this, and I say, Yeah, okay, you can't help it but do you have to be mean about it? He says he was never going to be mean about it. I just go to sleep because I don't know what else to say.

I wake up in the morning and Brett is still there and we're both still happy. We get dressed. We decide we're going to go downtown to the main street and we're going to go to Gionini's and eat some breakfast. Brett has some money. I have a little bit. We'll go see if we can have hash browns. I love hash browns.

When we get to Gionini's we talk about how pretty soon I'm going to get my license and I'm going to get my car and Brett tells me again, "You have to have a man sign for you."

I say, "Okay, Brett, will you sign for me?"

He says, "No, I mean a man who has a job and a family, a bigger man, like a dad."

Oh, goddammit, that just makes me nuts! Who needs those people anyhow? I'm the one making the money, how come I can't just sign for this? He says, "That's just the way it is."

I figure I'm going to ask my supervisor at work. Maybe he'd sign for a car.

Back at work at the Geriatric ward, I work really hard and I put Vicks under my nose so I don't get sick, and I clean everybody the best I can, and I peroxide their sores and I pour all that medicine on 'em and I turn 'em and I try to feed 'em. It's a bad job and it makes me unhappy. These people aren't going to live but worse than that, they're alive, only kind of.

Psychiatric Technician

Dr. Jamison calls me into his office. I've been on that Geriatric ward for a month. He's going to send me to Evanston for some training at the mental hospital, and I ask him what the hell's the difference between that hospital and this hospital, how come I can't have the training here because I don't want to leave because I want to be with Brett and Shorty? He says that it's a mental hospital instead of mentally retarded and that means that the people have brains but they're crazy. I don't understand that. He says that I'm a good worker and I'm smart and he wants me trained in every kind of training I can get. With this kind of training you get to be a psychiatric technician. It takes a whole year. First I have to do three weeks of training, then I come back here and work at the hospital another year, then I do three more weeks of training, then I'm a psychiatric technician. If Dr. Jamison thinks it's a good idea, I'll do it. He says after my training, at the Wyoming State Hospital, I can come back to this Wyoming State Training School and I won't have to work on the Geriatric ward anymore. They'll put me with the people who are teenagers. Okay, I tell him. He says they're called "trainables."

That means you have enough brains to train you to do some things. I like that idea because then I'll get to work on the ward where you can train the mentally retarded to do things and I won't have to put Vicks under my nose and I won't have to feel bad every day.

The Wyoming State Hospital really is different. All of these people were born with all their brains and all of these people can move all their bodies. They tell me there are some people in the cells in the basement that can't do all this, but that's because they've been crazy for so long. Crazy means that you had all your brains and you lost your ability to use 'em. I wonder if that's what happened to my brothers.

In the training you learn how to get the crazy people to do what you ask 'em to do, without making 'em mad or making 'em even more crazy. That's where that thing Dr. Jamison talks about, called "encouragement," comes in. Somehow I know how to do this without upsetting 'em. I think it's just being nice to 'em, but I see a lot of people be nice to 'em and still the crazy people won't do what they're told to do. Sometimes they won't do it for me either, and when they make me really mad or they hit me or throw things at me, I hit 'em back on their arm and throw unbreakable things at them too. My supervisor says I shouldn't do that. I also have training every day in reading what they call their charts. Their charts means everything that everybody writes down about 'em, you know, like where they came from and how many kids are in the family and what happened to them and when they went crazy. All that kind of stuff is in their chart including all their medication and when they've been sick. I found out that a whole bunch of 'em went crazy because of stuff that happened to them. Worse than that, the stuff that happened to 'em isn't as bad as what happened to me.

I get off work and I go into my room, and I want you to know I'm really scared. I think the thing that's making them crazy is going to come and get me. I don't want to be crazy. Even if you can move all of your body parts, like the wrecked-up people can't, you can't take care of yourself and you can't say where you're going to go. The charts make me feel terrible because if they can go crazy about their stuff, it's for sure I can go crazy about mine! I wonder if crazy is just a place in your head or it can come on like a cold. The nurses and supervisors tell me, you don't get to know when you're going to go crazy. That just makes me sick! I go home and stay in my room. I don't want to go crazy! I talk to my spirit guides about it.

They put me on the unit for this training of the people who are crazy but can still do a lot of things. I guess that the whole point is I'm supposed to learn how to deal with this so when I go back to the hospital where the wrecked-up people are I can learn how to get them to do these things. I really don't want this thing to come and get me too! A lot of these charts don't say anything except that they're mad at their parents, or they got pregnant and their parents put 'em here. They're all pretty young. Some of them were out having a whole lot of that sex. Why they would do that on purpose, I don't know, but they do.

I'm afraid of this crazy. I'm going to learn to understand it, and I'm going to figure out how you can tell when it's coming to get you. 'Cause before it comes to get me, I'm going to shoot myself. That would make me really mad, too, that those goddamned assbite boys that I lived with when I was young could make me go crazy later and they aren't even around. That's the nightmares I have, I go crazy and nobody is even doing anything to me anymore.

In the training program, though, I do very well, they say. I can get people to do things because I am like I am. I just have what they call an "encouraging attitude." I have to be on some of the other wards for a day or two, just to see what kind of people are not trainable and can't do anything. Some of 'em are called catatonic and they don't move. You put 'em in a position and they stay in that position all day. I put up one of their arms and he stayed there standing with his arm in the air all day long! Do you know I couldn't even do that if I wanted to. How's that for crazy? I'll be glad when this training's over because the supervisor told me that the longer that crazy people are around each other, the more they act like each other. If I have that crazy thing in my head, I shouldn't be here very long because then it would really get me! Besides, I have to go back home and get back at my job with the wrecked-up people so I can get my car. I'm going to be sixteen pretty soon. I have to be really careful. I almost told that to my damned supervisor but then I stopped because I was supposed to be sixteen to work here.

The training went really well. I learned a lot, and I got a certificate that says I'm a psychiatric technician. Now I have two certificates, one that says I'm a nurse's aide, and one that says I'm a psychiatric technician. Beats the hell out of rattly rides on a train. It even beats my rag house. I loved my rag house but that seems like a long time ago now and obviously, I wouldn't live in a rag house. I don't have to anymore.

After the training is over at the Wyoming State Hospital I head back to the Wyoming State Training School to see if I can train people to do things that they can do. I hope I'm good at this.

My Chevy

I'm sixteen today. I don't tell anybody about it, but I go down to the Department of Motor Vehicles and I apply for my license. It takes a couple of weeks for me to actually have it, but I have a piece of paper that says that I going to have it. They had me drive a car around. I did fine. As soon as I get my license I'm going to go get a car. I have a hundred dollars. I've been saving this whole year — I have a hundred dollars and I'm buying a car.

I'm on the trainable unit at work. I train the patients to serve trays in the cafeteria and not piss people off, and not play with the food, and not rub their noses, and not do weird things. I train 'em to mop floors and to do a whole lot of kitchen work. It feels a lot better than being with people who can't do anything.

I try to get a car. Brett was right, I have to have a co-signer. Shit. I ask my supervisor at work and he says no. I run over to Brett's house really upset. Brett's dad said he'd sign for me. What did ya think of that? He's been mad at us ever since we stuck that damn car over a ravine! But he says he thinks I'm a hard worker so he's going down on my day off and sign for me to have a car! I already saw the car I want. A '56 Chevy, and it's bronze and tan. It has a bull on the hood. Its horns light up!

Brett's dad signs for me and Brett and I drive that car away and I have to keep up these car payments and I will. I pay all my bills. I like me like that! My dad never pays his bills. My brothers never do anything right, and my mom sits around. I don't want to be like them.

Brett and I invite everybody we know, we fill the whole trunk of my car with ice and beer and take it out to the prairie and raise hell with my radio blaring. There are so many of us that some of the people are riding on top of the hood and on fenders. They're riding and we're laughing and having a good time. We dance and we drink beer and it gets almost sunlight and we go home. Brett calls that a celebration of all celebrations, and he stays with me the next night after I get off of work, doing that cuddling up and sleeping he calls it. I like that cuddling up and sleeping.

Brett says we never can have sex because once we start, we won't be able to quit, and I say, "Oh, huh, I could quit any old time, I don't even like it."

He says, "Yeah, most women don't like it."

I think, Right, so why do they do it all the time? I think women who don't like it should only have to do it when they're going to have babies. Brett says, "So, okay, if that's going to be the way it is, then when are men going to do it?"

I say, "When women are going to have babies" and Brett says that men have to do it a lot. I say, "I saw the way my brothers do it when they don't have a woman. They call it jacking off, how come guys don't just do that? What the hell is the problem?"

Brett says, "'Cause they don't want to."

I ask Brett, "Who the hell cares what you want? I mean, why should I have to do something you could do yourself?"

He says, "Really good women enjoy sex if they really love their husband."

Did you hear that? I don't think that's true. Either that or I never met a woman who loved her husband. Even Mrs. Sawyer does it but she doesn't run around singing and whistling. She never says a word about it, so I don't believe she loves it all that much. She is never happy about it when just the topic comes up. I don't know what the hell the matter's with me. I just don't see why I should have to do a husband and sex. That must be why I wanted to grow up and be a deer because they only have sex when they're going to make a fawn, and the rest of the time they stick together and then the bucks go away. They just don't bother each other. Besides, deer take good care of their babies, and they're not like cows. Cows are so dumb that they sit on their babies and squash 'em and don't even know it. Deer also teach their babies everything they know, and then the babies go out in the woods and they're fine.

I have my new car. I have Brett and Shorty and I have my room and my apple butter and my job and I'm happy. I'm going to live as happy as I can because if that crazy thing comes and gets me, then I won't be happy anymore. Everybody says that I'm fun so they invite me places, even adults invite me all over the place. I learned a thing called the waltz. I like that dance. They do it down at the bar. They let me in the bar, I'm not old enough to drink, they said, I told 'em I already drink anyway but they're totally unimpressed by that. They let me stay in there and dance and drink seven-up if I behave myself. I behave myself and I get to dance with everybody. Now people invite me to their house to baby-sit their kids or they invite me to their house to have dinner or just to be around. I like this happy life.

Next month, Jack will be back. Brett says he doesn't like that because he won't get to play with me as much and he won't get to run around with me and he won't get to sleep in my bed. I ask him how come, and he says, "Well, you promised Jack that you wouldn't do any of that with anybody but him." I say, "I did not! I promised Jack I wouldn't do any making love and I didn't. I can hang around with anybody and sleep with anybody I want."

He says, "You wait till Jack gets back, he's not going to think that's one bit cute."

I think that's stupid.

Singing with Jack and Getting Married

Jack's going to be back tomorrow and I'm excited about seeing him. I almost forgot what he looks like. I know he's tall, has brown, wavy hair and very, very blue eyes. I'll be glad to see him. He has a friend named Charlie who lives in town here, but Charlie has a whole bunch of animals out at somebody else's ranch, and I have to go over to Charlie's to see Jack tomorrow morning.

I get ready for bed, I'm excited, tomorrow's the big day. There's a knock on my room door. I open it, I hope it's not somebody telling me to be quiet because I'm not making any noise. It's Jack! He grabs me up, picks me up, hugs me and tells me he missed me. He really missed me. We hug and we kiss and we hug and we kiss and he asks me if I will go out to Sinks Canyon and just hang around a little bit with him, so I go out and get in his truck and we take off. We're at Sinks Canyon and he gets his stuff out of the truck and he puts down a blanket and he starts a fire and he makes a steak and tomatoes and the gins-and-tonics. I drink 'em and I eat the stuff. He starts to take off my clothes. He asks me if I waited for him. I tell him, "I didn't have any sex with anybody."

He hugs me, kisses me, and thanks me, and he starts taking off some more of my clothes, and I tell 'em we should have another gin and tonic, so we do. I need to have gin and tonic so I don't get mad when we make love. It's starting just barely getting light out, and we both wake up. He wants to make love again. I don't know why that makes me so mad, but I'm out of that sleeping bag ready to punch him. I hate it. I've not been this mad for a long time, since Mrs. Jones killed Sally. He asks me what's wrong, and I say, "I don't know. I don't — maybe I can't — I don't know. I just don't want to do that, ever in the morning, not ever. Not before gin and tonics, and not in the damn morning."

Jack says most men like sex better in the morning, and I say, "Too goddamned bad. I hate that."

I don't know why I'm so mad, but this is something we better not do again, even thinking about it makes me mad.

Jack says, "Okay, okay!"

He takes me back to the rooming house and he says he'll pick me up later that day.

I say, "I have to work today."

"Oh," he says, "okay, how about I come and get you after work?"

This is terrible, but I think, Oh yeah, so we can make love, and I say, "Nope. We can't do anything till my next day off, unless we have breakfast or something in the morning."

Jack looks really weird. I know he doesn't like it. I don't think he understands that I have to have gin and tonic to like sex and he needs to goddamned get it. He needs to understand, he gets to do that, but not till I really don't care about it. We make a date to have breakfast at Gionini's the next morning. He tells me he's been working really hard and I say, "Where?" He doesn't answer me. He says it's really important that I don't worry about what he does when he's not with me, and he won't worry about what I do. I tell him I think that's really stupid, and he says, "Well, for right now, it's just important."

When he says things in that tone of voice, I guess I just believe him. Okay, right now, I won't do that. I don't care. It's all right.

I tell Jack about my friends, Brett and Shorty, and I tell him about my new car, and I tell him how much I like running around and I like waltzing, and he tells me I can sing with him at Bud and Blackie's. He says we have to practice a whole lot of songs so that we can do them really good at Bud and Blackie's. I tell him, okay, I want to do it. He asks me when I see Brett and Shorty, and I say, "On my days off."

He says, "Well, how are we going to see each other on your days off if you're with Brett and Shorty?"

I just think, boy, you know what, Jack, you get dumber by the day. I say, "I won't do that for the time you're here, I'll only see you."

I tell Brett about that the next day when I see him downtown, and Brett says, "You're not a very good friend. You mean I'm not going to see you until next September? That's not being a good friend. I thought we were really close."

"We are, Brett," I tell him, "we are, but — I have to — well, okay, goddammit, Brett, what do ya want me to do?"

He says, "Well, let's pick a day, we could at least see each other one time a week. If it's not your day off, that's okay with me."

"Well, that's a good idea, Brett, I think."

We make arrangements to see each other one of the days in the morning and then right after I get off of work. We do that on Sundays because I have to work on Sunday evenings. He doesn't have to go to school, so I can see him all morning, and then I can see him at night. He asks me if he could cuddle up and sleep in my room and I tell him of course he can. He says, "What would Jack say about that?"

I say, "It's none of Jack's business. Jack said that we shouldn't worry about what each other does when we're not around, so I'm not."

Jack and I start practicing the country and western singing. Jack sings really low, so when I sing with him, it sounds really pretty and I'm not harmonizing, it's just a high voice and a low voice. I love singing with him, and he plays the guitar. He says when we're at Bud and Blackie's, I'm just going to sit on a stool in front of him. I want to know how come I can't play the guitar, why won't he teach me, and he says, "It would look better, everybody will like it if you just sit there and be pretty."

I say, "Jack, don't fuck with me. I'm not going to sit anywhere and be pretty. I've never been pretty. What you mean is I'm just going to sit there."

He says, "Yeah, I want you to sit on a stool in front of me. I'm going to get you an outfit," he says, "I'm going to get you pink pants and some boots and a pink western shirt with a scarf. You're just going to be pretty."

He always wears a hat called a fedora, he looks so handsome in it when he sings. He has a gray hat and gray shirt and gray pants and gray boots. We'll be pink and gray. I like that. We practice and practice and we gin and tonic and we talk and we walk and we do all the things we always do, only mostly now we just practice singing. In a couple weeks, he says, I'll be ready to sing at Bud and Blackie's with him. I like that. He says I can't go anywhere near the bar, though. I just have to stay on the damn stool, on the little stage, and sing with him because it's against the law for me to go anywhere near the bar.

I tell him, "How can it be against the law, I drink gin and tonics with you and I drink beer with Brett, I drink whenever I goddamned want to."

He says, "A lot of things are against the law that I do, but it isn't that they're bad, it's just the law."

"Okay, so I'll sit on the stool and sing."

We're going to be singing at Bud and Blackie's every Friday and Saturday. I can't sing on Friday nights, I tell him, I have to work. He's going to sing there on Friday nights, and I'm going to sing with him on Saturdays. Then I'm going to play with Brett on Sundays.

I'm happy I can buy what I want, and go where I want, and sing all I want, and take care of all the people I want, and I have my friends. It's a good life. My mom should know about this life but she'd probably just tell me to shut up. She writes me once in a while, tells me her and Tom aren't getting along, or she's having another baby. Another baby. Way to go mom. Anyhow, my little brother got my address from her and he writes to me. He wants to come out to Wyoming and live with me. I talk to Jack about it, he doesn't think it's a very good idea, but I think I'm going to have him come out and I'll take care of him because he doesn't get along with my dad and who could get along with my dad anyway?

Tonight's the big night. The first time I sing at Bud and Blackie's. I have my pink outfit and my country and western self looks good to me. I wish I had a different face, but you can't have everything. We get to Bud and Blackie's and I sit down in front of the stage because Jack says he's going to sing the first song by himself. Jack starts singing and it's "Tumbling Tumbleweeds" and he's looking right at me. I love Jack. When he sings the words "See them tumbling down, pledging their love to the ground, lonely and free I'll be found" then he changes it a little to "Drifting along with my tumbling tumbleweed" and then after he sings the song right to me. He announced that I'm going to be singing with him, that I'm his tumbleweed and so I get up on the stage and sit on the stool. The first song we sing is Hank William's song "You Win Again" and the next song we sing is "Hello Walls." What a happy night! Then we sing Jim Reeves' "Four Walls" and then we sing "Tender Years" and then we stop and drink some soda and talk to people. I have to sit right on the edge of the little stage if I'm going to talk to anybody. Everybody's calling me "Tumbleweed." I like that name - it fits me. A rolling' weed.

We get back up on the stage and we sing "Whispering Pines" and then we sing "The Window Up Above" and then "I'm So Lonesome I Could Cry" and then "Slowly." Then we take another break. The next song is "Indian Love Call," then on to "Long Gone Lonesome Blues," "Send Me The Pillow That You Dream On," and "From a Jack to a King." The last set of songs we play is "Cross The Brazos At Waco," "Please Help Me, I'm Falling," "Let the Rest of the World Go By," and then we sing "Tumbling Tumbleweed" together. That's the whole night. He says we're going to do those songs almost every Saturday. I wish we could sing the Everly Brothers, but he won't sing 'em, he doesn't like 'em. The Everly Brothers are great! I like their singing better. We have to sing songs both of us like, he says, so I'm doing it.

Everybody applauds the songs. They must like 'em. Jack says if people don't like songs, they don't applaud, and besides that, they get mad and leave. Nobody got mad and left, everybody talked to us when we took a break, and they applauded every time we sang a song. It made me so happy. I've never been this happy, I don't think.

Every week I work at the training school, and every Saturday night I sing at Bud and Blackie's. Every Saturday I spent all day with Jack. Then Saturday night we stay in his truck at Sinks Canyon and do that gin and tonicing and eating. He takes me home on Sunday morning and then I get to be with Brett and Shorty. Then Brett stays in my room on Sunday night, cuddling and sleeping.

Jack says on the Fourth of July, which is only a week away, he has a surprise for me, and Charlie's going to come with us to the surprise. Jack says he loves me and he wants to marry me. We're going to go to the Grand Tetons, they have a chapel there, and Charlie's going to marry us. I tell Charlie I didn't know he could marry us. Charlie just chuckles and tells me that life is full of surprises. I ask Jack if we're going to live together, are we going to get a place like a little house, baby and a dog or what are we going to do? He says, "Well, for now we just have to keep things the way they are and we still have to keep quiet."

I don't know why we have to do that! He said to trust him, he knows more about it than I do. I guess he does, but I don't like this. I tell Brett about the wedding anyway because I just want somebody else to tell it to. Brett wants to go. I tell that to Jack and he damn near has a stroke again. He says, "Absolutely nobody can go" and I'm not supposed to talk about it anymore. Okay, already! I won't talk about it! Brett says, "Okay, then I can't cuddle and sleep with you anymore if you're going to be married."

I don't want to be married if we can't be cuddling and sleeping! Brett says not to be stupid. We can run around together, we just can't cuddle and sleep anymore.

I say, "Well, what about when Jack's not even here all winter long?"

Brett just gets really sad. He says, "I don't know what to do. I'd marry you if I was old enough."

I tell him I'd marry him too if he was old enough. We are quiet and sad together.

It's the Fourth of July and we drive to the Tetons with Charlie, and when we get to the chapel, Jack gives me flowers to hold and I'm wearing my perfect pink country and western singing outfit and he's wearing his gray and Charlie says all the marriage words out of the Bible and I repeat 'em, and Jack repeats 'em, and Jack gives me a gold ring. What about that! A gold ring! He gave that to me! It's really true.

On the way back, I ask Jack, "Can we have a baby now?"

He practically drives off the road, he says, "Absolutely not!"

He's always going to wear a rubber and we're not going to have a baby until we're ready. I'm ready, I say, but he says, "You're too young and we don't make enough money and we're not together all the time. No baby until we're together all the time!"

It makes me so mad that I don't get to have any say. So I stay quiet. I want to have a baby so we better be together all the time pretty soon. I tell him that and he says he knows it. We drive back to town and we go to the Sinks Canyon again. We sleep there. He says it's our wedding night. We gin and tonic and make love and talk about when we were going to be together all the time and have babies. If we have a boy we're going to call him Joe, if we have a girl we're going to call her Sara. I was going to call her Tumbleweed, but I guess that really isn't very smart.

On Sunday morning I ask Jack, "I want you to tell me really, why do we have to keep all this quiet? It's important. It's a happy thing."

He promises me that someday he'll explain the whole thing and it will be okay.

I ask Jack, what am I going to say if somebody asks me about my gold ring? He says, "Tell 'em it was a gift and don't tell 'em anymore than that."

When we make love, he doesn't talk to me like he used to and he doesn't — I don't know how to explain it, but he doesn't really do it the same way. He just does it. He doesn't kiss me all over and it just seems to go quicker.

We add a new song to our Bud and Blackie's routine, it's called "Dear Heart" from Jim Reeves. I talk Jack into playing the chords for "Bye Bye Love" and I sing it by myself. It scared me but I did it.

Here Comes Little Brother

My brother's going to come next month. Then Jack's going to be leaving. Jack says we have to get him a job or something. I had to send him money to come out on the Greyhound bus. I haven't seen my little brother for a long time. I've missed him.

He's here, my little brother is here, with all his stuff. I rented him a room at my rooming house, he's right next door to me. I drive him around in my car, and I introduce him to my friends, and I take him down to Gionini's. I pay my bills so good that everybody in town says anything you need, you just come in and get it and you can pay us when you get paid. I introduce my little brother to all of 'em, and I tell 'em anything he needs I want him to have it. I'll pay for it when I get paid.

I like it that he's here. We run around together and have such a good time, and Brett's really nice and Jack's really nice to him, and Shorty — Shorty's nice to him but I think Shorty doesn't like him very much. That's probably because my little brother is a smart-ass to Shorty. My little brother and I got in a fight about it because he makes all these cracks about how tiny Shorty is. I took him aside and told him, I said, "Do you want me to whop you one or what? You shut up, you stop making cracks to Shorty."

He shut up about it, but I don't think Shorty's very impressed with him at all.

My little brother comes and watches us at Bud and Blackie's and he says I don't sound anything like I used to.

He says, "You used to sound like a dying cow," and I think, You know what, I hate you. "I don't need to hear that ever again in my lifetime," I say. "Besides that, you assholes wouldn't know what sounded good anyway. None of you fools could sing at all — ever. "He shut up about it.

Jack says that my little brother could work out at Sandy's ranch and come back in on the weekends, so we got him a job out there. I take my little brother everywhere we go on the weekends and Jack doesn't like that. He says that can't happen all the time. I think that's because he likes making love.

In another month Jack will be gone so I won't have to worry about it. I leave my brother by himself a few times so that I can stay with Jack overnight after we sing at Bud and Blackie's. I ask Jack where he's going to be but he tells me it is so far out in the woods there's no way anyone can reach him.

My little brother likes his job out at Sandy's. He gets paid and he buys some of his own stuff. He took me to Gionini's for breakfast one morning with Brett and he ran out of money. I couldn't believe it. I ended up paying for Brett and me and he paid for his own breakfast! I told him not to do that again. My little brother always says he's going to do things, but he doesn't do 'em. I guess I'm just not going to believe what he says until it happens.

Jack left today, so it's back to playing with Brett and Shorty and my little brother on the weekends. That'll be neat, though, I like that. I'm going to miss singing at Bud and Blackie's, but I can't go in there to just hang around, so I don't.

My little brother came out of his room and came into mine and he had carved X's on his chest with a knife and they were all bloody, bloody X's. I was so upset. I don't know why he did that! He doesn't know why he did that. Then he cried a lot. I don't know what's wrong. I just don't know. I cleaned off his chest and I made him promise not to do that anymore, and as I was cleaning off his chest, I noticed that there were carve marks on his arms too. I asked him, "How much of this shit do you do, fool?"

He says that sometimes he just wants to carve on himself. That's just nuts. I think maybe that crazy stuff is coming to get him. I clean him all up and I hold him all night. He sleeps in my bed now, for awhile. Every weekend when he comes in he just stays with me. I told Brett about it, and Brett says, "Boy, that's weird. That sounds like he's trying to die."

I asked my little brother if he wants to die, and he says sometimes he does. I really hate that. That really scares me. I tell him no one's hitting us, so why die now? I tell him I love him and I don't want him to die, and he says that it's too lonely out working at Sandy's because there's nobody there but the old man and him. Maybe he shouldn't work and I should just pay for him. He seems old enough to take care of himself now he's nearly fifteen. But maybe I'm wrong. I don't want him to carve himself all alone out at Sandy's. I don't want him to carve himself up and die.

At Christmastime I'm going to tell my little brother not to work at Sandy's anymore. I found a little Quonset hut they used to use in the war, they have several of them, and we can live in that and make our own food and stay together and he won't be so lonely and it won't cost as much money. I figured it out so it'll work out a whole lot better. He likes the idea too. I found out that when I left him alone when I was staying with Jack, he drove my car without permission, the little fucker. I told him not to touch that car or I'd take his head right off his body.

We move into the Quonset hut. It's kinda rounded and metal on the outside. Inside we make a nice little place. It's kind of like a really wonderful rag house that doesn't leak on you, and he has his bed and I have mine, and Brett comes over and stays sometimes. I like that. He sleeps on the floor in the sleeping bag, though. Since I married Jack, he doesn't ever sleep with me at all. I didn't tell my little brother about marrying Jack. He asked me about the ring and I told him it was a gift. I tell that to everybody, they just look at me. Never mind. I didn't think anybody was going to really believe it. They don't know what else to believe, so I guess they're stuck with it. Brett says when he gets married, he's not going to keep it a secret and he's not going to leave his wife, either. That hurt my feelings, so I swat him one. I also thought maybe I should marry Brett, but now it's too late.

Brett says once you get married, you have to stay married. I guess I will. Besides, I want the babies. My little brother hasn't carved on himself since we moved into the Quonset hut, and in a couple of months Jack will be back. This life is good again.

All of a sudden my little brother gets really sick — he has this thing called the flu. I asked the people at work if I could stay home with him until he can take care of himself because he can't even get out of bed. So they let me. I feel like I've been taking care of this boy all his life, but the truth is I haven't seen him for a long while. I don't mind taking care of him. He's my little brother. I get strep throat all the time. I don't care, I just take a bunch of aspirin and keep right on going. I'm tired of getting strep throat — I don't remember a winter in my lifetime without it. My tonsils are really bad, and they're supposed to take 'em out. I don't know when, though. I don't know what makes me have strep throat all the time, either.

My little brother's better, but he doesn't go to school, so all he does is run around town. He got to know a lot of people. Some people like him and some people don't. Lots of people tell me they can hardly believe he's my brother because we don't look alike, and worse than that, he doesn't act like me. What they mean is that he's not very nice sometimes. I tell him, "You ruin my reputation out here and I'll beat you to death."

He says he's mad, he wants a car of his own. He wants a car of his own! He wants to sit on his dead ass, he doesn't want to go to work, and he wants a car of his own? I don't know why I should care about that. Actually, though, I do. I'm going to try to think of something to get a car that's super cheap or something.

It's April. Jack's back! We get to sing at Bud and Blackie's. Jack has to work at the Grand Tetons National Park this year and he asks me if I will quit my job and go up there and work with him. Quit my job? What the hell? He says I could work up there cleaning cabins at the resort. I don't like this — and what the hell am I going to do with my little brother? Jack gets really mad because he says he should be working out at Sandy's, and I tell him about him carving on himself and how unhappy he is, but you know, sometimes I think Jack doesn't care about anybody but himself. Whenever he wants something, he just doesn't care about other people being in his way a whole lot.

He asks me to make a deal up at the training school with Dr. Jamison, that I work three days there and then I go to the Tetons for four days a week. Change my schedule and keep my job and let my little brother live at the Quonset hut and he could do some work around town. He could be cleaning up at the motels or something like that. My little brother gets a job like that, he's doing the janitor work, and I'm spending four days at the Tetons with Jack. We're teaching mountain climbing! First Jack teaches it to me, scares me half to death! I'm good at it, though. He says I'm real agile, which means I can move really quick and easy, so I help him teach other people how to do mountain climbing and then on the weekends we come back and I work at the training school and then on Saturday nights we sing at Bud and Blackie's. My little brother seems to be okay. He runs around with Brett sometimes, but mostly he runs around with this horrible kid, named Walter, who hasn't had a bath in his whole life, and doesn't do anything, and talks stupid and he chews snuff, and I don't like him. My little brother likes him so that's what counts, I guess. The whole summer goes like that and I'm happy with it. But once in a while I find those carving marks on him, and talk to him about it, but he seems to be all right.

I think I'm just going to enjoy a lot of things before the crazy thing comes and gets me. I'm going to be happy with my little brother and my friends Brett and Shorty and I'm going to be happy with Jack and pretty soon maybe I can have a baby.

Jack leaves in September as usual.

My Mom

Mom is writing more letters to me. She tells me that in May she had another baby, that makes three. Boy, I'll tell you, that woman just isn't very smart. She says her and Tom aren't very happy and then she tells me they are happy sometimes. I ask her if she wants to come to Wyoming and I'll take care of her, and she writes back and tells me I'm an idiot. Nothings new, right? She says she's tired all the time but she doesn't know why. She says her legs ache really bad every night. I don't know what to tell her, I just write back and tell her how my little brother and I are doing, and she tells me she doesn't like it that he never writes to her. I tell it to him, he doesn't care. I try to send her a Christmas present and a card and she got it, she liked it, she thanked me.

She doesn't talk mean in her letters like she talks in person. I call her on the phone and she sounds different. She sounds tired. She doesn't sound as mad anymore. She sure doesn't talk as mean as she used to. She asks me if maybe we can come and visit her in the winter. I tell her no because we can't drive that far in the snow, and besides that, I can't take off of work because I took all that time in the summer and Dr. Jamison said I could only do that for the summer, and then in the winter I had to work full time, so I am. She says, "Well, what about in the spring?"

I say, "I'll see, but in the spring is when Jack comes back, so that's going to make it really hard."

We just write back and forth. She brags about how cute the babies are.

Having my little brother here, and starting to hear from mom like this, just feels really weird. I don't know why it couldn't have been this good a long time ago. I don't know what the problem is. I never knew what the problem was in the first place. She lives down at Tom's, she likes her babies, maybe — maybe I was just awful and — I don't know. Who the hell knows.

It's April and Jack's back. That means Bud and Blackie's is back. I'll be glad when November comes this year because I'll be eighteen then I can go to Bud and Blackie's by myself. Jack doesn't have to work at the Tetons, he has to work here. That's good, that's better, I don't want to take off any more work, I need the money. My little brother quit his janitor job, he got another job some-place else and quit that too. He has a lot of new things so he must be working somewhere. He doesn't carve on himself so much anymore. It's been months since I've seen that. He has a better friend than Walter, except that he still hangs out with Walter, who still hasn't taken a bath, still chews snuff, and I still don't like him.

I got a call from mom. She's very, very sick. She's had an operation, she had the operation in February. It's April! She's going to have to have an-other one, she says. She says she has cancer of her female organs. I checked around, cancer's bad. Cancer kills everybody. But mom writes that she's a lot better and the doctors think they got it all, but they have to do some more surgery to make sure.

It's May. It's May and my mother's in the hospital and she says she might die. I'm going to get in my goddamn Chevy and I'm going to drive me and my brother to see her. This is very important. Jack thinks I'm out of my mind, but he thinks I should go see her if she's that sick. I tell Jack I'm going to tell her that I'm married and that I'm going to have his babies, and Jack says he has to talk to me when I get back and not to tell anybody anything until then. I tell him okay, I won't. We start the drive back to Wisconsin to see mom, my little brother and I in my '56 Chevy. We sleep in the car every night on the way there. He drives some, I drive some, and when we're both too tired we just go to sleep. We get lost a couple of times on the way, but we do all right. We don't get in any fights. I brought my bread and apple butter so we could eat in the car if we can't afford to stop. We didn't have any money to speak of, so we have to be real careful. Dr. Jamison checked with the hospital. My mom's in St. Mary's Hospital in Superior, Wisconsin, and he called so that he could okay me leaving without getting fired. I thought that was really nice of him.

We finally get to Superior and we drive right to the hospital. My brother won't go in. He doesn't like hospitals, he says. I go in and I find where mom is. She's so thin. She weighs about ninety pounds. She looks so sick. She has a tube coming out of her side that drains her poisons from the cancer. She looks and smells like she's going to die. But she says the doctors tell she's going to be okay. Since she doesn't have money and Tom's paying for most of this, she needs a nurse around the clock and they can't afford it. I volunteer to do what-ever she needs that they don't do at the hospital. I have to go pick up some things called cancer pads at a place downtown, and I have to drain the tube thing. I unhook it and put on a new bag every time it's full. It smells really bad. The cancer pads have to be changed all the time. I give her a lot of back rubs and I sing to her and I tell her jokes and crack her up and make her laugh — she likes to laugh but she says it hurts her stomach. I rub her feet, but that hurts her so I quit it. She gets really high fevers and I put lots of cold towels on her head, and I just stay with her and I help her eat, and help her go to the bathroom. They finally put a catheter in because she can't go to the bathroom by herself anymore. Oh, I hate this. I just hate this. I feel so sorry for her. Days and days of this.

They took her down to surgery because she was in so much pain she was screaming and crying. I'd do anything to fix her, but I can't fix her. They brought her back from surgery, and there were days and days of taking care of her some more, and she looks better. She's moving around more and they took out the catheter and she can go to the bathroom by herself. They say she might be able to go home pretty soon.

The sheriff's department in Wyoming sent a telegram to the Sheriff's Department here in Wisconsin because I didn't make my car payment and they're either going to take the car or I have to take it back to Wyoming. I called Dr. Jamison and he says that he can't have me gone much longer or he's going to have to replace me. My mom is better. I talk to the nurses and they say that I have to do whatever I have to do.

I've been here almost a month. The doctors are going to send mom home in a couple of days. My mom and I are having a conversation before she goes to sleep and she says, "You know, I know I've ruined my life and everybody's life around me."

She knows? She knows that. She knows about it. I just stand there. Then she says, "I know I didn't take care of you and your brother like I should've."

I just stand there. It all comes back, all of the ugly, rotten, horrible, stuff, is on my mind again. When she goes to sleep, I put the sides up on her bed, I just stand there looking at her, so filled with hate, I can hardly think. I don't know what kept me from being reminded that all of that happened, I don't know what kept me from thinking about how mad and mean she was to me all the time. What she let everybody do to me. I just feel angry and weak, like my arms and legs couldn't move, and I watch her sleep. I write her a note telling her I'm taking the car back to Wyoming and that I'll be back as soon as I can. I get in the car and I get my little brother and we drive back to Wyoming. I go back to work and my little brother goes back to whatever it is he does.

I got a call today from the nurses at the hospital, mom is back in the hospital and she's dying. I'm going to try and call her. I want my little brother to talk to her. Do you know that all the days that we were there, he only went to see her one time? He can be such a pain in the ass. I call her on the phone, but she can't talk, I don't know what's wrong with her. She says she has taken some medicine and she's out of her head. This woman gets on the phone and tells me that if I ever wanted to talk to her again, I better come home. I went to bed thinking, maybe I won't ever see her again. She never liked me. Ever.

June 23rd, the Sheriff comes. My mom is dead. I have to figure out a way to get back for the funeral. I call Mrs. Sawyer and she says that all of my brothers and my older sister are going to the funeral. Why are they going to the funeral? They haven't spoken to my mother since 1959. It's 1963. My sister, the oldest one, would go to look good. The three babies aren't going. They're having her funeral in the church where everybody talked about her and never helped her. I go down to the clothes store to get my brother a suit because you're supposed to wear a black suit, and to buy me something black. The guy at the clothes store says I don't have any more credit because my brother bought all kinds of stuff for him and his friends. I owe the store a lot of money. He let me have the black suit. I tell him to never mind the black outfit for me.

I go around my happy town talking to people, I find out that my brother charged so much stuff at all of my places where I pay my bills that it's going to take me almost a year to pay it all back. I ask him about it. I can't believe he did that.

He says, "Well, you told me if I needed anything to have it."

I check at Gionini's and he had a whole bunch of meals charged for him and his friend Walter, the damn fool! I owe too much money to do anything. I borrow some money for his bus ticket home, get him his black suit, and tell him I don't want to go home because I owe too much money and I'll lose my job and my car and I won't be able to pay anything back. It's more important that he go than me. I put him on the bus. I don't mind not going to that goddamned funeral. All those people who never helped her, never took care of her, never even liked her, are going to be sitting right there looking just fine. If I go back, it's going to be with a 12 gauge. I'll blow their fuckin' heads off. She's dead. She's dead and she has three babies. I have to pay for all the stuff my damn brother charged. He says he's not coming back to Wyoming, either. Right now I just plain don't care.

Jack is being really nice to me. I feel very unhappy. I guess I never thought she'd die. I drink a bunch of gin and tonics. I cry and cry and cry. She never even liked me. Why was I the only one at the hospital when she took such good care of all the older kids and they never came around at all? I called 'em when I was there. My oldest sister sent her a get-well card. The whole time I was there, she screamed and yelled about the fact that they didn't come and she took such good care of 'em. I don't understand that, either, and I called my dad, and you know what he said? He didn't feel sorry for her, she brought it on herself. If she hadn't had all those babies, she wouldn't be dying. Leave it to that asshole to dream that one up! Even if it's true, who gives a good goddamn? I can't wait till he's dying, so I can tell him he asked for it.

I didn't go to work today. It's Sunday and I'm supposed to go to work and I'm not going to. I got Jack to give me a bunch of his gin and tonics and I'm just going to drink so I can feel better. I drink and drink and I just get madder and madder. I can't believe it. I was having such a good life. Why do I have to care about this? She didn't even like me! She didn't take care of me! She doesn't want me! She's dead. She's just — dead. She has three babies. I wonder what's going to happen to them. She made me promise when she was in the hospital if she died I'd take care of 'em, but I didn't think she was going to die, so I told her yes!

I drink the gin and tonics and finally I'm so goddamned mad I hate everybody. I hate it that they're all going to go to that funeral and they're going to sit there and look good and they didn't take care of her. I hate everybody. I tear up everything in the closet. I'm not staying in this Quonset hut. I just break everything, and I just keep up this stupid crying, "I want my mom! I want my mom!

Jack comes over, he's really surprised I tore everything up. He's also really mad that I'm this drunk. I don't give a good goddamn what he thinks. I tell him I have to hurry up and pay off my bills and go back and take care of the damn babies because I told my mom I would.

Jack says, "Your mom never did a goddamned thing for you. Why are you going to take care of the babies?"

I tell him, "'Cause, stupid, they can't take care of themselves. Since we're married, I think you should go back with me."

He says he can't this year. I'm beginning to think things are going to stay this way with Jack and I until I drop dead.

I tell him, I say, "I can't even write you letters and things in the winter. I don't like this anymore."

He say, "Okay, I'm going to get a post office box and you can write to me all winter."

I say, "Okay."

It's September and Jack left. It didn't take me a year to pay everything back. I'm going to go home and take care of the babies. I got a letter from Jack today that gives me a post office box and guess what? The post office box is in Wisconsin! It's in some little town I never heard of. I don't care about much of anything. I don't want to go back there. I don't want my little baby Peggy Sue, and the other two babies, to be upset. Alone, like I was.

Today I'm going to take my car down and sell it back to the dealer. I don't know if I'll get any money. I'm just going to try.

Mom's Babies and Jack's Lies

I get back to Wisconsin, and Mrs. Sawyer's and I go down to Tom's and I see the babies and they're just as cute as they can be. The new one is only a year old. My little brother is staying at Tom's. Wonder how come Tom's letting us stay with him now? Tom kept us from staying anywhere near my mother all this time. I stay at Tom's too and take care of the babies. I don't like this, I can feel mom everywhere. I know that's crazy, the crazy that will probably just come and get me finally, but I can feel her, I mean it. The other day I saw her walking in the living room. She's dead. She's not walking in the living room. I'm not liking this at all.

The babies cry a lot. They want their mom, I think. I think they know — I know Peggy Sue knows. I think even the little teeny one knows I'm not their mom. They're kind of funny, though. I sing to 'em and I tell 'em stories and I play with 'em and I drag 'em around outside so they'll get tired and take a goddamn nap. Then I drag 'em around outside after dinner, too. I chase 'em and everything so they'll go the hell to bed and go to sleep. They are pretty good babies.

I don't know why I miss mom, but I do. She didn't even like me! Tom never liked me after the first baby was born. Now he's being really nice to me. I can't stand it. I feel absolutely crazy here. I don't want to be here and I don't want the babies not to have anybody. I don't know what the hell to do. Tom says, "Well, I'm not so bad. You can stay and take care of the kids, it's okay with me."

I drop the potato I'm peeling thinking to myself, How'd you like me to stick this knife through your heart, you son of a bitch? You didn't let me anywhere near my mother ever, and now that she's dead, you want me to come in here and take care of you and them just like she did? Well, she might have been that dumb, and I'm not. I don't say anything to him. I pick up the goddamned potato and start peeling it again. How could he be so stupid? He could apologize for being a prick for years to me, just like mom in the hospital. She didn't even bother saying she was sorry! She just said, "Oh, well, too bad, I wrecked everybody's life including my own."

I wrote all the news to Jack and told him what I was doing, and he wrote me a letter back and commiserated with me about how awful it must be. I ask him where this little town was, but he didn't answer that part of the letter.

Every day I feed and fix these babies. Goddamn. That's all you can do when you have babies, there's no time for anything else. When I have my babies, I'm going to think of a better way of doing this.

It's been almost a month. I got a letter from Jack today, again. Jack says he has to tell me something, and it's going to be hard for him. First he tells me he really loves me in the letter, and he tells me that the ring I'm wearing is really a wedding band like he said it was — in his heart, he's married to me. In real life, Jack's married to somebody else and better than that, he has six kids. Six kids. Jack is married to someone else and has six kids. He says he didn't tell me all of the story before because he's been trying to get a divorce, and that every time he tells his wife he wants a divorce she threatens to kill herself, so he can't get a divorce! I don't care if she kills herself.

I write back how mad I am, how stupid this all is, that I took the ring off and that I don't care if she kills herself. I ask how old are your kids and how come you kept leaving 'em every summer? What the hell's the matter with you? Now what are we going to do, Jack? I'm not going to get to have a baby, right? Even if you do love me and I love you, you lied! You lied a lot! I hate liars! Jack writes back and tells me that his kids are all grown — they're older than I am! Of course, Jack's a lot older than I am too. He says it'll take him about a year to get a divorce, so he and I can really be married. Jack, you're a jack-ass! Oh, goddamn you! I'm getting out of here. I'm going back to Wyoming. I don't care what happens.

I go down to Mrs. Sawyer's and I ask her if she'll take the babies, and she says yes, and so I take the babies and I pack 'em all up and I take 'em to her house. Then I leave a note for Tom and I go to town to get some more stuff that they need for the babies. When I get back, Tom is really mad. He asks, "How could you take the babies to Mrs. Sawyer's?"

I start hollering back at him, "'Cause I'm not goddamn staying here, Tom, and that's what you get for being such an asshole to me when my mother was alive! I didn't get any part of her, thanks to you! Not to mention the fact she didn't like me at all. Besides that, Mrs. Sawyer knows exactly what to do with babies and I don't. On top of it all, I'm going back to Wyoming. Besides, Tom, you have to pay for those babies at Mrs. Sawyer's. She's not going to keep 'em for free. You have to go down and talk to her."

Tom drove down to Mrs. Sawyer's and they made the money arrangements and that's the way it's going to be. I'm getting the hell out of here with no money. Here we go again. Mom's dead, Jack lied, and you know what my little brother did? He told everybody around here I didn't care about my mom, I didn't like her, and that's why I didn't go to the funeral. He didn't tell anybody around here that I couldn't afford to go, and that I had to buy his ticket and his suit, and that he charged everything on earth in goddamn Wyoming, and that I took care of him in Wyoming and he never said a word to anybody! He's also not even going to talk to me! Fuck him! All of 'em!

I scrounge around Tom's house, looking for things that were mom's because I'm keeping 'em because I feel like it. She didn't have much. The babies won't need it, they're too little. I take a bunch of things I pack up everything. Tom had a bunch of money in his bureau drawer and I stole it. I'm not sorry. I wonder what a train ticket would cost if I didn't rattle-ride it, if I got in an actual sit-down place on it. I get a ride from Mr. Sawyer when he goes to work and I check at the train depot and the bus depot. The train still goes to Billings, Montana. I don't know why, but I just want to go there instead of back to Wyoming. This time I get a train ticket where you sit down in the train and you don't rattle-ride yourself to death. I'm going to Billings, Montana. I wonder what else is going to happen in this life before the crazy thing gets me.

I wonder if I'm ever going to like my little brother again. I think him letting everybody think that I didn't help him was awful! He didn't tell the truth about me. I tried to take good care of him ever since I ever knew him. I can't believe he did that! I can't believe all those hypocrites went to the funeral, either. I think what he did was mean. That's as mean as mom or the assbite boys would do, just make themselves look fine and I look terrible. He didn't help with mom, even when she was sick. I don't know what made him do that and he won't tell me. I feel like punching him to death. Tomorrow I get to get on a train, in a seat, and go to Billings, Montana, again. Maybe it'll be a good luck thing again. Last time I went to Billings, Montana, my life was good for a long time. Even if it was the worst rattle-ride on earth in that damn box car. Maybe Billings, Montana will be good luck again.

I write Jack a letter and tell him I'm going to Billings and I'll write him when I get there. I tell him I don't know if I like him anymore because he lied to me and I don't believe he loves me, but I still love him. I write Brett a letter, tell him what's been happening, tell him that I'll write to him when I get to Billings, and I go see Mrs. Sawyer and I talk to her and the kids and Mr. Sawyer, and I see my mom's babies and I hug 'em and I hold 'em and I like 'em. They like me. I don't talk to my little brother. It's going to be a long time before I'm not mad at him, I think. Mrs. Sawyer says not to be too mad at him because he's just young and stupid. He's only 14 months younger than me. He might be stupid but he's also mean. I've never seen him be mean before. Except charging all that stuff, and not telling me, and charging it for his friends too, and not telling me, that's kinda mean. My little brother and I didn't do really mean things before. He reminds me of the rest of the dreaded family.

I'll just get on the train, go to Billings, and hope that good luck starts all over again. I had some good life since I went to Billings on that rattle-ride. I just want that one more time. I don't want to stay here because that crazy thing is going to get me and I know it.

Tonsils

I go up to Superior to see if Lucy is still at the counter at the depot. She's still fun and she still likes me. I tell her about my mom and that I'm going to Billings, Montana. She says, "You were going to Billings, Montana, the last damn time I saw you!" I laugh a lot with her. I tell her about where I've been and what I've been doing and that I married Jack but it wasn't really true because he's already married. I tell her about my mom and my brother and my baby sisters, and she says, "Girl, you have more problems than a hound has fleas." I thank her for that tidbit. "Take that back, Lucy, or I'll swat you one. I'm not a dog."

She says, "Okay, already! I take it back."

Lucy's pregnant again. I asked her how many kids she has now. This is the fourth one. Four kids! "Lucy, you aren't very much older than I am."

She says, "Well, you know, when you're married, you just have kids."

I say, "I'm not ever going to get married. I thought I was married and I'm not, and I'm not ever getting married."

She says, "You'll change your mind about that."

I ask her, "Lucy, how do you stand that sex all the time?"

She says, "Oh, that's easy. You just get through it. Think about something else." She goes and waits on another customer. Think about something else? Why would I want to do this if I have to think about something else? Why is she doing it and having one baby after another if she has to think about something else? Damned if I understand this world. It reminds me of all those manners I had to learn when I was in the first grade. I know they have a purpose. There's something I'm not going to get if I don't follow the rules, but goddamned if I know what.

Lucy comes back and asks me if I'm going to take a boxcar again. I rattle just thinking about it! I tell her, "No more rattle-rides for this girl."

I say, "Besides that, I have money enough for a ticket."

"Whoa," she says, "That's really something new. You have money."

I say, "Yeah, and I meant to give you the dollar back you gave me" so I give it to her, and I pay for my coffee, it isn't free this time. I even had breakfast, and that isn't free. Lucy asks me if I'm feeling okay, and I say, "Hell, no. I haven't been feeling okay for so long I can't remember. My mom died, my brother's an asshole, I was in debt forever, and now I'm back here in horrifying Wisconsin. My throat is sore again, too. My throat's been sore every winter of my life. It's really sore this time. I hope it goes away in a couple of days. Usually it takes a week or so. I really get hot and tired and I can't eat very good. Sometimes it's even hard to swallow water."

She asks me if I want to stay at her place for a couple days, so I feel good when I get on the train to go to Montana. She says, "You're not going to be feeling like getting a job or anything if you're half dead when you get there. Besides, I could use a baby-sitter." Just the goddamn excitement of my life, I get to baby-sit her kids. I didn't say that to her, but boy, the idea of baby-sitting three babies is really not fun, I think. I don't feel good, and my head's hot, and my ears hurt, and my throat hurts as usual. One time somebody told me it was strep throat in Wyoming when I had it checked. They also told me my tonsils were really bad. I told 'em, "Well, they must have been bad all my life because it's been going on for every year that I ever knew about." The doctor in Wyoming said, "You're going to have to have those out pretty soon or they'll just rot out by themselves." I hated that bit of information, so I didn't go back, and I figure I've been having it every year so who cares?

After Lucy gets off work I go home with her. Her husband is really icky. He's big and fat and doesn't talk. How much fun can you have in one day? When she goes to work the next morning, I baby-sit the kids. I feel worse than I did yesterday. I baby-sit the kids by way of turning on the TV. They sit in front of that TV and gawk at it for hours. That TV has the dumbest things on it I ever saw in my whole life. I like movies. On TV, everybody talks all the time, and there's commercials all the time and I just hate it. They watch it, they watch anything that comes on. We spent that whole day sitting right there in front of the TV with me sweating like a stuck pig. I have a fever again.

Lucy comes home from work and she tells me, "Good God, girl, you look like hell. Go to bed." I get in one of the kids' beds and she brings me some aspirins. I start to go to sleep. I'm so hot and my throat hurts really bad. In the night I wake up and I'm so hot I can hardly even breathe. I'm really scared, this doesn't feel right, I don't feel good. I try to go back to sleep. A little while later I wake up again and I'm cold, very cold, but I'm sweaty, too. I usually get these kind of fevers but I just don't usually feel quite this bad. Maybe by morning, though, I'll feel better.

In the morning Lucy wakes me up because she's going to go to work at the counter and I'm going to baby-sit the kids. I'm going to do TV again today. Lucy said she already made sandwiches for 'em so all I have to do is get 'em out of the fridge and give it to 'em for lunch. She already fed 'em breakfast. All I have to do is get out on that couch and listen to 'em scream, yell, cry, and holler. Talk to 'em and play with 'em and try to get along all day. I don't know if I'm going to get over this very quick. I feel sicker by the hour. I take some more aspirin, I try to play with the kids, but I just can't. I just lay on the couch and keep falling asleep and waking up and first I'm hot and then I'm cold and then I'm hot and then I'm cold, and now I'm only able to swallow water.

Lucy comes home and I get back in one of the kids' beds, take more aspirin, and go to sleep. I'm sicker than ever before. Lucy wakes me up and I think it's morning, but it's the next afternoon. She got somebody else to babysit the kids, and I didn't even hear anything. She says she has called the doctor and she's taking me down to the hospital.

We get to the hospital emergency room. I feel like objecting but I'm just too goddamned sick. They put me in a hospital bed and they give me a shot and I go to sleep. I wake up the next morning with a nurse. I don't know if I'm going to like her but I'm hoping that she's not a hag for sure. Finally they tell me, "As soon as we can, we're going to take out your tonsils. You have strep throat, though, and we have to get this antibiotic working before we take them out so it'll be in the next few days."

I tell her, "I don't want my tonsils out, and I don't want anything, I just want to feel better and get the hell out of here."

She says, "Well, you're still underage, so you just don't have anything to say about it. Since you don't have any money, we're going to have the welfare doctor take out your tonsils. Just lay back and get well."

They give me a shot everyday for three days, and they feed me lots of liquids and soups and broths and juices, and I want coffee and I get to have some once in a while. The nurse is really nice, she's not a hag, and one night she came back after her shift and brought me a chocolate malt. Tomorrow morning they're going to take out my tonsils. They say I don't have to worry, usually they take out your tonsils and three days later you get to go home. Your throat's sore for awhile and then you never get to have this tonsillitis and strep throat again. I guess that's a good deal. I don't mind if that's going to be the way it goes.

It's time to take out my tonsils. They take me down to a room and they put me in a chair that I just sit up in and it has a kind of like a head-rest. I'm sitting there and the doctor comes in and he tells me to open my mouth and go "Ah" and all that and I do it. Then he takes out a silver needle. I never saw anything like this in my life. That needle must've been a mile long! He shoots it into the back of my throat. I'd like to have a screaming fit! Then he shoots it again! Then he shoots it again! I'm not happy, I am not happy. I wonder how this guy would like me to get up and shoot him a lot with that goddamn thing. That needle was attached to this big round silver thing with curly little things for his fingers to fit in the handles. He says it's Novocain, it will numb the back of my throat and then they can take out my tonsils. Fine, fucking get on with it.

The doctor's glasses look like the bottom of coke bottles, and he has a thing around the top of his head with a shiny thing on it, and he just really is going to do it with me sitting in this chair. By now I can't talk. The fact is, I try to talk and I can't make any words at all. My tongue is numb and everything's numb. This is really screwy, I've never even heard of anything like this. Then he comes back in and he opens my mouth and puts a thing between my teeth on both sides so I can't close my mouth. Then he goes snip snip. Blood squirts out of my mouth, all over him and all over that shiny thing on his head. He takes off his glasses and wipes 'em off, I can't believe this is happening! He comes back and he picks up something, and he goes snip again. I grab it. Him and me are in a fight over this snipping thing he's doing in my throat. Blood is pouring out all over the place, and he pulls the thing out of my throat, it's long and silver and looks like teeny scissors with a long handle. He yells at me that if I don't behave myself, he'll just quit and bring me back down here and do it again tomorrow.

I point to my arms. I want him to tie 'em down but I can't even make the words, I sound like the wrecked-up babies at the mental hospital. I make all these grunting noises and point to my hands and he goes out of the room. He comes back with a nurse and they tie down my arms. That'll keep me from grabbing the thing he sticks in my throat. How the hell does he expect me not to grab this, I don't want it in my throat. Besides, it hurts like hell, I can still feel it. I can't tell him I can still feel it because my tongue won't work. He snips some more. I'm screaming now but the only sound that's coming out sounds like an old tired bear. When it's over, I barely remember what they did, but I'm in a bed with ice packs on my throat. I go to sleep.

I wake up later on, I don't know whether it's this day or next day or what day. I just keep hearing him tell me if I don't behave myself, he's going to send me back upstairs and do it again. My tongue works now so I ask the nurse, "Is it finished? Does he have to do that to me again?"

She says no. She looks at me, pats me on my cheek, and tells me that she knows that was awful but I'll be well pretty soon.

Pretty soon turned into eighteen days. I had a massive infection, they say. I can't wait to get the hell out of this hospital and go to Billings, Montana.

Lucy comes and sees me a couple of times. She can't come very much because she has to work and then she has to take care of the babies. I didn't realize this when we came in but I'm in the same hospital my mother died in a few months ago. I'm not on the same floor. I just have to get over this infection and then I can leave.

Finally I leave for Billings, Montana. Lucy kept all my money while I was in the hospital, and she didn't spend any of it. Pretty nice of her, I think. She could use a lot of that to take care of her babies. Her husband doesn't work most of the time. He sits around and gets fatter and goes down to the bar and drinks more beer. He doesn't take care of his own babies, even. If I ever did get married and my husband did that, I'd slap his head in his sleep. Lucy says I'm not going to make a good wife if I keep acting like that. I have no intentions of making a good wife. Unless somebody's going to make a good husband. I don't tell her that. For some reason, I think that would really hurt Lucy's feelings. I'd like to tell her, though, you know what, you married your big fat beer-drinking icky thing, but I don't tell her that. She says if you're a woman, you have to get married. I heard that before. I heard you have to do all these damn dumb things to have a baby, too. I heard about this, I'm just going to figure something else out, I guess.

I tell Lucy good-bye, I hug her, and she gives me a dollar. Another dollar! Lucy, you screwball. I take the dollar and I get on the train.

Part Four

The Young Adult

Back to Billings

I'm on the train — it isn't like the boxcar ride, and isn't as long, either, and the rattling that happens doesn't bother you when you're in a seat. I talk to everybody on the train. I play cards with some people, I have a good time, I wonder if there's a way I could work on a train, I could go everywhere. They told me girls can't do that. What the hell is it girls can do besides put up with big fat beer-drinking men? I think, well, I already did a whole bunch of things that aren't like that so I'll just keep that up. I'll work at hospitals and I'll do good things and I won't be having a whole bunch of babies and going to work while some fat thing sits home or sits in a bar and he doesn't even help with the babies.

I get off the train in Billings, and I think, okay, smart-ass, you're off the train in Billings, and you don't have very much money at all, now what are you going to do? I'm going to get a room. The woman at the depot tells me, "You should go down to the YWCA and get a room. They have the cheapest rooms for anybody, if you're single, and you don't have any men in. They even have a kitchen at the Y, you can put your own food there, and they have their own bathrooms, and you'd like it, you get to be with a bunch of other girls and you just get to be there and get a job and not have to worry about anything." I found out where this YWCA is and I go there. I have this idea of how much it's going to cost me and how much I get to pay for it and how much money I really have and I figure when I get there I just won't say anything till I find out the facts. As I'm talking to the administration woman at the YWCA, I find out I'm in trouble. I don't have enough money for this, but she made the mistake of telling me that if I didn't have anyplace else, or if it was going to keep me out of trouble, that I could stay there for free until I went to work.

I lie. I tell her I don't have any money and that I'd have to stay with my boyfriend downtown if I didn't stay at the Y. The reason I said I was going to have to stay with my boyfriend downtown is she said earlier in the conversation that if I had to do something bad like stay with a man or whatever, then they would help me more. So I lied. I wish I could just tell the truth and they would help me anyway, but they won't. They give me a room, and there's a lot of other girls here and there's a TV room and there's a kitchen and there's a bunch of bathrooms and my room's right across the hall from one of the bathrooms. When we're in the TV room watching TV, I make fun of all the shows, and everybody in there's laughing. I really enjoy that.

Also everybody tells me their secrets. I don't tell 'em mine. They talk to me when they're really in trouble or upset, they come in my room and cry and scream and yell and holler and some of 'em even go get in my bed, snuggle up to me and go to sleep if they're really upset. I ask one of the girls, "Why is this going on?"

She says, "Well, you've got a kind of natural talent for talking to people. Everybody here trusts you." What do you think of that? I'm interesting, I have some sort of natural talent, and people trust me. They wouldn't if they found out that I stole the money to get here, and that I don't take care of mom's babies, and that I lied to get the room here in the first place. I don't tell 'em that. I like being liked. I like it a lot. I get to go places with the girls and run around, laugh and meet their families. They ask me not to swear when I meet their families. Okay with me.

I met a guy named Archie, he's not too much older than I am, but he's already bald. I like him, he's really nice. One night he says, "I'd like you to come to my place and sleep."

I say, "Archie, everybody who lives at the Y has to go to their own place to sleep. Besides, I have an interview tomorrow for a job at the Broasted Chicken Inn so I have to sleep at my own place."

He says, "Well, let me sleep with you."

I say, "Archie, I told you, I can't have any men at the Y and I can't stay out all night without permission." He says okay, all right already.

I write back and forth to Jack and his wife's still going to kill herself if he gets a divorce and nothing's new. I don't trust him anymore. He tells me he misses me and he misses making love and he wishes we were together. I just don't know if I believe him anymore.

I get a job at the Broasted Chicken Inn. What you do is put a bunch of chicken in a basket and a bunch of french fries in a different basket, and you put it down in this boiling, boiling grease and you bring it up and you serve it to people. The woman that I work for says I'm very good at it right away. It only took one day to train me, and she brought me a blue coat to wear because I didn't have a good winter coat. She's a very nice lady. She's a Mormon and she wants me to go to Mormon meetings. She gets some Mormon missionaries to talk to me, and they tell me that I must be a really special spirit and they say a lot of really nice things to me and they explain to me that people don't just go to heaven or hell, that they go to all sorts of different kinds of heaven, depends on what kind of good works you do on earth. Now I like that idea, that's different from the Baptists who believe you go to heaven or hell, not to mention that they lie their asses off while they're here. They molest people and sing in church every Sunday. I go to the Mormon classes and I work at it and I work at it and then they say they want to baptize me because I'm such a special soul. Now they're going to baptize me a Mormon. I told that to Jack, he liked to have had a fit. He sent me two letters pleading with me not to be a Mormon. I don't know why he's so bothered by that. It doesn't bother him to commit adultery. It doesn't bother him to leave his family. I don't know why being a Mormon would bother him.

A lot of people don't like the Mormons. They say they're not really Christians because they believe Joseph Smith found a bunch of tablets. Of course, nobody ever saw the tablets. I don't know what the difference between that and nobody ever saw the people actually write the Bible yet. Everybody has different ways of believing. I'm baptized. Now I'm a Mormon. In the Mormon Church, they say that women are really special. Everybody's special, actually. Everybody has their special jobs they do. All of the women get together and put food together for families who don't have enough food. They do a lot of good things.

I work at the Broasted Chicken Inn and I go to the Mormon church and I run around with the girls at the Y, and I run around with Archie. Archie is fun. He takes me to lots of places and we run around in the hills. We go up on this one really high place and you can see the whole city from there, the whole city of Billings is lit up.

One of my friends in Billings invites me to go up to Haver, it's at the very, very top of Montana, almost on the Canadian border, to meet her family, so I go with her for the weekend. It's so much fun. I meet a guy up there named James. James and I hit it off. We like each other. James has a mom and a dad and a brother, and he's really friendly and really warm. He cuddles up in the car and talks to me.

We get home from the weekend and James promises he'll come down and visit me in Billings. I go back to my job and to going to church and to laughing a lot at the YWCA.

Archie is very mad that I like James. I told him about it, and the girls at the Y said I must be out of my damn mind, why am I telling him about it, that makes boys mad. I don't know why that makes boys mad, except I remember being really mad at that girl who really liked Brett. That dumb broad thought she was going to be Brett's girlfriend! I drove right up to her on the sidewalk in front of the school one day so I could smack her one and tell her I was going to smack her every time she even mentioned she was going to be

Brett's anything, ever. I guess it must be the same feeling. Brett hated that I did that but we laughed about it for a long time after.

Recruiter

I meet this Army guy at the coffee counter. He asks me if I'm over eighteen years old. I ask him what the hell does he want to know for? He tells me he can get me a great job. He says I can go to school and get paid for it. He says I can be whatever I want and the Army will take care of me. I tell him that's great except I'm not going to war in Nam and kill a bunch of people I'm not even mad at. He says women never go to war and kill — only men do that. "No shit," I say, "only men could dream up that kind of rotten stuff." Well, he wasn't happy with that crack.

After a bit he says that he thinks I'd be really good in the Army and I could have a job, go to school and get taken care of all at the same time. I ask him if I can be a nurse. He cheers right up and tells me that's what most of the women in the Army want to be. To be fair I pipe up and say, "No shit, only women could dream up that kinda stuff." After I say that I think the look on that Army guy's face was the strangest look of I've ever seen on any face.

He tells me he has to go, but if I come down to the recruiting office he'll show me all the brochures and how and where I'm going to live and what my uniform looks like, what they'll do for me and I tell him, "All right, I'll come down and see about it."

He says that if I do it before April that he gets an extra commission, and he'd really like that, and I ask him what a commission is, and he says it's just extra money.

Just think of it, school paid for, clothes paid for, food paid for, room paid for, and extra money every month. Boy, what a lucky break. I want to be an RN, then people like Mrs. Jones can't kill babies in my face and I won't be able to do anything about it. Being an RN is a great idea! I'd be able to really do something. Mrs. Sawyer would approve — she says it's important to do things that matter to you in this life. Maybe I could make enough money and later I could take better care of my sisters, or send money home so they get better taken care of. I'm not going to give my little brother any money now. I'm going to join the Army. That's my decision.

I go back and tell the girls at the Y and they all had a cow. They're yelling at me that good girls don't go in the army and that the women in the army are more like men than women and nobody wants their daughter to go in the army. I went to my room. Fuck 'em! I kept trying to tell 'em, they're not listening, they just had a fit about what girls don't do. I'm sick of hearing what girls can and can't do. I'm going to do any goddamn thing I want.

After a while they all come in, piling in my room and sitting on my bed, and sitting on my everything. They tell me that they're sorry they yelled at me, but they just know that everybody tells 'em not to go into the military and I ask 'em, "How do you think I'm ever going to get through school, and how in the hell is it I'm ever going to get anywhere? I'm going to be working at the Broasted Chicken Inn for the rest of my life." Well, yeah, they agreed that might be true. They all have families who take care of 'em. As a matter of fact, half of 'em are going to Northwestern University and staying at the Y because their parents pay for it, and their parents pay for their car and their clothes and everything and all I do is work my ass off! I might as well work my ass off, get my education, get my clothes, get my food, get my housing, and get extra money, I say! I'm yelling at the top of my lungs by now. They're all laughing. "You're so funny, Louise." I oughta funny you one, I want to go in the army and get where I need to get. They finally agree that I probably would be good at it, even if I'm not supposed to go in the army and I say, "Besides that, when was the last time you saw me running around caring what girls do and what's ladylike? I don't give a good goddamn about any of that." They all agree with me. As a matter of fact, we all end up laughing about it, and they hug me a whole lot and go to bed. I think all the goddamn time I'm going to sleep, What a lucky break! Counters at coffee shops are just lucky. That's where I'm going to die someday, sitting at a counter in the coffee shop having a good time.

I work a lot of hours at the Broasted Chicken Inn, and I do a really good job, and she pays me good and she compliments me and I get one meal a day like every restaurant gives you and I have to pay for my room and all my clothes and everything. I don't have a car anymore, so I have to pay for transportation. You can make quite a bit of money but by the time you pay for everything, you don't have very much money and because I want to send money home for my sisters, I'm saving up and I'm not eating very much at the Y. I feel bad that I just can't take care of 'em.

I wrote a letter to Jack telling him I was going to go in the army. He didn't have a fit about that like he did about being a Mormon, he thought it was a good idea and that we could see each other on my furloughs. I asked him what in the world was a furlough, and he wrote back it's when you get to take a vacation from the army.

I go down to the recruiters and I sign all the papers. They have to get a whole bunch of information on me before I can actually go in the army. The recruiter says it will probably be March before I go in. I'll be nineteen by then. I go to the Mormon church meeting and at the church meetings, you get to get up and say anything you want, anybody can say anything they want in there. I get up and I explain to everybody that I'll be leaving because I was going to go in the army. They all have a fit. As a matter of fact, they do a laying on of hands that night. Laying on of hands means the elders come and they put their hands on your head and pray for you. They don't want me to go in the army. Nobody wants me to go in the army, but Jack! He just wants me to get my education because I really want it. Besides, right now, he can't leave anything because his wife's going to kill herself. I think somebody should kill her and hurry up! Anyway, after the laying on of hands, these sisters come and see me the next day and try to talk me out of it. I just won't be talked out of it. They say it's not good, that I will be exposed to a whole lot of things I shouldn't be exposed to, and I think, "Boy, if you only knew!" I mean, what else could I be exposed to? War? Huh! That would be easy, at least I'd have a gun too this time!

Anemia

I woke up out of a sound sleep. I'm so hot I can hardly breathe. I think I'll get up and go to the bathroom, put some cold water on my face. I get to my door and I open it, but I can't walk. I crawl. The bathroom is right across the hall from me. It's a little hall, so I get in the bathroom and I pull myself up to the sink and I put water on my face. I don't know what happened. I might have fainted, but now I'm crawling around the bathroom, I run into the bathtub with my head, I run into the toilet, I run into the bathtub again. I'm running around on my hands and knees in circles. The only thing I can see is a light. Every time I look up, I can see the lights on the ceiling but I can't make out anything. I wonder if I'm going blind? I don't know what's wrong with me. I keep crawling and crawling and crawling. This is the biggest bathroom I've ever crawled in my life, I can't get out of here. Finally, finally I find the door. The reason I know I'm in the hall is it has a rug on it and the bathroom doesn't. I keep crawling and crawling and I get against the door and I just start banging my head on the door so they'll open it. I don't know whose door it is, but they open the door, and they take me and put me back in bed, and all of the lights go on, I can see the lights barely, but I can't see anything else. Am I going blind? What's wrong here? I can't go blind and go in the army!

I wake up the next day — I think it's the next day, but it's two days later and a doctor is there, telling me I'm anemic. He gives me shots every day so I won't be anemic anymore. He says that I'm so anemic I could've died. He says that's why I feel like I'm going blind because if I hadn't taken care of it I would've gone blind. He says anemia is when your body isn't making enough iron and your blood just can't take care of you so you get really sick. I've been tired for awhile, but I didn't know I was that sick. I spend a whole week in bed. The whole week!

I go to church on Sunday. There's a whole lot of dumb people and a whole lot of not dumb people, but I just figured out another thing today. There's a whole lot of dumb people who are harmful. They're mean. A whole lot of dumb people who are not mean. A whole lot of smart people that are mean, and a whole lot of smart people who aren't mean. I figured that out, and I'm not going to forget it. Today in church, we have a black couple. They're black like the people who are in Florida. We only have one black couple. They can't be anything in the church. They can come, and they can pay their ten percent tithing every month, and they can't be anything at all. That's because they're black. We're back to goddamn dumb Cain and Abel, right? Boy, am I mad! Really mad. I get up to the microphone and I tell 'em that it seems like just a bunch of rotten no-good stuff to me. I'm not going to be a Mormon if you guys are going to act like this. Well, here we go again, they're going to do the old laying on of hands and pray for me, and I'll bet tomorrow the sisters will talk to me a lot. I'm not changing my mind about this. I don't give a good goddamn if Cain did kill Abel, that's just like Jesus dying on the cross. I don't believe for a minute that there's really a God that cares about anything if he's doing stupid things like this.

I don't go to church the next Sunday because I go to Cody, Wyoming with a friend of mine to visit her family. I have a good time. They have good family and good babies and a lot of laughing. I'm going to have a family like that when I get out of the army, if I ever can figure out how to do this without having to do what a man tells me to do, and without having to have sex because I really don't like it.

Jack was really good when he was gentle and nice, but I just can't get all the memories out of my head, and I can't get that bad thing out of my body! That makes me really mad. Every time I think about it, I think, Okay, I'm not able to do that and where's the applause for everything I do? I do lots of good things.

I go back to work at the Broasted Chicken Inn. They didn't fire me when I was off all that time with that anemia. They were really nice to me and she brought me a pin that goes on the blue coat she gave me. I never had such a pretty, brand-new blue coat, and a pretty pin. My mom was wrong. You really can go out in the world and have nice things and be nice and know nice people. She was just wrong. She wasted her life being really pig-headed and wrong. Even she said so.

I go to church on Sunday. I haven't been for a few weeks. They made me mad over the black people thing. I go back to church because I think, okay, maybe there's something I don't understand. Today I think, their name shouldn't be Mormon anymore, it should be Moron, like people joke about. A woman who fell in love with somebody who wasn't her husband and made love with him — they called it an affair — five years ago, and today they took a vote — they voted — on whether they should let her back in the church or not! We voted? I thought forgiveness was up to God! They've been telling me the only person who can do judgment on earth is God. We're supposed to forgive and not to judge. They took a vote! That's a judgment! That does it! I get up to the microphone again. This is my last day as a Mormon. I tell 'em what a bunch of assholes I think they are, and I leave. I'm never going back, either. Not ever. They're not doing any laying on of hands, either. They tried that. I told them to get the fuck away from me, I'm not kidding. I'm not going to belong to any of this religious stuff that does mean things to people. Then the sisters come to see me the next day to try to convince me that I don't understand it, that I'm a special spirit, and that I should come back to church. I say, "Even if I'm a special spirit. I don't believe in your religion. I'm sticking with the spirit guides my grandfather taught me about. He's an Indian and he's not a Mormon. I'm not coming back to church. You people do not do good things. You people run around acting like you are God instead of you have a God, and that's the end of that."

A few weeks later I go in the army. I leave from here by bus for Idaho and from Idaho I go by plane to Alabama. Anniston, Alabama. Ft. McClellan for basic training. The recruiter told me that in basic training they try to make you as unhappy as they can make you. They try to test your will power, and they try to test what you're made out of. I thought, Well, so just test away, smart-asses. That will be nothing new to me and I'm strong enough to take lots of things.

I'm going to do six weeks of basic training when I get there, and then I get to have one of those furloughs. Jack and I are supposed to meet. We just didn't decided where yet. After basic training, I'm going to be a nurse, a WAC, that stands for Women's Army Corp.

I go to the Induction Ceremony which means you raise your right hand and all of us in a group promise to take care of our country and don't do weird shit to it and don't make it mad and defend it and stick up for it and be loyal. I always am anyway.

Basic Training

I don't know if I was scared or what on the plane because I fell asleep. I slept almost the whole night flight. They take us out to Ft. McClellan, and the first thing that they do is yell at us. They yell at us to get in line, they yell at us to stand straight, they yell at us to suck our bellies in, they call us "ladies." We can't call anybody anything but "ladies." It has to be "Private Burnham" and "lady" or nothing. The first thing we learn is how to take care of our uniforms. But then we get our uniforms, they don't fit, we have to ask for better ones, and we have to wear the ones that don't fit, until they give us better ones. We have to starch everything so it stands up by itself. I'm allergic to starch!

It's March, and in Alabama it's hot. It's hot and wet, just like Florida. It's really something. We have black people and white people and Mexican people, all of us women are different, but we all get to do the same things and have the same things. I like this. I like this better than the Mormons and better than the Baptists and better than everybody. Better than Florida. We have to march until we turn purple. It's so hot that when we march everybody's hair flattens out and is soaking wet, and we're sweating from head to toe. I'm going to be a good WAC. I'm going to do a basic training, and I'm going to make everybody proud of me. Everybody who cares about me, anyway.

Jack writes me letters and tells me to be good and make him proud and I'm going to do it. Then he says he's going to get a divorce. He doesn't care if his wife is going to kill herself, he's going to get a divorce anyway. Yeah, sure.

I'm good at marching. They call it a cadence, where it's almost like drums only you do it with your feet. It's really pretty. I don't like the heat and I don't like being so hot that we don't know what we're doing. They make us stand for a long, long time. As a matter of fact, a couple of these WACs fainted while we were standing. We just stand at attention until we turn blue. I don't know what the point of this is, but I'm just going to be a good WAC, then I'm going to go to school and be a nurse.

At dinner they give you boiled potatoes that have grease on 'em. How in the hell do you boil a potato and have grease on it? I get to find out, Sgt. Zabo says because pretty soon I get to have KP. Everybody gets to have KP which is when you go to the kitchen and wash pots and help fix food and clean floors. Some of the food is not recognizable. It's almost funny, all of us laugh about it. You can't throw your food away, you have to eat it. We make up names for it, laugh a lot, then we eat it. Some of it really doesn't taste good.

We have a lot of field practice and we have a lot of drills and marching. We have to go through buildings that they have put chemicals in and try to breathe through our gas masks. We have a lot of first aid training, and then we have a lot of the rules of the army training. Memorize the books. Memorize the rules. They give us tests and classes on everything.

I just keep spit-shining my shoes and shining my brass, doing my uniforms, marching and doing my cleanup duties. We clean things when they're not even dirty. Even the toilets have to be in uniform. Uniform, for the toilets, means that all of the tops have to be up in uniform position in a row so they all look alike. But when you go flying out of your bunk at night, and you go screeching into the bathroom because you have to pee, you land right in the water because you're half asleep and all of those toilet tops are standing at attention believe me it's very cold on your ass. You have to do your beds so you can bounce a quarter on 'em. These beds are old, wobbly, lumpy beds. To fix 'em so that you can bounce a quarter is really a trick, but I figured out how to do it, and I get a good mark on my locker and footlocker and bed every time.

I get good merits on my jobs, and now I'm a squad leader. A squad leader means that you get to boss people around after the sergeant bosses you around. I don't do that, I just walk in the bay. The bay is where we sleep. Everybody sleeps in a row, just a lot of beds in a row. I walk in the bay and I say, "You know what you're supposed to do, fucking do it," and they do.

We get our first weekend pass this weekend, and we're going to go into Anniston, Alabama, and look it over. I'll be so glad to go somewhere besides this damn military base. Everything is hup-two-three, hup-two-three. When they play "The Star Spangled Banner," and when they play any of the marches and we march to 'em, I get tears in my eyes. I don't know why. I asked somebody about it in my platoon and they said that I'm patriotic and it is touching. So there I am, patriotic and touched.

We go into town and I want to go to a coffee shop. I want to go to a coffee shop, sit at a counter, talk to people, and drink coffee. Private Washington is with us, and Private Washington can't go in. We're standing inside this coffee shop and they tell her she has to leave. I can't figure this out. We're all in the same uniform, and we're all serving our country, and she can't come in. I ask 'em why? They say it's because she's black, and nobody black can be in here. That does it! That does it. I start throwing stuff around at the restaurant and knocking off the salt and peppers and I'm really mad now. I'm so tired of this black thing. I wish Cain had fucking refused to kill his stupid brother Abel, and even if he did, I wish somebody hadn't written it down and then made it up as a big rule for the rest of everybody else's life. Just a pain in the ass, is what I think. Private Washington can't go in there, I'm not going in there anyway. All the rest of the WACs went in there and Private Washington and I went to a place where blacks can go. If you're white, you can go into a black place. They're very nice to me in there. We get to sit at the counter and have coffee. I'm not going to white places if they're going to act like that. I can't believe this. We're all Americans and we're all in the United States Army, and they're not going to let her in the restaurant. She says that's nothing new, just nothing new. I wonder why they let her in the army in the first place if they're going to be mean to her. While we're on the post in the army they're never mean to her. She does everything I do. Oh, the hell with it, I don't get it. Rats — all of 'em.

Basic training's almost over and I'm getting a good grade in all of it. If you don't get a good grade they do a thing called "recycle" which means you have to go right the hell back to basic training, which really makes you want to get a good grade because nobody wants to do this again.

We get our first dance with the guys. What an excitement. We actually get to go and hang out with a whole bunch of guys. We get up to the dance place, and there's a whole bunch of booze that the guys smuggled in, and a whole bunch of guys, and we can drink, even if we're not of age. I drink and dance and talk to the guys, and I watch a whole bunch of my platoon go outside with the guys and come back looking like hammered hell. I know they're having sex. The guys that I dance with ask me if I want to go outside, and I think, And get fucked? Are you out of your mind? I don't say it. I just say, "Oh, no thank you, I'm drinking and dancing" and that's what I do.

In one week we graduate and then we get our furlough. I'm going to go to Wisconsin and see Jack, and I'm going to see Mrs. Sawyer, and I'm going to see my baby sisters, and I'm going to go see Lucy at the counter. I'm feeling okay. I don't like what they do about the blacks. We're all saying good-bye to each other at the base because we're all going by bus and train and airplanes and whatever to go home for our leaves. Some people can't go home for their leave, they don't have a home to go to, so they're going to go right straight to Fort Sam Houston, Texas. Fort Sam Houston, Texas, is where I'm going to go for my nurse's training.

As we're getting ready to go, lots of people hugged me and tell me they're going to miss me and how much fun I've been, and what a riot it was to have me stand my uniform up. I made it stand up all by itself in my position in the platoon. The sergeant didn't think it was funny, but everybody else thought it was hilarious. I just waited until they figured out I wasn't in it and started hollering, and then I came right out in the rest of my clothes and got into my uniform. I got a demerit for acting like that, but it was sure funny. We say good-bye to each other.

On Leave

I get back to Wisconsin to see my sisters. I take a bunch of pictures of 'em. I see Jack and he tells me that he's going to have a divorce by the time I'm out of the army. I'll believe it when I see it. He says he's sorry that he lied to me, but he really loves me and wants to be with me. I don't really trust him anymore, I wish I did. He and I are going to Canada for a weekend, up to Thunder Bay, and beyond. They speak French up there. I felt like he was a pal of mine. We stayed in a hotel. He likes making love but I don't care about it at all. I did what Lucy told me, which is just think about something I like. I sing songs in my head and drink gin. I didn't tell him what I was thinking the whole time. Jack didn't even notice the difference. It works! I wouldn't want to do it a lot forever, but there is no other way to have a family that I know of yet. Jack and I talk about books and stories, and we talk about the army and we talk about the United States Military and the war in Vietnam. That's why I want to be a nurse, maybe I can help.

Mrs. Sawyer still takes care of my baby sisters, and their dad still pays for them and sees them on the weekends. When they get older, he's going to take 'em full time. One thing I can say about that damn fool is that he takes good care of the girls, as good a care as he knows how. I know mom would be happy about that.

I have to go to Ft. Sam Houston, Texas, now and get my nurse's training. I'm so excited, what a lucky break this army is. There's always a whole bunch of good, like Mrs. Sawyer says.

Fort Sam

So this is Ft. Sam Houston, Texas. It's hotter than backing your ass up to a potbelly? They have a huge barracks here for the WACs. The barracks is three stories high, it's a big red brick building. It has these things called verandahs. We're on the bottom floor. Our whole platoon is in an open bay which means just like basic training, everybody's bed's just kind of lined up against all the walls and the lockers are in between the beds. You can hear everybody snoring and moving. I don't know why I like that.

Today was orientation day. They drag you around in this blistering heat to every place that you're going to have to be and you have to march in full dress. It's so hot, you're dripping wet. Everything's dripping. This is too hot for marching. They march us anyway. They march us to all the places that we're going to take classes. Then they march us out on the drill field and march us around that. The drill field's bigger than a football field. It's huge. We're marching and marching and marching and I'm dying of the heat, everybody's dripping wet, and Private Brown falls over, and we're not supposed to stop. We already had instructions this morning. Anybody who falls over, we step over them like you would in battle, you can't stop, so you just keep marching. Sgt. Hark says, "She just fainted. Sometimes when people get too hot they faint." Why the hell would they march us around if they know we're going to faint? Brilliance at its peak, I think. Every morning we're going to go to classes, and every morning we have to be marched through the men's barracks section to go to classes, and today, when we march through 'em, all the guys are out there making all kinds of rotten cracks, and we can't break formation to go hit 'em a lot. I don't get this. First they march us around till we faint, then they march us through these stupid men who are standing on the lawns making horrible cracks to us. They said if we talk to each other like that, we'd be in deep shit. They don't get in trouble. They just stand there and make those cracks. I fell like walking up and decking 'em one. Can't break formation, though. I'm not going to fail. I want to be a nurse, so I'm not going to walk over there and knock those fools on their asses, but I want to.

We have nurse's training every day, and then we have details, a job like chores, and you either are cleaning up something, or you're doing KP. I finally found they get grease on boiled potatoes by not washing the pans right. They're half the size of me. I can stand in 'em, and they're almost up to my waist.

We put Sgt. James in there, just for laughs because he's really tiny, and rolled him around the kitchen for awhile. It was an absolute scream. He's really a comical guy. Unlike Sgt. Hark who's our sergeant, the women's sergeant. She's huge. She was going to be a man and changed her mind. She's enormous, and she looks at us funny. I mean, she looks at us like guys look at us. She gives me the creeps. I don't know why she does that.

When we march past those guys in the men's barracks on the way to the training class center, the guys actually make propositions. They stand on their lawns and ask us how much we cost, and ask if we want to do this or we want to do that. It's all about sex. That's what it's all about. I just want to leave the formation, go over, and bloody a nose or two. I wouldn't get my nurse's training, so I'm not doing it. I hate those guys! I hate it that they can get away with that. They give orders around you all the time. If they say bend over, you better be bending over. How come they don't tell these guys to shut their goddamn mouths? I don't know why. I don't know why we can't turn around as a whole unit and scream, "Fuck you!" and be right back in cadence with our next step. If I were running this, that's how I'd do it. That's not how Hark does it. Hark just marches hup-two-three ourselves to death to the training center, and we just take that nasty talk from those dumb guys. I can't believe people that stupid are defending our country. No wonder we can't win the war in Vietnam, they're probably standing alongside the roads making rotten cracks to women!

Our training classes are exciting. We give blood, learn how to take blood, we give shots, we learn how to dress wounds, we learn all kinds of things. When I get out of here, I'm going to be able to take care of almost anything that happens. I know how to stop bleeding and I know how to put a bandage on something or pressure on something, and save somebody's life. If you have something in your body, like something stabs you, a piece of shrapnel in your body, the worst thing to do, until you get to the operating room, is take it out. They teach us how to bandage that and leave the thing that's in your body in your body because if you take it out, you start to bleed to death.

Sgt. Hark likes me. She pats me on my back. She's not even supposed to touch me. We're not supposed to touch each other. Nobody is supposed to be touching anybody. The best we can do is salute each other or shake hands. She pats me on my back and then she runs her hand down it and my hair practically walks right off the front of my head! There's something about her that's really creepy. She has a whole bunch of birds in her room — parakeets. She's not supposed to have any birds anywhere, and she has 'em. That's against the rules. Patting people on their back and having animals is against the rules, and she does it anyway. Maybe it's because she's a sergeant. Maybe when you're not a private anymore you can do stuff like that.

The dumbest detail they give us, as far as I'm concerned, is called policing. When you police an area, you go out and pick up every little thing that's in the area that's not alive and growing. If they're so busy making rules, why don't they make one against people throwing that stuff around. Stupid sergeant Hark took us out to police the men's parking lot area! The guys are up in their barracks screaming all this rotten stuff at us, and we have to pick up their junk. How about some shrapnel in their bellies and not dress the wound. The guys really piss me off.

It's a lot of fun in our barracks. We sing a lot and we laugh a lot and we make jokes a lot and tell ridiculous stories. I never heard so many weird things in my whole life. I laugh until I go to sleep around here.

Half of our time is spent scrubbing floors and waxing floors, and you know, scrubbing things down. They call it a "GI," and you start from the ceiling and work your way to the floor. That's not a lot of fun. The only thing that really does make it fun is that everybody gets along and they are a riot. We do such crazy things — I didn't know people had this much fun.

Sgt. Hark is never satisfied with it, though. She had me come in her room with all her birds and I'm allergic to 'em, so I get to sneeze my way through talks with her. I don't want to talk to her. It's against the rules for me to tell her, "Yoo Hoo, I do not want to talk to your stupid self." I have to sit there and listen to her and answer her questions. I don't like the way she looks at me. I don't like her, period. She's never satisfied with anything. She tells me how well I'm doing in the nurse's training class, and I say, "Why do we have rules that we can't do a whole bunch of things, and the guys don't?"

She says, "Well, all we worry about is what you do, we don't care what they do, it's up to their officers." What can I say about that? She says I get to carry the guide-on from now on because I'm the highest in the class. The guide-on is a flag, it's our platoon flag, and it's an honor to carry the guide-on. I'm pretty excited about that. I tell her that, and then when I'm leaving her room, she put her hand on my back and slid it all the way down to my ass. That's what Jack does! Why is she doing that? I look at her like, "Get your hand off my ass!" She doesn't. I leave. Creepy bitch.

I find out that if you're homosexual the Army will give you a dishonorable discharge. Homosexual is when you make love with another girl. I wonder why they give 'em dishonorable discharges. Who cares who makes love with who? I don't know why they care about that. They gave a dishonorable discharge today to Pvt. Grant. This is really rotten, but the first person I thought of was Sgt. Hark. She acts like she'd like to make love with a woman — me. I can't figure out how they make love because they don't have any penis. I ask one of my buddies in the barracks and she just laughs. She says, "Boy, you really are from out in the country, aren't you?" I ask her just what the hell she means by that? What's wrong with being from out in the country? She says, "Well, in the city, you learn who homosexuals are really quick."

"Well, tell me who they are! I want to know about this thing."

She says, "Well, homosexuals have their ways of making love and they really like it. They like it better than they like making love with men. Besides that, there're homosexual men who like making love with each other better than women." Well, that's a head spinner! I never even thought about that. You can't have any babies, though, so what's the point? Pvt. Good just looks at me like I've lost my mind. I get that look a lot, you know that? She says, "For pleasure. It feels good." Another head spinner! What a concept! It feels good? How does it feel good? She says, "Haven't you ever made love before?"

I say, "Yeah, but it wasn't like it really feels good. Mostly, it's kinda boring."

She says, "Well, who have you made love with? Men or women?"

I say, "Just one man! Why would I be asking you all these questions if I already knew how women make love? Obviously it was a man!"

She says, "Well, maybe if you made love with women it wouldn't be boring!"

"It would be even more boring than with a man, Pvt. Good because I wouldn't even know how to do that."

She says, "A woman would teach you."

"Just never mind. You could just tell me."

She says, "Well, it's a pretty private thing. I wouldn't like to just give you the details." "Well, you could give me the details, Pvt. Good, and then I'd know how the hell they do it. Boy, for confusing!" Pvt. Good says she doesn't want to talk about it anymore, so I said okay, fuckit, never mind.

Private Sanders is pregnant. She's pregnant and she's out of the army. You can't be pregnant and be in the army too. You can't be homosexual and you can't be pregnant. How come they're not discharging the guy who got her pregnant? He's in on it. It doesn't count. Oh, am I surprised? I know, it doesn't count, it's just like when they make all those rotten cracks when we're marching by. That doesn't count. Anything they fucking do doesn't count.

We get a whole talk on medical corpsman training, and I find out that when you get out of medical corpsman training, and you go back to civilian life, your certificate for medical corpsman means you're a nurse's aide. I already was a nurse's aide. I feel numb. I can't believe this. What happened to the RN training? I thought I was in RN training. Registered nurse! I was a medical corpsman before I ever came in here. What the hell is wrong with that recruiter?

I make an appointment to talk to Captain Ramsey. I need to know if this is really true, or if I get a different kind of certificate, or if I go to a different training because the way it works is you have a thing called an MOS. My MOS is medical corpsman. When I get out of medical corpsman, then I go to work in the hospital, an army hospital. That's the end of the training! That means I'm not going to be an RN and I want to know if that's true. It just goddamned better not be true!

I get my appointment with Captain Ramsey, and I go in and I stand at attention and I salute like I'm supposed to. She returns the salute and tells me to be at ease, so I stand at ease. She says, "What is it, Private Burnham?"

I say, "I want to know if after the medical corpsman training, do I get the RN training? When is the RN training going to happen? If all I get to be is a nurse's aide, well I was already a nurse's aide." Captain Ramsey tells me, "In the army, you're a medical corpsman. In civilian life, that's a nurse's aide."

I says, "My recruiter told me I was going to have RN training! That's why I came in here! That's why I'm in the army! I was already a medical corpsman, and a psychiatric technician."

Captain Ramsey says, "I don't know what you were told. In order to go into the registered nurse's training, you have to be twenty - one, with two years of college. You can't even do that yet, you're not old enough for one, and for two, you don't have two years of college. When you came in the service, you had to take that test, remember, the GED test because you never even went to high school! We still don't know how you got college credits since you didn't go to high school."

"Captain Ramsey, if I have two years of college, and I'm twenty - one, I'll be out of the army by then. Then I won't get my nurse's training."

She says, "Private Burnham, you have been misinformed, and you should have checked that out before you ever came in the army." I just stand there. I stand there and think to myself, Here we go again. I'm so tired of people lying to me, so at the top of my lungs I tell Captain Ramsey, "I'm fuckin' sick and tired of people lying to me!"

Captain Ramsey stands up behind her desk, and says, "Private Burnham, you will be on detention for the weekend. Don't you ever use that kind of language in my presence again. You're going to graduate from medical corpsman training at the top of your class, and don't disgrace yourself now. Now go back to your barracks and this weekend you're on detail."

I go back to the barracks. I can't believe this. I go through the motions of going to class, and I go to the marching and I go to what I'm supposed to do. I'm really mad. If no one ever lies to me again on this planet, it's going to be too goddamned soon. Besides that, I'm a Sagittarian. I read that book on Sagittarians, and they always tell the truth and they always want the truth. I'm going to have it. Fuck this goddamned army, you lying sacks of shit. How could Capt. Ramsey just sit there and not care about the fact that somebody in her army lied to me? I'm in here for three years, and then I have to re-up to get the training! I have to be in here six years! I'll be old by then! I'm not going to do it.

For the detail for the weekend, Sgt. Hark tells me to go out and police the officer's parking lot. I'd like to police that parking lot with a few grenades is what I'd like to do. Well, I'll tell ya what. I'm going to put the junk in this damned garbage can and I'm going to take it right over to the non-com's which is for sergeants and dump it in their parking lot. They probably won't even notice. I work all goddamned morning policing the giant parking lot, and I drag the garbage can across the street to the non-com's parking lot. I distribute that garbage evenly. Then I go back in and I tell Sgt. Hark my detail is done. She looks out the window, and she says, "Well good, now you can start on the non-com's parking lot."

I just dumped everything in the non-com's parking lot! I don't believe this! But it's an order, I have to go do it. I go down to the non-com's parking lot and I pick up all the junk that I threw there before and all the junk that they threw there since. I stand there thinking, Chortle chortle, hee hee, ha ha, ho ho, and up your parking lot — this is going right back to the officer's parking lot. I drag the garbage can across the street and I dump it all, distribute evenly, very uniformly, all over the officer's parking lot.

I go back in, it's two in the afternoon now, and I should be through. Sgt. Hark looks across the street and sees that the non-com's parking lot's done, then she says, "Good grief, Private Burnham, you didn't police the officer's parking lot, look at that!"

I think, I just hate this. How could she be so dumb, I mean, it's pretty obvious that the garbage is going back and forth. She doesn't get it — I'm back out there and I'm cleaning the officer's parking lot again. I want you to know it's going right back across the street to the non-com's parking lot. I'm really mad.

I drag all the garbage from the officer's parking lot back to the non-com's parking lot. Sgt. Hark is standing there when I get back in, saying, "Private Burnham, have you been taking the garbage from one parking lot to another?"

I think, Christ, Hark has had a brilliance attack. I say, "Yes, ma'am, I have. First I take it from one, then I put it in the other. Then you send me out, I pick it up, I take it back to the place I got it."

She says, "Private Burnham, you go back out there and you clean up both of those parking lots and you bring that garbage to me."

Okay, your fatitude, you asked for it.

I go back out and it takes me until five in the afternoon. Sgt. Hark is gone. She's gone! I take the garbage can and I put most of the garbage in the parking lot behind the kitchen which is everybody's parking lot. I bring the garbage back in and I tell the desk person that I have the garbage Sgt. Hark requested. She says, "Okay, Private Burnham, put the garbage where the Sgt. told you and go to your barracks, you're restricted to quarters, you know that."

I put the garbage by Sgt. Hark's door. I go back to my bed and I sit there and I sing and I write songs and I play around and I like it. I wonder what Hark will do when she finds out she has what garbage I didn't throw in the kitchen parking lot. Chortle chortle.

Sgt. Hark is out in the hall screeching for me. Guess she doesn't want the garbage. I get up and take it out laughing all the way. Outside I can hear everyone in our bay laughing and Hark hollering to be quiet. More restriction for me.

I think, I'm not going to be an RN, and I still have to put up with all of this shit, all this marching, all this bed-making, all this listening to those guys holler rotten things at us, all this stupidness, for nothing! For nothing! I can stay in this dumb army and be a nurse's aide and do what they tell me to do, like clean up parking lots, for three years and then if I want RN training, I can re-up! I can stay here another three years! I'll be an old lady! I'm mad now. I'm going to finish the medical corpsman training but I'm not staying in the army.

I look up from my bed and Private Jose is standing there. She has something behind her back and she's grinning like a skunk eating shit. I ask her, "What the hell's up?"

She says, "I have a surprise for you, to cheer you up."

"Oh, an honorable discharge? That would cheer me up. Is that what you have behind your back?"

She laughs and she says, "No."

Private Jose takes out two little hands with turtles in 'em. Teeny tiny little turtles! They are so cute! "You can't have animals in here," I say. She says, "Sgt. Hark has a whole goddamned room full of birds. I don't know why you can't have these two turtles."

We put 'em down on the floor and they took off. Turtle races — what an idea! "What do they live in?" I ask her.

Private Jose says, "We have to get a bowl and put water in it. They live in that. With a rock in it, so they can climb out of the water."

"Where am I going to get that?"

She runs over to her locker and comes back with a bowl and a rock. Okay, we put water in it, we throw the turtles in it, they love it. Okay, I'm going to have these turtles.

Everybody comes back, we're all sitting around the bay talking, and I say, "How about we have turtle races? We can bet on 'em."

We start the turtle races. We laugh and bet on those turtles. We had to mark out blocks on the floor of the tile so that we could call it a race because they'd take off in all directions at once. One of 'em keeps winning, one keeps losing, so nobody bets on him. Now the race doesn't mean anything because there's only one turtle to bet on. Okay, so then I say, "Why don't we clock how long it takes the one turtle to go these three blocks on the floor, and then we'll bet on that."

We started betting on that, and then we took the little turtle and started betting on how long it would take it to go the three blocks on the floor. It was a lot of fun.

I keep doing my detail and being restricted to quarters and playing with my turtles. I just love 'em. Private Jose, you're a sweetheart! Thank you for the turtles. I named 'em Don and Phil after the Everly Brothers. It makes me feel good that they're in my locker, playing on their rock. When nobody's around they're out on the windowsill getting some sun. I got something called Turtle Food. It's like fish food, pretty weird, but they eat it.

Five o'clock in the morning and we hear this "Attention!"

That means we're out of our beds, still stupidly asleep, standing at attention as if we're in our right mind. Sgt. Hark comes flying through on her broomstick and tells us "We're going to have a surprise inspection in one hour."

We can't have a surprise inspection. I have turtles. I'm going to be in trouble. Graduation is next week. What the hell am I going to do with the turtles? Private Joseph says, "Throw 'em out the window!"

I can't throw 'em out the window. The glass will break and the turtles will die. We're on the ground floor, but it's a long way down anyway.

She says, "Well, I don't know what the hell you're going to do with 'em."

I decided that after I got my place all cleaned up for inspection, I'd throw the bowl and the rock out the window separately and hope they didn't break when they hit the ground.

When you're having inspection, you have to stand at attention, and you have to hold your hands a certain way so it makes a little cup. I put a turtle in each hand and hold on to one of their little feet and make cups of my hands and just stand there. In comes the Captain and the Sergeant for inspection. They walk through and Captain Ramsey looks at me and says, "Private Burnham, what do you have in your hands?"

"Nothing."

She says, "Private Burnham, attention and salute."

I had to salute. I can't believe this. So I saluted, still hanging on to Don's little foot. Don is saluting too, I think, he's waving all over the damned place.

"Private Burnham, what is that?"

"That's a turtle, Captain Ramsey, a little baby turtle."

"Private Burnham, do you have another turtle in the other hand?"

I hold it up. I hold on to their little feet and they're wiggling and wiggling and I say, "See? They're really glad to see you."

"Private Burnham, you are not amusing."

I don't say anything, but I think I'm incredibly amusing. Everybody else is trying desperately not to laugh. When you're standing at attention, you're not even supposed to blink, let alone laugh. There I stand with two turtles, waving in the wind. Captain Ramsey is madder than hell.

"Private Burnham, you will dispose of those animals, and you will be on restriction again next weekend."

Inspection is over, everybody dies laughing. They're rolling around on their beds, that was the funniest thing they'd seen in a long time, and I'm not about to get rid of those turtles. I have to figure something new out, but I'm not going to get rid of the turtles.

Liar!

I'm really pissed I'm not going to be an RN. I hate being lied to and on top of all that, the United States Army, of all the places on earth, shouldn't be lying to people. I mean, this is our country! Captain Ramsey is always reminding us we're serving our country. How could you serve your country if you lie all the time?

I have one week to go before graduation. At the end of this week, I'll have my medical corpsman certificate, which means the same as being the nurse's aide I was before I came in here. Then I'm getting out of here. I'm going to go tell the captain that I'm pregnant. Then they'll give me a discharge and I'll leave. So far it looks like I'm going to be the one that gets top honors in the class. Me and another girl. She doesn't even talk to me, but we're getting the top honors. I also decided I've had it with those stupid men. When we march through there this week, I'm not going to take any shit from them. I have a great idea. I'm really agile. I can do somersaults, walk on my hands, flip backwards, and land on my hands, and I'm going to change the way those guys talk to us when we march down for graduation. That's what I'm going to do.

The graduation march has begun. Hup-two-three, and nobody knows my plan. I'm carrying the guide-on. The big fat honor of the big fat lying army of the United States of America. The goddamned lying recruiter and the goddamned captain that doesn't care about the recruiter lying. We're marching along when we come to those guys. For eight weeks, they've been giving us a bad time. They say things to us that I wouldn't take from anybody. If I break formation, I can get in a lot of trouble. I'm not going to break formation. I wait until we get right up to this guy who's on his haunches who gives me the rotten time, I lower the guide-on and act like I tripped and hit him dead in the face with it. Knocked him on his ass, absolutely. He didn't move. I did a forward somersault as if I fell over. He's on his back. He's out cold! I hit him hard enough to knock him out! What a deal! Hup-two-three, yeah me!

Sgt. Hark calls us all to a halt. We stop, I get up. I looked a mess, but I'm happy. I knocked him right on his ass and I'm happy with it. Sgt. Hark asks me if I'm all right, and we march right off to graduation class. I graduate. I'm now another kind of nurse's aide. First I was just a nurse's aide, now I'm an army nurse's aide. Big goddamned hup-two-three deal.

Captain Ramsey calls me to her office. She wants to know if I hit that guy on purpose.

I say, "Oh, I'd love to hit him on purpose. That would be really neat. The truth is, that I did a somersault on my way to graduation. Sorry."

She just looks at me. She doesn't believe a word I'm saying, and I know it. That's okay. I don't fucking care. She can't prove it — she can't prove it. I smacked him and I'm glad. I wish I could have gone around and smacked every goddamned one of 'em rotten mouthy men. I told her I needed to talk to her about something else that was very important and she says, "Now isn't the time and you come back tomorrow afternoon."

Tomorrow afternoon I'm going to tell her I'm pregnant. I've dated guys on this post, I could be pregnant. I'll just tell her, then they'll have to let me out of the army. I go to the PX with lots of guys. They're just friends, we dance, laugh, drink beer, but she doesn't know that. How does she know I didn't have sex and get pregnant? She doesn't know about that. The next afternoon I go and I tell her, "Captain Ramsey, I'm pregnant."

Captain Ramsey's face drops and she says, "Oh, for crying out loud. How in the world did you do that?"

I just look at her, I think, she doesn't know how you do that? I don't have anything to say to that. She sends me to the doctor, I tell her I don't need a doctor, I don't feel sick, I'm just pregnant. She sends me to the doctor anyway, and so they make me pee in a cup. Every time you go to a doctor in this army you have to pee in a cup. When we came in we were peeing in cups and we're still doing it. I peed in a cup and I left.

I'm on restriction for lowering the guide-on that smacked that dumb fucker. I have to be on restriction all weekend. Sgt. Hark is really pissed off. She asks me to come to her little room with all the birds because she wants to talk to me. She's going to be gone for the weekend and she wants me to take care of the birds that she's not supposed to have, and she also is really mad that I'm acting up. Okay, fine, be mad, who cares. My detail for the weekend is to feed that icky woman's birds. I don't like her, I don't like the army, I don't like being lied to, this isn't funny...I don't care about this place anymore. She's gone for the weekend and I feed the birds the first night. Sunday morning I think, You know, she's not supposed to have those birds. I mean, the army should tell the truth. It should be the same for everybody. Everybody gets to have stuff or they don't. Everybody should have to follow the rules. She doesn't follow the rules and she's not on restriction. I'm on restriction when I don't follow the rules! I decide her birds would be a lot happier out in the fresh air. Out the window they go. All of 'em. They fly, they stand there on the ground looking around, and then they go away. Happy birds, I think to myself. Pissed off Sgt. Hark when she gets back, I'll bet.

Sgt. Hark careens around the corner of the barracks, and up to my bed, screaming at the top of her lungs, "Private Burnham, what happened to my birds?"

I say, "They wanted to fly around for awhile, so I let 'em. They all took off."

She says, "Private Burnham, you are restricted to barracks for one week. Do you hear me? You can't leave these barracks."

Okay. Okay, monumental Sgt. Never mind. I won't leave the barracks.

"Private Burnham, you have become a problem. I'm going to take care of the problem you have become."

Oh, no, she's going to take care of my problem. Good. Maybe that means she's going to let me the hell out of here. They lied to me! Whole damn thing's a big hoax. It's the same as when used car guys tell you nothing's wrong with the car and you drive it down the road and it falls apart. I hate liars. A lot of people must like lying, though, because there's sure as hell a lot of it going on.

Sgt. Hark comes in, gets me in front of her, makes me stand at attention, and tells me, "Private Burnham, I want you to take off the wax on this floor and then clean it and put new wax on and buff it. I want this floor so shiny I can see myself in it."

She leaves. She wants this floor so shiny she can see herself in it. The floor's almost white. How the hell could you see yourself in it? Oh, hark, an idea! I strip it of wax, then I put can after can of black shoe polish and I do it in swirls like they taught us to do for our shoes and I rub it in and rub it in and rub it in and then I get the buffer and I buff it and buff it and buff it until the whole damn hall is shiny black. Then I wax it like I'm supposed to. Do you know what? You can see right up your dress in this floor.

Again Sgt. Hark, careens up to my bed again. The woman is pissed. I'm enjoying this. I like making her mad. I'd like making anybody mad at this point, I want out of the army. "Private Burnham, what the hell did you do to that floor?"

I say, "You said you wanted to see yourself in it and you can. You couldn't see yourself in it when it was white, though, so I had to make it dark, you know, the dark thing behind mirrors and stuff that makes you able to see yourself, now you can see yourself. I thought you'd be happy."

She turns purple. I think the woman is going to explode where she stands. No more rubbing my back, though, she's been mad at me a lot.

Now I'm on restriction until I'm transferred to Ft. Meade, Maryland, which is where I get to go pretend I'm a nurse, right? Nurse's aide in Ft. Meade, Maryland. Fuck you. I'm not going to do it. I'm restricted to barracks until I go. Okay, fine. Everybody's laughing and singing because all of us are going to be leaving in about a week and a half for our new assignments. Private Georgia always sings the "Ave Maria," it's a beautiful song, she has a beautiful voice. She sings and she sings and we all just go to sleep afterwards. I like hearing her voice and I like that song. I can't sing it very well, but I like it.

Everybody's really quiet, and I'm laying there thinking to myself what I'm going to do is go back to my psychiatric technician job and be a psychiatric tech and nurse's aide. I guess I won't get any damned school and I won't be an RN. I don't care. I'll think of something. I'll have my babies and I'll think of something. I'm laying there thinking and thinking. I must've dozed off because I woke up and somebody's sounding really sick. I mean, what a weird noise. I jumped up and turned on the light. Okay. Not only are they not sick, but I finally see how homosexuals make love. They do that with their mouths. Almost like when Jack used to kiss me, everywhere on my body, and I want you to know something, I found out that noise isn't sickness. That's happiness. Surprises me! Everybody in the barracks is screaming, "You stupid fool, turn off the light." I turn off the light and go back to my bed.

I do my details like I'm supposed to. I do a lot of dumb things. In the army, if anything holds still, you paint it green, if it moves, you shoot it, that's the motto. The other motto is, you get to hurry up and wait. The other motto should be, we make you do stupid things to keep you from doing nothing. Better stupid than nothing, I guess should be the motto. They have details here in which you strip and wax the same floor twice in one day. Sgt. Hark has not asked me to do much of anything, though. That's important because I want her to just fuck off. They don't care that I got lied to and I'm in this army for nothing, and I don't care what they do either.

The tests came back from the peeing in the jar act. I'm not pregnant. No kidding. Next, I'll tell her that I'm homosexual. Now if she asks me any questions, I can give her the lowdown because I saw all I needed to know from turning on the lights the other night. I get an appointment with Captain Ramsey, and when I'm there I sit down and I tell her, "Well, I have to tell you I'm a homosexual."

Captain Ramsey looks absolutely weird. I can't tell if she's going to laugh or throw up or cry or what, it's a really weird look. She says, "How long have you been a homosexual?"

I say, "Oh, gee, I don't know. You want me to tell you how we do what we do?"

She says, "No, I don't."

She sends me off to a shrink! Sends me to a shrink! I don't need a shrink! Just because you make love to another girl, you don't need a shrink. I talk to the shrink, he's stupid. He asks me questions and more questions, and I keep saying, "Don't you want to know how I make love because I'm a homosexual? I mean, don't you want to know about this so you can get me out of the army?"

He just keeps asking stupid questions, and he makes me take a couple of tests. Then he sends me back to the barracks. Captain Ramsey calls me to her office and says that the shrink doesn't believe for a minute that I'm homosexual. I say, "I don't care what he believes. I should know."

She says, "Well, Private Burnham, you're not going to get out of the army. You're not pregnant and you're not a homosexual. You might as well just straighten up and do as good as you did before."

I say, "I'm never going to do good again. You guys lied and nobody cares about your lie. That makes me mad."

She says, "You're in for a lot of trouble. You're going to get court-martialed if you keep it up."

I say, "I don't care, as long as I get out of the army, I don't care what you people do."

She just looks at me and tells me I'm excused, and I do an about-face and leave. I don't care what they do, do you hear me? I'm getting out of here.

Ft. Meade, Maryland. I'm here. I'm figuring out that the only way I can get out is if you go AWOL. AWOL means you're absent without leave. Actually what it means is you ran away. I'm good at running away. I'm just going to have myself an AWOL and then they'll let me out of this stupid army and then I won't have to wear this dumb uniform anymore, and nobody else can do anymore lying to me here.

I work in the hospital during the day, and I go out with the gang at night. This other WAC kissed me. Are you ready for that? I was in the laundry room doing my laundry and she came in, grabbed me, and kissed me. It was a great kiss. But then she's a girl, I thought, no babies here, never mind.

I told her, "Never mind."

She said, "Okay."

Pretty easy, huh? Tomorrow morning when I leave for work at the hospital I'm going to walk right off of this base and I'm not coming back. I'm going AWOL. Then I'll turn myself in when 28 days is over and then they'll let me out of the army. I have a friend who lives in Indiana that I was in basic training with, so I guess I'll just go visit her. I leave the post, go to the bus depot, get a ticket, and I'm gone. I just leave. That makes me laugh. I go to Indiana to visit my friend, we run around together. She's homosexual. She takes me to some bars where homosexuals hang out, then she takes me to regular bars, and her mom and dad don't care that I'm visiting. They don't care that I don't stay in the army and they don't care if you're gay and they don't care what you do, actually. I'd care what my kids did, I think. I stay with her and stay with her and run around and now it's twenty eight days so I have to turn myself in.

I go to Ft. Sheriden in Illinois and turned myself in. They thought they would recycle me. Recycle me! Re-fucking-cycle me! Because I did so well in basic training and so well in medical corpsman training, they're going to recycle me. Fuck that! I'm not going to do that. The captain at this post has me on what they call house arrest, which means you have to stay in the barracks, and they have these two stupid WACs that I could break in half with one hand guarding me. Then they take me out to do details, to work. Then they bring me back, and I have to stay in my room with them standing there stupidly, and then they're off duty and two other people show up. As if they could do anything to me anyway. Who cares? All I want is out of the army.

Today is that I find out that a lot of my private stuff was missing. I don't give a good goddamn about most of it. There was a picture I found at the dump years ago of a big boy and his little sister smiling and holding hands. I wanted that picture. I've had it a long time.

The sergeant at this base comes up and says, "Private Burnham, I want you to clean out the air conditioning unit, I want this building completely cleaned out."

Okay. You asked for it. I tried to figure out a way to clean this building out, and the only thing I could think of is to pour ammonia in the central air conditioning pan and clean out the building, and it works, everybody is outside. The sergeant is screaming at me, "Private Burnham, what did you do?"

I say, "You wanted the whole building cleaned out, here it is cleaned out, we're all out here. I put ammonia in there, otherwise it wouldn't clean out the whole building."

Now I'm so restricted that I don't even have any jobs. They don't even let me out of this room. They take me periodically down to this Major Bennett.

Honorable Discharge

Major Bennett is a black guy. He asks me why I want out of the army. All of a sudden I'm crying and screaming and knocking things off his desk and I'm really upset. I tell him about getting lied to, and I tell him I was already a nurse's aide, and about Sgt. Hark. I sail his books through the air yelling, "I hate everything!"

He keeps saying, "Okay, okay, settle down."

I sit in the chair and try to settle down. He orders lunch for us. While we have lunch, Major Bennett asks me why I hit a soldier with the guide-on flag. I try to be calm but I end up yelling, "Those were a gang of rotten guys making disgusting cracks to us every goddamn day! Guys like to do shitty things and the Army thinks it's okay too."

The Major just sat for a moment and very quietly he said, "Men of ethics don't do things like that."

We just sat there. I don't know what he means and I don't know what else to say.

He asks me a few more questions, and then he tells me he's going to recommend that I get a general discharge under honorable conditions because I'm not "adaptable to military life."

Ah ha! Finally, the truth! I'm not adaptable! I'm not going to get adaptable. I'm not going to be adapting to military life. I'm getting discharged. I don't lose my rank of E2, and I don't lose any money, and I don't lose any benefits, and I have an honorable discharge. My spirit guides do like me, even if I'm a brat, they like me, and I wanted out of this army and now I'm getting out.

I'm going back to Wyoming to take care of my wrecked up-people. That'll be good for me, and I'm good for them, they said I'm encouraging. I'll just go and encourage them a lot.

I pick up all my papers and my severance pay and all the stuff I'm supposed to do before I leave this damn army, and I go and get on a bus. Ft. Meade, Maryland, to Cheyenne, Wyoming. I'm going to go home.

There's a lot of people from this army that like me and I like them, so we'll just write and someday maybe I can see 'em. I could hitchhike or I could take a bus or something.

I make it back to Wyoming to the Wyoming State Training School. Dr. Jamison says that he's going to transfer me to the Wyoming State Hospital where I got the psychiatric tech training before. He says he thinks I'd be really good there. They've already filled my position here. I'm on my way to Evanston, Wyoming, to work at the Wyoming State Hospital. That's where the truly crazies are. That really makes me nervous. Pretty soon I get to see Jack, too, in the spring, so I'll go and just do my job.

I write Jack a letter telling him where I am and he's really disappointed that I didn't behave myself in the army and he hasn't had his divorce yet so we're both disappointed. I ask him why is it a bigger deal that I behave myself in the army, than that you keep your promise and get the damned divorce so I can have the damned babies? He doesn't say anything about that. Whenever he doesn't like a question, he just doesn't answer it. Dumbbell. When I do that to him, it makes him really mad. Fact is, he just chases me down and says, "Why won't you answer my question?"

I do that with him sometimes. It works. I don't know why a person should have to ask somebody to answer a question a hundred times. Why can't he just answer me? I don't know, I never did know, and I still don't know. He also says the best he can do is work at the Tetons which is a little ways from Evanston, but not so far we could see each other on the weekends. On this new job I only have Sunday off. He says, well, he could drive down and see me on the weekend.

I make friends with a Mrs. Simpson and a Mrs. Wiltzen. They all have kids and husbands and everything, and they're funny. They make me laugh a lot and we talk about everything. I baby-sit their kids sometimes. I go out and help 'em on their little farms. They have what they call ranches here, but they're really like farms. They're not big ranches like Bauer's used to be. When I was in Lander I tried to look up Brett. He went away, and he has a job somewhere else, but worse than that, he's married. I'm always going to miss Brett. He was my friend.

I have a lot of fun on my days off, either at Simpson's or at Wiltzen's because it's really neat. They're good people, and now I have some friends. Simpsons have three kids and Wiltzens have seven. A lot of damn kids. I hang out with them. I learned how to make sourdough and then I learned how to make sourdough bread and sourdough pancakes. I like cooking. I didn't know I liked cooking. I have a room downtown, but this other friend wants to be a roommate. My supervisor is named Mrs. Smith and her sister's named Sherie and her sister wants to be somebody's roommate, so we may get a thing called

an apartment which is bigger and has a kitchen and bathrooms and everything but a yard. Mrs. Smith has a cleft palate, which means that when she
talks you can barely understand her. There's some problems with that, but I'm
getting better at it. Sometimes she has to write things down so I can understand her. Sometimes, when she's not around, I practice talking just like her.
To my surprise, I can do it.

Every day after work I don't tell anybody about it, but I go for a whole
hour in my room by myself and talk to my spirit guides so the crazy thing
won't get me. Sometimes I feel like it's really close to me.

Full Blown Bat-Shit Crazy

At work there's a very long tunnel. Underground corridors with cells in 'em, and you can go from one building to another without even going outside. Dr. Reese is in charge of this hospital. He said he was impressed with my accomplishments at so young an age. I didn't ever tell anyone I went in the army because Jack had told me a long time ago if I'm not going to stay in the army, I shouldn't tell anybody I even went because it gives girls and women a bad reputation for being in the army. Crazy fucking world, I'd say. Anyway, I didn't tell anybody here. I just said I was back home and decided to come back to Wyoming and Dr. Reese and Mrs. Smith gave me this tour of the grounds. In the underground tunnels the creepy thing is that in the sides of the corridors, in the cells is where they keep the criminally insane — those are people who have killed people, or people who are real dangerous—they jump the psychiatric techs and they try to kill people. They keep them all down here in the dark, in little cells. They look horrible, and you walk by their cells and some of 'em sit back there and just growl like animals, and some of 'em run up and try to grab you from the cell and it's just horrifying. It's a horrible place. Lucky me, I don't have to work down there.

I'm on a teenage unit. The teenage unit is the one I trained on in the first place. Those people are in there for things like getting pregnant. Get this! Your parents can lock you up and keep you there. All they have to do is say so. Can you believe that? They can get away with that. They put you in a crazy house, for being pregnant! Goddamn. And they can put you in for running away. It's a good thing my parents didn't care about me at all. No one even bothered to lock me up. The units are called wards here, and on my ward they're in there for things like that. They're in there for a thing called promiscuity. That means that you're running around fucking whoever you please, all the time. Well, does that sound like something to get locked up for? I mean, I've done worse than all of that. I don't run around fucking anybody because I don't like it, but if I liked it, I'd do it. I run away. I'm not pregnant. The parents can say when they can get out. If my mom and dad had locked me up, they woulda never let me out. This is crazy. Whoever made this law is crazy.

There's some people on my unit who don't know who they're talking to. There's schizophrenia...that's one of the diseases where you really do hear voices in your head that nobody else knows about but you. The voices tell these people to do the goddamnedest things. Like eat the paper cup to the medicine. Then they gag and choke and take a drink of water and go away. That's pretty bizarre. Some of the voices in their heads tell 'em to jump ya and hit ya a lot. Some of the voices tell 'em never to get out of bed. It's really sad that a voice can just go on in your head and be the boss of you. I tell 'em, "Oh, tell your voices to shut up."

They look at me, and they smile at me sometimes. They don't know what I'm talking about, I don't think, but sometimes they follow me around after I tell 'em that. They're not following me around to hit me or anything, they're just kinda like puppies, they just follow me around. Maybe if you yell at those voices, it shuts 'em up. I don't know.

Dr. Reese gave me some books to read on this and it's really interesting. There's a real difference between somebody calling you crazy and you really being crazy. In the books it shows how the truly crazy people have some horrifying things going on inside of 'em that nobody knows about, and they don't understand either. As a matter of fact, it's so bad that they can't tell you what's wrong. They can't even explain it. They see things that aren't there, hallucinations. They think they are people like, like Jesus or whatever, I mean they think they're somebody that they're not, but they can't talk to you either.

I tried lots of things because I want to know about this. I talked to this one guy who calls himself somebody else and I tell him, "You know, you're really not that person, did you know that?"

He just stares at me. He just stares at me like there's no way for him to understand that he doesn't know that. When I call him by his real name, he won't answer, so I get in the habit of not doing anything until he responds to his real name. Then he gets it — like if you call him his real name, he waits a minute, he just stands there, and then he takes his food or he takes the orange I have for him, or he takes his medicine, but he has to wait awhile. If you call him by his pretend name, he does it right away. That's the difference.

There's one person here, who'll yank your head off if you get too close to her. We push her tray toward her, but you always stay far enough away from her so she can't grab ya because she really has hurt people who work here. She gets hold of 'em and twists their heads off, she's really scary. Her name's Pearl. She sits on the floor in Indian cross leg, and then she rocks back and forth and growls and rips sheets into shreds. They give her a whole bunch of rags and she makes shreds out of 'em. That's what she does all day, every day. When you get her up to put her to bed, she doesn't attack you if you say, "Okay Pearl, you're going to bed." If you say, "Come on, Pearl" then she just rises up and tries to take off your face. I mean, it's really hard catching on to what each one of these people can do and can't do, what they'll do and won't do, but it's fascinating.

Mixed in with the really truly crazies are these other kids who just do things like I'd do, like they run away. Some of the things they say, I know they have a whole bunch of things going on at their house just like I used to have going on at mine, like getting beat up and getting jumped up and down on and being hated, so they feel crazy. Dr. Reese says that after awhile if you feel crazy long enough, you just are crazy. That scares my eyebrows right down to my chin. I'm not going to think I'm crazy, then. Maybe that's the key. Maybe the big secret is that you have to remember to keep thinking you're not crazy. Sometimes, though I don't know if that works with the really crazy people because I don't think they can think that. I don't think they know to think that.

Mrs. Smith, my supervisor, tells me that I do an excellent job, and I have to tell ya, I have a big secret that she doesn't know about, and I don't tell anybody because I already know it's against the rules. When one of the patients smacks me, I smack 'em back. I don't hit 'em in the face and I don't double up my fist or anything, but if they smack me, I just whop 'em back. Then they just stand there. Then they don't ever hit me anymore. I like that. Mrs. Smith can't figure out how come they don't swing at me and stuff like they used to when I first started, and I can't tell her it's because when nobody's looking, I clobbered 'em one. I only had to do it one time with each one of 'em. They don't hit me. Pearl is a whole different thing. I'm not going to smack Pearl. She's strong enough to break me in half. I'm not doing anything with her, so never damned mind. Then Mrs. Smith keeps talking to everybody about the fact that when I tell these people something, they really don't swing at me and try to bite me. She thinks that's special. I can't say it's because I punched 'em out when nobody was looking. See, the way I do it, is that they hit me — one of 'em smacked me in the back of the head — but I can't hit 'em in their head. I turn around and punch 'em in the arm or smack 'em really hard on the arm or whop 'em one in the back with my open hand. Then I just stand there, like you want to fight, asshole, you're in the right place, and they look really confused. You know, like they're looking at something that's important. Then they don't swing at me anymore.

The one's who aren't really crazy, the ones who are in here for not doing what their parents want, they don't hit me because I tell 'em, "You touch me and I'll knock you on your ass."

I have to do all of that when nobody's looking because it's against the rules and I know it. I'm telling ya, it works. You have to treat these people like they're really people. If I had a person at my house and they hit me, I'd hit 'em back. I don't hit the people that don't hit me. You have to remember some of these people can't think and they don't know what they're doing. Those people you just can't hit because that would be just like beating up babies.

Today was a nightmare day! I thought that I was asleep having a horrible dream, and I wasn't. They give me two days on Ward C, and you know what, Ward C is the place for people who work here who finally go crazy. They are on Ward C all by themselves till they get better. You can just go crazy! One of the things Mrs. Smith told me while we were touring Ward C in the first place is, "A lot of these people aren't really crazy. They're in DT's, when you drink so much alcohol your body is poisoned then you imagine things and you see things that aren't there and you're just nuts. That goes away after you eat good and you rest right and you don't drink any alcohol."

Why the hell anybody would do that on purpose to themselves is beyond me. I like that alcohol stuff, but I'd never drink enough to not even know who I am. They call 'em alcoholics.

They have a program here for these alcoholics. A bunch of the people who work here are also patients in the program. How weird. Still, it's like a nightmare. That you can be taking care of these crazy people and all of a sudden you're just crazy yourself. On Ward C it's kind of like special treatment and special attitude and they aren't any better than the people on my ward. I don't understand this part of it. The other thing I don't understand is if some people are, like Dr. Reese says, truly crazy, and some people are just acting out, why do they put 'em on wards together? That must make 'em all feel terrible.

In the ward I'm on, there are only girls, they never put boys and girls together because even if you're crazy, you still have sex, and you get pregnant. Who in the hell wants a crazy for a parent? I agree with that one. The men here can work on all the wards. The women can only work on the wards where women are, or they can work in the glass enclosures. They can't go out on the wards where men are because the men attack 'em. Boy, even when they're crazy it's still the same, right? It's a bizarre thing.

Incest Is Normal

Our unit is such a horrible mixture. Pearl, who sits there and rips rags for a living, has been truly crazy forever, and then there's Tammy, who's simply pregnant. She doesn't seem crazy to me. From reading all their histories from their files, every woman on this unit has been sexually molested or raped. Seems like it happens a lot!

The people here don't have the physical disabilities that the people at the Wyoming State Training School have. All of their body parts work and they can talk and they can see and they have all their arms and legs and all of that. Mrs. Smith gave me a book called "One Flew Over the Cuckoo's Nest," and that book is really very interesting. Whoever wrote that book must've seen the same thing I see because they really do some ugly things, like when they take one of these kids who just ran away or doesn't "behave themselves," they take 'em down for shock treatments and you hold 'em down and then they shock 'em a lot and then they don't even know who they are for a couple of days. I think that's awful. I don't know what the point is. Some of 'em they give 'em so many drugs they don't know who they are, either. That can't be helping them. If you're taking a whole bunch of drugs and shock treatment, no wonder they can't think right. When I'm doing the gin and tonic thing, I don't think right, either. I'd hate to have to spend all day every day like that. How would I ever get well, get not crazy, if I don't know what the hell I'm doing every day?

Tammy tells me a secret today, she says that she's pregnant because of her dad. I just stand there. I can't believe that she's in here. "So, how come your dad doesn't take care of you?"

She says, they lied, they won't admit that she's pregnant because of him. Well, I want you to know, I turn right around and stomp into the nurse's station and tell Mrs. Smith, "Yoo Hoo, this girl is pregnant because of her dad. How come her dad's not locked up? It seems to me he's a lot crazier than she is."

Mrs. Smith says that there was no proof of that, and so they just have to believe the parents instead of the kids, and besides the dad is a really good guy, I mean, he does a lot of community work and has a business of his own, and everything, so they believe the dad didn't do that and the girl's just making that up. I just stand there, and ask Mrs. Smith, "What the fuck would make somebody say that if it wasn't true? That's stupid!"

She just looks at me and says she never thought of it that way. I'm really mad and I say, "Well, probably about time you did."

She tells me not to be a smart-ass, so I shut up. Why would you say that your dad's the father of your baby? I mean, what a sick thing to have to say anyway, why would you say that if it isn't true? These guys are really stupid around here sometimes. I keep remembering Major Bennett saying, men of ethics don't do things like that. I looked up the word ethics because I didn't understand it. I believe it! Men of ethics wouldn't do things like that and women of ethics wouldn't let them get away with doing it.

Then there's marvelous visiting day on Sunday damn afternoon, when everybody who locked up these kids comes and looks at 'em a lot, pisses 'em off, sends 'em up the wall, and it takes me two days to scrape 'em off the ceiling. I mean it, they come and visit 'em and if the kids say they don't want to see 'em, they don't get a choice, and they have to go sit there. Every time, her dad comes and visits her and he brings her presents. Her mom just sits there as if she were in her right mind, too. By the time they leave Tammy's a screaming mess. We have to put her in restraints. I don't think she should be put in restraints. I think she should have a fucking screaming fit, and then I think she should get out of here. I don't know why this makes me so mad. So today I made a big mistake. Her father says hello to me, and I say, "Why did you get her pregnant and then lock her up? You're not a man of ethics, you know that?"

He just sits there. He doesn't move. His wife, however, goes straight in the air. She jumps up so fast that it flips the chair over backwards and she starts screaming, "Why did you say that? What's wrong with you? Why are you working here?" and on and on and on. Mrs. Smith has to come out and get in the fray and get me out of it. She takes me into the office and asks me what the hell I thought I was doing, and I say, "I just wanted to know why they lock up Tammy when he's a creep."

She says, "We don't believe that. We believe she's making it up."

I say, "Mrs. Smith, why would she make it up?"

Mrs. Smith say, "You and I get along really well. We can't talk about this thing anymore. You just have to understand that's all. Dr. Reese is in charge of who's put in here and who isn't, and he knows a hell of a lot more than both of us."

Okay, okay, already, Mrs. Smith, fine, fuckit, never mind. I have to see Dr. Reese this morning because I talked to that damn father about him being responsible for this, and Dr. Reese tells me that the next time I did that I'd not work here anymore. I tell him okay, I won't do it again, but can I ask you a question? He says yes. I ask him why he thinks a person would make up a story like that. He says Dr. Freud said lots of girls make up that same story. I think, I'm not going to tell him that I know that those stories are true. That they happened to me. 'Cause I'm going to end up on Ward C, right? Oh, boy. I hate lies. I hate 'em. They cause all problems on earth. I can't tell Dr. Reese, I can't tell him that even though he's a doctor and I'm not, that I know that stuff goes on all the time because it happened to me because they'll just lock me up! What a scary fucking world!

In the book "One Flew Over the Cuckoo's Nest," they do all sorts of shitty things to the patients and get away with it, too. It's kinda like having really bad parents. I'm never going to do anything that gets me locked up because once it starts, it looks like just like living with my brothers, you can't do anything, you can't help yourself, and you can't get away. I'm not going to do that.

Tonight I ask Mrs. Smith if she knew anybody who wasn't crazy who had their father's baby or had a lot of sex with their dad or brother or whatever. She calls it incest. Okay, so do you know anybody who isn't crazy who had all this incest? She says no. I think, what am I going to do? I mean, nobody even knows anybody who had this happen who isn't crazy. I spend a lot of my off time in the library reading about everything on crazy I can. Some of the people are crazy because they were beaten so badly when they were little, that they have brain damage. I wonder if I have any brain damage. They have to give 'em tests to find out, but the big deal is that after they give 'em the test to find out if they're crazy, if they find out that they're crazy from getting beaten and have brain damage, then they lock 'em up. I can't even go get a test and see if I have any brain damage because they might lock me up too. A lot of times I feel like killing people when they really make me mad. I mean really killing 'em, I'm not kidding. I feel like blowing this place up when I'm mad.

The longer I work here the more I think, this is really bad. This ward keeps people who are perfectly good people, and believes the liars. If you're a parent, you lie and get away with it, and if you're a kid, you're just fucked. I wonder what would happen if I took these trusty fucking keys of mine, opened the back door, and turned 'em all loose. Sometimes people run away from here, but they don't get very far, and then for a little while they lock 'em in those cells in the corridors in the tunnel and when they come back up, they give 'em shock treatments and medications. They don't run away for a long time after that because they don't even know who or where they are.

Mrs. Smith, Jenny, Larry and I were talking about "mental illness" and "normal." Larry is in charge of the teen-age boys' unit. I get it that "normal" is what "usually happens." Everyone agrees on that. I'm suddenly pissed purple. I just sit there because I can't even listen, I'm so mad.

The three of them ask me what's wrong. I feel like I just stepped in a deep, dark hole. I wish I were dead for some reason.

"If normal means usual," I mumble, "then rape and incest are normal."

There is quiet and we all go back to work.

Pregnant

Jack comes down on his days off now from the Tetons or sometimes he comes and gets me and just takes me back up there with him on my days off. I have Wednesday and Thursday off. I like it best when we go back up there. Mrs. Simpson has an old car, '55 DeSoto, that she's going to sell me. Then I can just drive up and stay there. It's very pretty. High mountains, lots of lakes, lots of animals. Jack has a cabin up there, a little tiny log cabin, just one big room, with a fireplace. We sit around the fire and we talk about when his divorce will be final. He has it, but it has to be a legal thing. Takes about a year, he says, for a divorce to be final. Then we can really get married. We plan what kind of babies we're going to have, and the first baby we're going to have is a boy. I decided that. We're going to have a boy and we decided we're going to name him Joseph Michael.

The only reason I make love is to have my babies and a family of my own. I wish I liked it like Jack does. Just another damn thing wrong with me I guess. It does make me feel good that he likes that with me because I can't be sickening or he wouldn't want to do that either. I hear guys talk about girls they wouldn't touch with a ten foot pole, at least I'm not one of those.

It's exciting to be with Jack because he does all kinds of things like mountain climbing and horseback riding into the hills. There's a lake behind one of the Tetons. You go in this canyon, and then you come out to this lake, it's just a beautiful hide-out. He also thinks of things to talk about, like what's going on in the world today and what do I think of this and what he thinks of that. I love to talk to him because he's smart. I tell him I was really sorry that he had such a bad time getting a divorce, and I tell him that I finally understand how terrifying it can be when somebody says they're going to kill themselves because at the hospital, whenever we're on a suicide alert, that's because somebody really is trying to kill themselves and it's scary. It's like if they're going to do it, they're going to do it, but it's still scary, running around trying to make sure they don't. I tell him I'm sorry about that and he tells me it's okay. I start asking him questions about it, but he never wants to talk about it. He just says, "I don't want to talk about it."

Jack thinks it's great that I'm taking a correspondence course from the University of Wyoming. I want to be a nurse. I really want to be a doctor, but they say it's too hard for women to do. Everything's too hard for women to do. It makes me mad, but I can't argue with it, I guess. We'll see, though. After I'm a nurse, maybe I'll just be a doctor anyway. The correspondence courses give you what they call credits for college. You have to have so many credits and then you get to be a like a sophomore and a junior and a senior and then you graduate. All the courses that I'm taking are in psychology. They go with my psychiatric technician certificate.

Jack says he's really proud of me, that every woman should be able to take care of herself. I ask him, "So okay, if every woman should be able to take care of herself, why in the hell do men make sure that I can't do what they can do or I can't do the things I want to do. How come there're so many rules about what women can do?"

Jack says, "There's a bunch of rules about what men can do, too. Like men can't stay home and take care of babies, and men can't find a husband and have him support 'em."

I say, "Who in the hell cares? Who wants that? If you have a husband and he supports you, then all you do is get bossed around. Why can't you stay home and take care of the kids when you want to. If I support myself and then stay home and take care of the kids when I want to why can't you?"

Jack just laughs. He says, "You know, you were just born ahead of your time, goofy."

Okay, so I'm born ahead of my time. I don't care. I want an answer to that, Jack. Why does everybody make rules for each other when they don't even know what each other wants. Fact is, they don't even know each other period. They just make up a bunch of rules and then everybody runs around doing them. I just think this is screwy. How come we can't just do what we want? We're the boss of ourselves. Jack just tells me I don't understand yet, I'm not old enough.

I say, "You know what, Jack, that used to fly when I was really young. I'm not that young anymore. I think people can make up what they want in their lives and just have it. I did it."

Jack says, "You did do it but not everybody can do that. There has to be some rules."

"Why do there have to be some rules? What is it about making rules, anyway?"

Jack says, "If they didn't have any rules, everybody would just go wild. Do whatever."

I say, "Jack, the idea that everybody would just go wild and do whatever is bullshit. Everybody would just do what they want."

Jack says, "Well, how would you keep law and order and how would you do this and how would you do that?"

He drives me nuts with those questions.

I tell him, "People don't want to get hurt and people don't want to be without money and they don't want to go without everything. People would just get jobs and pay their bills and do what they really wanted to do, but at least they'd be happy."

Jack asks me if I think people would do pretty much what they do right now, and I say no. They'd work and pay their bills and have their babies but they would do what they really want to do. Like, I'd get to be a doctor and somebody — some man — could stay home with his kids if he wanted to. Nobody would be talking about the stupid rules. That's the only part that would change. Everybody wants to have things and do things. People aren't going to just quit doing everything they like because they don't have to, that's stupid.

We have a lot of conversations like that. We don't argue about 'em, we just talk about 'em. I keep thinking Jack has answers to it but he doesn't have 'em. He says he doesn't know. I feel really stupid because I thought he knew. Actually, most of the time, I think Jack knows almost everything. Jack says that's being childish.

"Well, thank you, Jack, you asshole. Thanks a lot for childish. Okay? You don't know everything and I don't know everything. I just think you're really smart, is what I mean. I get surprised when you don't have answers and so what?"

Jack says, "Nobody has all the answers."

That makes me even madder. "I never said everybody had all the answers. I said, it's surprises me when you don't have answers because most of the time you do."

Jack says, "Oh."

I just sit there, he just sits there. Sometimes I think he argues just to hear his face bang together. We just drop it when it starts to get like that because all you can do then is just kind of say stupid things and wish you didn't talk at all. Jack says he's never talked to anybody on this whole earth as much as he talks to me. I tell him I've never talked to anybody as much as I've talked to him, either. Then I think to myself how many things I haven't told him because if I did I'd hear about how creepy my imagination is, the things I make up in my head, or he'd just do like some people have done and just not talk to me anymore. It makes me feel bad that I have a secret — a bunch of secrets but I'll be goddamned if I'm going to tell those secrets and have somebody knit my eyebrows together because they don't believe me or they don't like my story. So I'm just never going to say it.

Mrs. Simpson sold me her '55 DeSoto today. It's a horrible car. It's a stupid big giant car that almost goes, you know, it kind of crawls everywhere it goes, not like my Chevy. This car is slow, but sure. It's big enough to live in. When I take it up to the Tetons to see Jack, I have to start out early because it takes a damn long time. I always get back really, really late at night. It's worth it.

The swing shift is really best for me. In the last couple of weeks all I do is throw up in the morning. I hope I'm not getting anemic again. I can't be getting strep throat because my tonsils are gone. I throw up and then I'm fine, so by the afternoon, when I go to work, I feel great. I've been thinking about talking to somebody at work about it, but I'm afraid if they find out that I'm not well, they'll make me stay home and I can't go without the money. I'm not saying anything. Maybe it'll just go away. It seems weird to throw up and feel fine afterward. I never did that before.

I talk to Mrs. Smith. She says to see the doctor. She says that sounds really serious. Throwing up every day isn't good for anybody. I'm going to see the doctor tomorrow. I hate doctors. I'm afraid of 'em.

I don't go to the doctor. I go to the Tetons instead. I tell Jack that I'm throwing up every morning and he looks like I hit him. In the face. With a board.

He says, "Could you be pregnant?"

Pregnant? Could I be pregnant? Could I? I don't know. Jack just looks white. I've never seen him look like that. He looked like he was going to throw up.

Jack says, "Well, we've been really careful. You shouldn't be pregnant."

I say, "Jack, I'm not pregnant, I'm just throwing up. In the mornings, that's all."

He says, "That is a sign of being pregnant."

Oh. Well. I don't know if I'm pregnant. He says to go back and find out.

I say, "I'm not going to do that without you."

He says, "All right, next week I'll drive down on your day off and then you can find out. Make an appointment for your day off and then we'll find out if you're pregnant."

For some reason, on this visit, Jack didn't want to make love. I thought it had to do with me throwing up. I mean, what's he upset about — he's not pregnant!

The doctor takes some tests this morning, the pee-in-a-jar test. I wonder who dreamt that one up. Anyway, he says he'll call me tomorrow. Jack is here, but he's not very happy. He seems really mad about something. He says he's just worried about me. Well, we'll find out tomorrow.

The news is I'm pregnant! I am! I'm pregnant and I'm going to have my first baby! It's going to be a boy and I'm going to name it Joseph. I tell Jack, and I'm so happy, and Jack isn't happy. Jack's really upset. I keep asking him, what's the matter? He says, "Well, it's just bad timing. We aren't ready, and the divorce isn't final, and we just weren't ready for this."

I say, "I'm ready for this! I've been ready for this forever."

Jack goes back to the Tetons really upset. I go back to work feeling great. Jack says he'll come down on my day off next week again. He says to make sure I don't tell anybody at work because I'll probably get fired.

I tell him, "I've seen women at work who are pregnant. I can take care of myself."

He says, "Yeah, but they're married."

I just hate these rules! Pregnant's pregnant! Who cares if you're married or not! Everybody gets pregnant the same way. What difference does it make?

Jack says, "I really want you to stop acting so stupid. It makes a difference. I don't know why. It's just the way it is."

I just say, "Okay, already, all right! I won't tell anybody at work. What a drag. I have to tell you Jack I think you're the stupid one. People who have sex get pregnant, you know that and you know about being married. You didn't care about any of it this whole time so what's the big deal now."

Jack doesn't say a damn word.

I tell Mrs. Smith at work that the doctor said that I was really nervous, which is what Jack told me to tell her. I ask her not to tell anybody else that I'm so nervous. I feel like a total dumb-ass, standing here lying to my friend. Besides, I'm so excited, I feel like squealing. I'm pregnant and I'm going to have a baby boy and I'm going to name him Joseph and I'm going to keep him forever! I'm just going to be a good mom. I have to have a boy. 'Cause there's no way I could be a good mom to a girl. Everybody tells me I don't even act like a girl half of the time. I'm not going to know how to teach anybody to be a girl.

It's my day off and Jack's here. He seems different. I'm worried. He's not talking very much. When he starts to talk, he loses track of what's he's saying. I don't know what's wrong. I keep asking him and he keeps saying that he's worried about me.

"Jack, bad things have happened to me that didn't have any good reason and I didn't even get to have a baby, either! They were bad things and

I did fine. I'm going to be happy with a baby. Lots of things have happened to me I was unhappy with, this one I'll be happy with. It's like the applause for making love." He's not cheered up at all. My Jack cries.

Oh, now I get it. I woke up this morning and Jack left me a note. He's not going to stay in the Tetons, he's going away. He's going away and he's not coming back. He really isn't waiting for a year for a divorce. He lied. Again. He never even started to get a divorce. Now he's just gone. He says he knows I'll make a good mother, and he loves me, but he can't stay, and he's sorry. Jack, you son of a bitch. You rotten, fucking, no good son of a bitch. You liar! You yellow-bellied coward. I'm never going to believe a thing you say, again, not ever. What am I going to tell Joseph, that you're just a goddamned rotten liar?

I built a fire in the fireplace and just sat there. Drank gin and tonics. What am I going to do now? How could he lie so long? What is the damned thing here? 'Cause his wife's going to kill herself. I'm going to kill him, and then he won't have to worry about the whole damn problem. Never mind. Just never mind. Fuck you. I'll just do this myself. I'm sick of your goddamned lying and I'm sick of you disappearing all the time and I'm sick of you acting like you're such a good person when you're just a rat, that's what you are, a fucking rat! I hate it. Fact is, you don't care! I hate this. I hate liars. Besides that, he left his other kids. So he wouldn't mind leaving Joseph. Yoo Hoo, Louise — you are a dumb person.

What am I going to tell my baby? Your dad's a liar? I don't want to do that. I'm not going to do it. I'll be the liar.

I just sat, watched the fire, madder than a wet hen, drinking gin and tonics. Then I decide, it's almost noon, that I'm kinda drunk but not a lot, and I call Mrs. Smith at home, and I tell her that I'm pregnant and going to have a baby boy. She laughs, and says, "How do you know it's going to be a baby boy?"

I say, "'Cause I said so."

I tell her that Jack left, he went away, he left me a note.

She says, "I'd call that trouble, girl."

Trouble! Well, it's a big problem, but I've seen women at work pregnant, and she says, "Yeah, but they're married."

Oh, goddammit, I know they're married. She says, "They aren't going to let you work there pregnant."

"Why? Why, Mrs. Smith? Why aren't they going to let me work there pregnant?"

"Because you're not married. You can't work there if you're not married and you're pregnant. They think that bad people do that."

"What? Bad people? How could they think that when there are women up there that are pregnant?"

"Louise, you just aren't listening. They're married. If you're pregnant and you're not married, everybody thinks that you're bad."

Oh. I ask her if she thinks I'm bad, and she says no. But, she doesn't run the hospital, either.

"I know you don't run the hospital. I just want to know if you think I'm bad."

She says, "No, I don't think you're bad. But you're pregnant, and the whole world thinks that if you're not married, and you're pregnant, you're bad."

Bad girl. An unwed mother. Oh, Jesus, now I've really done it. She says, "Yeah, it looks like this time it's going to be a big problem."

"Where am I going to work? I could be a waitress again. I could work at a counter."

Mrs. Smith laughs and she says, "I've never met anyone like you. I'll talk to you at work tomorrow. As a matter of fact, tomorrow morning we'll just have coffee and talk it over, okay?"

Okay. She hangs up and the gin and tonics come back up. I really hate that. I don't have to work the rest of the day so I just sleep.

At night I sit there by the fire. I guess I just don't believe all of this. I keep waiting for Jack to walk back in the door because he was just mad and he changed his mind. I don't think that's going to happen. He didn't get a divorce so he can't marry me. I'm going to have this baby boy by myself. I can't work at the hospital. Mrs. Smith and I are going to figure out how long I can work and what I can do about this. I don't know what to do, except sit here and watch this fire. I don't even know where Jack is. I can't even go talk to him or tell him okay, we don't have to be married. Why do we have to be married, why do you have to go away? I want to know. We haven't been married the whole time and you didn't go away, Jack, so why do you have to leave now? I don't get it.

The next morning I do my throwing up and I go and meet Mrs. Smith for coffee. She says, "I know, you've told me that you don't have any family, but do you have any friends anywhere else?"

I say, "Yeah, I have a lot of friends that live in different states."

She says, "You know, it might be a good idea if you talked to 'em and see if you could go to a different state and work. Because they're not going to let you work at the hospital."

"Well, they let me work so far. They don't even know."

"Pretty soon," Mrs. Smith says, "pretty soon, Louise, you're going to start getting to look pregnant and they're going to fire you. Besides, you should quit before you get fired because it looks better. Like you're smart enough to know when to quit."

"Thanks a lot. Well, I have a friend from the army who's in California, and she says she makes a lot of money."

"Why don't you write to her and see if you can go out there and maybe you could make enough money out there to take care of yourself and the baby."

I love the sound of that. "The baby." Me and the baby. I like that. I'll take care of the baby. He's my baby!

I go to work as usual and I don't say anything to anybody, and I write Anita. She's in San Jose, California. She's in San Jose and she makes a lot of money and she writes back and tells me I could make enough money to take care of me and the baby. They have a thing called "electronics" out there and it's easy to learn how to do it and you can just make quite a lot of money, she said, and I could stay with her at first till I get a place of my own. Fine. Now what?

Well, I'm going to work out the rest of this month, get some money together. I'm going to go to California. That giant '55 DeSoto probably will crawl all the way. I have to get a map! I don't even know how to get there. I tell Mrs. Simpson about being pregnant and that I'm going to take the DeSoto and go to California, and she's really worried that the DeSoto will fall apart before I got there. I tell her not to worry, hell, I've been in worse fixes than this. Besides, I get to have a baby! Anything would be worth that. She just tells me, "God, girl, you're really something."

We don't know what yet, right? I know I'm something. God only knows what it is.

I pack up my car and I have breakfast with Mrs. Simpson and Mrs. Smith. They're really nice and they give me some little presents, a scarf and a little shirt. My friends. I'm going to go a place I've never even been, I don't even know what's there, but you know, when I went to Billings, Montana, I didn't know what was there either. Maybe this is another just lucky good thing. Maybe I'll get to California and it'll be a lucky good thing.

I get in my '55 DeSoto, my giant horrible crawling car, and I marked out on the map how I'm supposed to go, and I'm going. On the ride I took my apple butter and bread and a whole bunch of pork and beans and I have to remember not to eat anything in the morning. I have a coffee pot, but I have to build a fire for that, and they told me to keep looking for places you could stop at the side of the road — just pull over, make like a little fire place and make some coffee. I'm going to do that. I have my blankets in the back so all I do is curl up and go to sleep. This won't be so bad. It won't be so bad at all.

Since it's June, it makes it easier to travel in this '55 DeSoto because it's not cold. Except high in the mountains. I have to go across these passes, mountain passes. This car just crawls up 'em. It gets up 'em and that's the most important thing. Soon I'll be in a state called Nevada. I've been in a lot of states. I'm going to have a baby, finally.

Reno, Nevada is a gambling town. A lot of my friends in Wyoming talk about it. They go there and they put money in machines and they get money back. I'm going to try that when I get there. Mrs. Smith told me to take ten dollars and get some quarters and nickels and dimes and try the machines and don't use any more than ten dollars because if you start doing that, pretty soon all your money is gone and you don't have any more and you just have to stay there. When I get to Reno, I'm going to do that. Maybe I'll get a bunch of money.

For lunch it's my apple butter and bread, and for dinner it's pork and beans and bread. Then I drive until I'm really tired and then I pull over and I curl up in my blankets and go to sleep. When I get to California, if I can't make enough money, I could just sleep in the car. I could always make enough money to buy bread. That isn't hard. I can do this. I can make it.

Jack, you rotten shit. You no good, no ethics, man. I'm not even going to miss you, you shitass. Never damn mind you, anyway.

Holy cow, I've never seen so many lights in my whole life. This Reno, Nevada looks like a giant Christmas tree! There's lights everywhere! I don't know where to go with this ten dollars so I stop and get gas and ask the man at the gas station, "Where do I take my ten dollars?"

He says, "Anywhere. Any of these places will take your ten dollars and you can gamble, and see if you can win. Most people lose, though, so you better be careful."

I just drive up the street and I pick a place and I go in and I get money and I go to the machines. They do take your money. Then they give you money. Then they take your money. Then they give you money. It's really screwy. Give me the money or take my money! I was there all day. I finally don't have my ten dollars anymore. I'm going to go back tomorrow with one more dollar. After I get some sleep, I'll see if I can make some more money.

It's morning and I'm back at the machine. I finally have five dollars back. I'm leaving because you never know what these machines are going to do. I'm taking this five dollars, least I only lost six dollars, and I have five dollars back, so I'm just going to call it even and get the hell out of here. People are so drunk that they're sitting and laying on their machines and going to sleep. People with aprons on come around and wake 'em up and make 'em stop that. Then they give 'em another drink! Does that make any sense? They're drunk, you stupid ass, you keep giving 'em drinks, they're going to get drunker and lay on those machines and you're going to have to wake 'em up and then you have to give 'em another drink. The drinks are free! I had some gin and tonics. I'm going to take a nap and take my extra five dollars and go to California.

They told me in the casino that California is just a little ways away now. I can't wait—I hope this damned DeSoto gets there. It keeps crawling along. They say there's a huge mountain pass in California called Donner Pass, that my car might not make it over. I just think, Oh, never mind. If my car doesn't make it over Donner Pass, I'll live in Donner. They laugh, they say there isn't a Donner. It's just a pass. Well, then I'll just stay someplace else — I don't know! There's always a place to go, though. They agree with me about there always being a place to go, so I'm not worried. I'm thinking, though, that my DeSoto might not get over that Donner Pass, and there I'll be. They say you can always take a Greyhound bus. Yeah! I've taken a Greyhound bus before. I could do that. I still have all of the regular money I had.

The bartender gave me a gin and tonic for the road. Pretty neat guy, I thought. I got in my car and I start to drive and the tire's flat. I hate Jack. I keep screaming at the tire and screaming at Jack. I don't know what the hell my problem is, I'm just mad, I guess. I change the tire and I get on my way. I'm going to have to stop and get that tire patched. I better do it pretty soon because I don't want to get on that pass and have another flat, and no spare.

California

Don't ever take a '55 crawling DeSoto over Donner Pass. That is the slowest — I could have walked faster than that car got up that pass and down the other side. We were coming down the other side when I thought, what if the brakes don't hold? I have to pump the brakes to make 'em hold, but they held. It took me forever. I'm getting madder by the damn day, here. I was so mad after I got over the Donner Pass that I had to stop the car and throw a screaming-and-hit-the-car-fit. It felt great, though, when I was finished. Maybe that'll be a new way to feel better. I'll just throw a fit, kick the car a lot, pound on its tires, pound on the hood, run around it screaming, and I feel a lot better. I'm back on the road and I'm in California. I'm in California, but I still have a long way to go to Anita's. At least there's no more Donner Passes to go over. The fact is, there's no more passes the whole way. I just go straight on the road, no problem. This car crawls a lot, but it doesn't crawl on the straight-aways, it goes just fine.

I've never seen so many flowers on the road. This is California, and in California, in the middle of the road, they have a whole bunch of flowers that divides one side of the road from the other. You have to be really careful not to get on the other side of the road because all the cars on that side are coming right at you. They call these kinds of roads freeways, but at least you don't have to worry about somebody hitting you head on cause you're all going in the same direction, and these giant flower trees are in between you.

I hate getting up every morning and throwing up. I'm getting tired of it. Mrs. Smith told me that it doesn't take very long for the throwing up to quit, but this isn't quitting yet. First I have to go through San Francisco and then I go down 101 Highway to San Jose. In San Francisco it's a nightmare. That's the worst damn place I've ever been. I made a U-turn on a street and they gave me a ticket. They say you can't make U-turns here on the street like that. They make U-turns in Wyoming anywhere we goddamn well please, and here you can't make a U-turn like that. Pretty bizarre, I'd say. It scared me half to death. Tomorrow morning I'm going to drive down to San Jose and tonight I'm just going to park this stupid car and sleep. I get up in the morning and throw up like usual and then I'm going to San Jose with my ticket. I don't know how I'm supposed to pay for this ticket, either. I'll ask Anita.

That cop was really mad. He told me that in California you don't do anything like you do in Wyoming. He said, "This is The City. You're not out in the sticks now."

Asshole! I told him, "Hey, I don't care if I'm out in the sticks or not. Just give me the ticket and leave me alone."

He told me to shut up and not smart off. He gave me the ticket, and then he drove away. I mean, who's going to argue with him, he's wearing a gun! Stupid person.

California is really different from Wyoming. There's trees and flowers and the houses have giant windows and giant sliding glass doors. At Anita's, you walk out the sliding glass door and you're on a thing called the patio, then you can look right down and they have a pool you can swim in anytime you want. You can look out the giant windows they have here and see everything!

Anita has a roommate named Terry. Terry's a nurse. Anita works for an electronics place. It's called Fairchild. Fairchild is the electronics plant that I'm going to work in. Anita's going to get me a job there. I told her I have to work in the afternoon or at night because I throw up every morning. She just laughed.

She says, "If you got up earlier, you could throw up earlier, feel better earlier, and work during the day. They'll probably put you on nights anyway because that's the shift that they have open."

On the corner down about two blocks they have a gas station and grocery store and a bar. The first thing I do is go down and make friends with the gas station and the grocery store and the bar. I feel really lost. This place is huge. I mean, everywhere you look there's houses. Anita says they have country here where you can get out of town, we're going to see it when she gets days off the same as mine. Anita says I should see a doctor about being pregnant, and I say, "What's to see? I already know I'm pregnant."

She says, "No, I mean, so you're healthy."

Okay. I'll see a doctor. First I have to get a job and some money because I don't have any more money.

I go for an interview at Fairchild and I get the job. I'm going to be a die attacher. You attach dies, little microscopic things that have gold on the back to the tops of things called headers. Then they put 'em in things like TVs and cameras. They pay you for doing a certain amount of headers per day. My first day of work I thought I was going to go blind. You look through this microscope and these little teeny tiny things called dies, you attach a certain way with the little dots going a certain way, with tweezers. I work really hard. I have to get some money. I'm going to have my baby!

Anita and Terry work during the day, and I sleep in Anita's room at night and Terry and Anita sleep together. I offered to sleep on the couch, but they said they like to sleep together. I have my room and they have their room. I have to wait until I get paid, I have to see the doctor, and then I have to start looking for a place of my own.

The doctor says I'm in great shape. He asks me about the father and I say, "He left."

The doctor says, "That's too bad, what're you going to do after you have the baby?"

I say, "I haven't thought of that yet, but I'm going to figure something out."

He tells me there's a thing called welfare, and I say, "Oh, no you don't. My mother used to do that, and we all went hungry all the time."

He says, "It's different in California. When you go on welfare, you can actually live. They actually give you money."

Maybe that's what I'll do after I have the baby.

Anita says they have a place called Agnews State Hospital, and maybe I could use my certificate, my psychiatric certificate, and get a job there because it pays a lot more money. I went out to Agnews and they don't accept my certificate! What do you mean, you won't accept it? The guy says, "It doesn't count. You have to have a California certificate." I ask him how I get one. He says, you have to go to school. School? I'm not going to school. He says I could use my nurse's aide certificate, though, because part of it's from the army. The medical corpsman certificate means that I'm a nurse's aide in California. They accept one certificate and they don't accept the other one. I ask him what the hell that meant. Why are they just doing that? He says, "Well, that's just the rules," and, "too bad."

I leave, get in my car, swear at him all the way home, get home and keep thinking, I can do welfare just long enough for the baby to get bigger. I'll have to pay for baby-sitters because Anita and Terry can't do it. We already talked about it. I have to get a baby-sitter and they cost almost as much as you make at Fairchild. I have got to figure out something here. I'm not supposed to have the baby until the end of December, though. What a Christmas present!

I have a lot of time to think this over. Anita and Terry tell me all the stuff I have to pick up for the baby, and I say, "I'm not buying any of that. Lots of babies are born dead, and whatever. I'm not buying anything until the baby Joseph is right here."

I found a place to live, but it's just a porch that they made into an apartment. It has a stove and refrigerator and a little tiny bathroom, with this itsy bitsy shower. You have to stand up, there's no bathtub. I guess when I have the baby, I could just put 'em in there with me, and hold on to him, to wash him off.

Terry, Anita and Goodwill

Terry and Anita bought a little bathtub, and they bought some diapers, and gave 'em to me. I went down to the Goodwill store, Anita showed me where it was, and I got a bassinet. It's a little tiny cradle crib-like thing, and I could put it right by my bed. Soon as I get a bed. Then I had to bring it home and paint it white because it was really dirty. This Goodwill place has all sorts of things I can have. It's almost like the dump in a store. I can go there and everything costs a lot less because it's stuff other people used and didn't want anymore so they gave it to the Goodwill. I wonder how come nobody in Wisconsin or Wyoming thought of that Goodwill idea. Maybe they did and I don't know about it.

I get the bassinet and paint it white. It used to have legs on it, but it doesn't have legs on it anymore so I'm just going to sit it on the floor.

Today Anita and Terry bring me a little teeny tiny dog. You can hold it in your hand, it's so small. They say it's a cross between a Chihuahua and a toy poodle. I keep looking at this little black thing and you can't tell what's the front or the back of it until it barks. When it barks, it makes me laugh. It's the tiniest bark I've ever heard in my whole life. Sounds more like a squeak. I'm going to name him Sam. He bounces around on my lap, he's so tiny! Sometimes you can't find him, he's so little. He gets behind stuff and I can't get him out. He just whines and pisses me off, so I carry him around in my shirt, and then he cannot get lost and I don't have to get mad. I decided that since the sides of two walls are all glass that I'll have to make curtains for 'em. If I don't want anybody to see in, I can close the curtains. There's mold on the inside of the windows and I scrub it off but it's already coming back.

Outside I have a little yard. The people next to me have the bigger yard. Here there's lots of wood laying around and all these houses look like they're going to fall down, they don't look anything like Anita's and Terry's. There's a lot of rocks and wood so I'm going to make a garden. Every morning before I go to work, after I throw up, I go out and arrange the rocks and I put dirt in between the rocks and then I water it and the next day I do it all again.

I'm going to have a great big rock garden in the corner of my little yard. It bothers me when the cars come by my window. I could reach right out and grab the driver by the neck if those porch windows opened. But they don't. The only thing that opens is the door.

Every time I get paid I go to the Goodwill store and get a couple of things I'm going to need when I have this baby. I have a chair now, and I have a little rug on the floor, and I have a mattress. That mattress puts me right about even with the bassinet so if I look in there I'll see the baby. I bought a little doll, one of those plastic baby dolls, and I'm practicing pinning diapers on it. I think it's smaller than a brand new baby is. I practice pinning it without stabbing the doll so that when my little baby boy gets here I won't stab him either. But I know that babies wiggle around a lot and this doll just lays there.

My friend calls Sam a "hairy pot roast." He's about as big as a pot roast now. He has these teeny tiny little legs. If he puts his tail down you still can't tell if he's coming or going. He's a crack up. Anything that happens, though, if somebody drives by, or somebody rattles my door, or anything happens at night, Sam starts to bark that goofy bark and it wakes me up. I think that's good because if the baby wakes up, then Sam will have a fit and I'll wake up. That way I won't sleep so hard that I won't hear the baby. Anita says she never met anybody who sleeps as hard as I do.

My rock garden is really looking good. I'm going to get some seeds and plant flowers but I can't plant any vegetables. There's not enough room and the ground is hard as a rock. I'll just plant some flowers. Back home I could plant a whole garden and I could feed my baby because I planted it and canned it and took care of it. You can't do that in California, there's no land. Anita says that I should marry a farmer, and I say I'm not marrying anybody. There's not a goddamned man alive that I'll trust ever again. Anita says, "I know the feeling."

I'm really surprised. Come to think of it, she never even has men around. I ask her why, and she says because she doesn't like 'em. All they want to do is get laid and that's it and she hates it.

I said, "Me too! Me too, and besides that, they lie. They're always lying to me."

She says, "Everybody lies. People who lie are liars. People who don't lie are not liars."

We laughed a lot about that. I said, "No shit, Anita! Wow. That's brilliant. How did you figure that one out!"

We just keep laughing.

Anita says, "Why do you want a boy baby so bad if you don't like men?"

I say, "I didn't say I don't like men. I said I don't like horny liars. Besides, what the hell does that have to do with a boy baby?"

She says, "'Cause he's going to grow up to be a man."

"He's not going to grow up to be a horny liar man. He's not going to grow up to be a man who doesn't keep his word and does bad things. He's going to grow up to be a good man with ethics."

Anita says, "Did you ever meet a good man?"

I say, "Yes!"

Anita says, "Well, I haven't yet."

I say, "That's terrible, Anita. You should go down to the bar. The bartender's a really nice guy."

Anita laughs and says, "You know sometimes you sound like you're a wise old person, and sometimes you sound like a little kid."

"Thanks a lot, Anita, but what the hell does that mean?"

She says, "Well, I don't know. There's an old saying like you're too old to be so young, and too young to be so old? I think that fits you."

I think I've heard that somewhere before but I don't remember where. Anyway, I don't know what the hell to do about it, I guess I'm just like this. Anita laughs and says, "You don't need to change. We like you just the way you are."

I tell Anita about Mr. Sawyer, and he was a really neat man. About some of the truck drivers, and she says, "Yeah, they're really neat men. They're not sleeping with you. When men sleep with you, they get stupid. That's why I don't sleep with 'em."

"Anita, how're you going to have a baby, then, ever, if you don't sleep with any of 'em?"

She says, "I'm not. I'm not going to have any babies. Everybody doesn't have to have a baby, Louise."

"I know that, Anita, I just want everybody to have a baby if they want one. I mean, you have to sleep with a man, but you don't have to be with him forever. I mean, look at me, Jack just ran off and I'm still pregnant. It isn't like they take the baby with 'em, you know."

Anita laughs. She says, "You're a nut, you know, you're the zaniest nut I've ever known. Even when we were in the army, you were a nut."

I say, "How do you know? We hardly ever even talked to each other in the army."

She says, "Aw, bull, I laughed a lot, everything you said cracked us all up. I really liked you in the army. I still like you."

"Good Anita because I like you too."

I finally buy the dresser. Anita shows me how to turn the top of it into a thing to lay the baby on and wash him off because you can't throw babies in the tub right away when you get 'em home. You wash 'em off and then you change their diapers right on top of the dresser. In the top two drawers are all my treasures for this baby boy I'm going to have. Anita asks me what I'm going to do if it's a girl? I say, "It's not going to be a girl, so don't worry about it. I said I can't raise a girl because I'm not a girl very good myself. I don't know what girls really do and don't do." Anita says that I'm out of my mind. She says, "You're a girl, you act like a girl, and you do know what girls do because you're a girl."

"Never mind, Anita, just never damn mind. I know how to do a boy better, though, I think. I think I'm going to be better at that. So never mind, I'm having a boy."

Anita says, "You don't get to say which you're going to have a boy or girl."

I say, "Anita, I know it's a boy. I just know it, that's all."

I'm getting bigger and bigger and bigger. I only have two more months to go and my baby boy will be here. Anita told me to tell the people at work that I was married when I got the job. They ask me why I never talk about my husband, and I laugh to myself because I think, well, let's see, so I tell 'em. "Well, that's because he's just nothing." Everybody laughs. Everybody talks about their husbands, so when I say my husband's just a nothing, they don't know that I mean that I don't even have one, and they all think it's funny. Who cares? As long as I don't get fired for being an unwed mother. It's so dumb. I mean, if you're a good mother, that's all that should count. Anita says everybody feels like that. I don't believe that — I think some people don't like unwed mothers. I'm an unwed mother — shoot me. Then shut up and piss off.

It's December and I put in my notice at Fairchild that I'm quitting. I have enough money to live for a whole month after my baby comes, and then I have to find a different job. Anita says to go around to the nursing homes since I can be a nurse's aide, and she says she swears I'm the only one she's ever met who threw up every morning for nine months. Anita thinks I should have seen the doctor more than just the one time, but I can't afford to see the doctor. I have to be saving up so I can stay home long enough for the baby to get used to me, and then I can take him to the baby-sitter. First I'm going to have to get another job or do welfare. I think I'll do the welfare thing — I don't want anybody else taking care of my little new boy. Anita and Terry bring me a lot of new things for my baby. Little rattles and little sweaters and little booties. I can't wait till he gets here. I hope he looks like Jack. I like the way Jack looks. I hope he isn't an asshole like Jack, though.

I'm so excited. This baby's supposed to be here right around Christmas time. It's only a little few days away. Come on, baby boy! Show up. Do some crying so I can change you and talk to you. We have your own private hairy pot roast dog when you get here. It runs around the house barking at everything that moves.

I scrape off all of the moss, the junk that grows on the inside of this porch because they say it's not good for babies. I use bleach. It works really good. Scrub and scrub. It's going to grow back, and I'm just going to take it right back off.

I talk to this baby who's sitting in my stomach waiting. I sing to him when I'm by myself. I feel like I already love him and he's not here yet. What a strange thing. I mean, just think about it. He's in there, hanging around, making me fat as a hog. For two months now I can't even see my damn feet. I go to bend over, there's no way. When I sit down, I have to sit down with my legs really wide apart, make room for that giant belly I'm dragging around. Pregnant! Fat as a pig. I have this one outfit called "maternity outfit." I have to wash it out every night. I like it, it's comfortable. He's going to be here pretty soon.

I met some people who live in the back cabins behind my porch, a couple called Laura and Teddy. Teddy's in the navy. There is a big navy base here. Laura's from Newfoundland, which is up farther than Canada, and they're really friendly. They bring me things, and talk to me, and we just hang out. Every once in a while Teddy has to leave on his ship and Laura's all by herself. She said maybe next time he gets shipped out, she and I can stay together. That would be really neat! There's a great big giant man who lives back there in one of the cabins and he always tells me he likes seeing pregnant women. I think he's an asshole, but I don't tell him that. I just say okay, you like seeing pregnant women. He asks me if I was going to nurse my baby when it got here and I say, "Of course! At first you have to nurse 'em."

Even I know that. Besides, who could afford to do anything but nurse him? See, the only way I can take all this time to be with the baby is because I'm going to nurse him because he'd cost too much. I wouldn't be able to pay for formula or milk.

It's the first of January. No baby. He's still in there. Anita says I should go to the doctor, so I did. The doctor says he'll come out when he wants to. The doctor says maybe we didn't get when you got pregnant right, and so then he says, "When's the last time you could've possibly gotten pregnant?"

I figure it out. This baby should be born right now.

The doctor says, "Well, then, that means that you're late."

"Late? I'm late? How did I get late?"

"Well, I mean, the baby is just staying in there longer than nine months."

"What the hell for?"

"Sometimes," the doctor says, "babies come early or they come late. They do whatever they want. Is this your first pregnancy?"

"Yes, it's my first pregnancy. What the hell? I told you I didn't have any other babies."

"Or you could have had a miscarriage."

"I didn't have anything. This is my first pregnancy."

He says, "Well, sometimes in the first pregnancy you just can't tell what the baby's going to do."

"Well, can you hear his heart beating?"

The doctor assured me he's in there, he's alive, and besides I can feel him kicking. He sticks his foot up in my ribs and I have to sit arched backwards for awhile while he exercises. If he wants some extra room, he should get born, he can have all the room he wants. My little baby boy hates broccoli. Anita said broccoli was good for me, so I tried eating 'em — that little baby boy wiggles around more than ever, and makes my stomach hurt. He also doesn't like it when I try to bend over. I swear every time I try to bend over he stands up.

Anita thinks I'm out of my damn mind. She says, "Babies don't do that. You're just making that up."

So what? I can make up anything I want. He better hurry up and get here, though, or the money I saved isn't going to last long enough.

Baby Joseph

I couldn't sleep at all last night. I have a backache and I just feel really weird. My back hurts like hell. This morning I told Anita and Terry about it so they stopped by.

Terry said, "Maybe you're in labor."

"Maybe I'm in labor?"

"The baby's going to come any day or any minute."

"Any minute? Should I go to the hospital?"

"Yes!"

They took off for work. I'm going to get in my car. They gave me directions for the hospital. It's called the Valley Medical Center. It's the only hospital that will take me.

I cleaned up my little porch and got ready to drive to the hospital. Now I don't think I can do that. These things — these pains — Terry told me they're contractions — that's when your body is getting ready to push the baby out. They hurt so bad! They happen so often, that I can't really walk around very good. Besides, they make me holler and hold still. How can I drive like this? I'll just have to do it, that's all. I go outside and the two guys next door are taking the garbage cans to the street so the garbage men'll pick 'em up. They say "Hi" and I start to say hi and I have another contraction. I'm leaning against the door crouching down and they started laughing. I hate them. I'm too worried to tell 'em off. I just have to get to my car and get to that Valley Medical Center. I tell 'em I have to go to the hospital, I'm in labor, and one of 'em says, "That's what happens when you get pregnant." No kidding! Another brilliant person heard from. I get to my car and it's a long drive to this hospital. I keep thinking that I'm not going to make it, but I make it.

I get there and I go into the emergency room and I tell 'em that I'm going to have a baby.

The nurse says, "That's pretty obvious."

She feels my stomach and she says, "You certainly are."

They put me in the hospital and they take my clothes and they give me this gown — I hope they don't do anything awful to me. I'm really not too scared — I just have to stay wide awake so they can't take the baby away from me or do anything I don't like.

Boy, do these pains hurt. I hear other women behind the other curtains hollering at the top of their lungs. I guess it hurts everybody. My mom told me it was really terrible. Mrs. Sawyer told me it was terrible, but it's worth it, and it's only terrible for a little while, and boom! You have the baby. I can do it.

It has been a long time with this pain, I'm tired of it. I feel like slapping everybody who comes in here to talk to me. Goddammit, baby boy, get in this world and knock it off! Pain everywhere, all over me. They keep checking to see if I'm dilated enough, which means, did I open up enough to let the baby out. Then they come in and they put something around me and give me a shot. Why are you giving me a shot? The doctor says it's called a saddle block. So you won't be in so much pain.

I said, "I don't want to do — I wanted to — is it going to put me to sleep?"

"No."

"Okay, okay. Never mind."

Since they gave me this shot, my legs hurt really bad. I called for the nurse and a nurse's aide came. I told her that my legs hurts. She rolled up the bed a little bit. That feels a lot better. I can barely breathe. I push the button for the nurse again. A nurse comes in and practically yells, "What the hell is the bed doing up?"

I feel like I'm going to die. She rolls the bed down and sits me up. They bring in ice and put it around my waist. What the hell is going on — my baby is going to freeze to death, quit it! They said you're never supposed to put your feet up when you have a saddle block, it makes all the stuff go to your chest! "Well, the nurse's aide did that, I didn't do it. What's the hell's the matter with her?"

They said, "Never mind, it'll be all right."

Now they have my bed up — I'm sitting up. I have to sit up for awhile till all of it goes back where it's supposed to.

I took off the ice. They're not freezing my baby, that's that. I threw it on the floor. They came back in a little while later to check me. I'm okay. They're going to put my bed back down. They were really mad at me for throwing the ice on the floor, but I don't care, we're not freezing my baby. Some more labor. I've been shaking from head to toe all day. They said that the labor has stopped. How could it just stop? Well, it's probably a big problem with the saddle block and everything. They put me in a room, I'm going to stay overnight in this hospital. Anita and Terry came by, they found out where I was, and they brought me some flowers and a gift to take the baby home in, with blankets! I love them. I love this. I feel terrible. I want Joseph to hurry up and do the labor thing with me and get in this world and quit acting up. It's already a damn month later than I thought it would be.

Well, it's about three in the morning. I'm tired. I'm in labor again. Come on, Joseph. Just be born, okay? Don't be pissing me off. About five o'clock, I'm still in labor. I'm leaving. I hate this hospital, I hate this baby, I hate everybody. This isn't going right, I'm not happy with this, I'm going home, and when this damn baby can get it straight when he wants to be born, then I'll come back. I get up and I go over to get my maternity clothes and get the hell out of here, and the nurse comes in and asks me what I'm doing, and I told her, "I'm going home till this baby decides it's really going to be here. I'm sick of this, I don't want to be in labor anymore, I'll come back when he wants to be born."

She says, "You can't leave the hospital."

I said, "I don't want to do this anymore, and I'm not going to do it! Get out of my way!"

She put her arms on my shoulders and she said, "If you go, you are taking the labor pains and the baby with you. Do you understand that? You're going to feel the exact same way at home with nobody to help you."

I hadn't thought of that. I'm so tired I'm not thinking straight. Okay, fine, I'll stay here.

It's seven thirty the next morning, I'm going in the delivery room. Joseph's going to show up. My little boy is going to finally just show up. By now the shots have worn off, and all of this hurts like hell. After a lot of yelling and crying and pushing and yelling and crying and pushing, they lay my little baby boy on my tummy. He turns toward me, he looks like he's putting his arms out to me. I tell him hello. He's here. It's my little teeny tiny baby boy.

The nurse picks him up and I grab her arm. "Where are you going with him?"

She says, "We have to clean him up, he'll be in the nursery and you can see him in a little while."

The doctor starts sewing me up. There's another doctor behind him telling him how to do it. They do that about three times. They take the stitches and put 'em in and then they take them out. They talk about how I was torn pretty badly, so there's three sets of stitches. This is the third time they're doing it because one doctor teaching the other how to do this. I leaned up, practically sat up, and I said, "Never mind. Leave it. I'll fix it myself."

I try to get off the table, but they have the leg stirrup things strapped to me. Both of the guys started laughing, and they said, "Okay, okay, this is the last time." They sewed me up and sent me back to my room. I went to sleep. When I wake up I'm going right out there and get my baby boy and go home. I was right, too, it's a baby boy.

It's afternoon and they bring me this little tiny thing. Talk about wrecked! No teeth, no hair, he's long, very long, and skinny. He looks like a little old shriveled up man. He won't eat. I tried to breast feed and he won't eat. Maybe he doesn't like me.

They come in to take him back to the nursery. The nurse said that lots of times they don't eat for a couple of days. Maybe he likes me and he's just doing that. Not eating for a couple of days because he doesn't feel like it.

Social Worker

A social worker comes in to talk to me. A dreaded social worker? She asks me a lot of questions. I don't have any family and I don't have any money and on and on and on. I can be on welfare. She fills out a bunch of papers, and I sign 'em. Every month now I get some money, she said, and I get some medical care, whatever my baby needs and whatever I need. She gave me a little book that tells me about his belly button and his tiny little head gets this crust on it they call cradle cap, and how often to feed him, and the signs to worry about like if he gets a high fever or whatever. She gave me all of that and said that every month she'll come to my place and check on me.

She said it was a pretty courageous thing I was doing, and that it would be very hard, taking care of this baby by myself. She says it's too bad my baby doesn't have a father. I ask her how in the hell she thinks I got pregnant, if he doesn't have a father. She says that she means he doesn't have one at home. She just pisses me off.

I tell her, "Big goddamned deal, I had a father and all he did was hit us, yell a lot, and run off. Sometimes having a father at home is just as bad because they molest you, and hit you, and don't take care of you. Some dads are good and some are just bad."

She asked me if I knew that I could give Joseph away for adoption. Adoption? I waited for this baby boy forever. I should give him away now? I tell her she's out of her fucking mind. She doesn't say anything. She looks really surprised. Then I tell her that I'm going to take good care of him and he's my family now. I get to have a family. She tells me how much hard work it is and how she'll keep checking on me. She asks me if I had anybody to help me.

I said, "He's going to be all I do so I don't need any help."

She says, "When you go home, you're going to be very tired and he's going to wake up in the middle of the night and want to eat a lot. He might wake up a lot during the night."

I told her that I'll wake up a lot during the night, I can't sleep with the baby howling anyway. She just looked at me. I don't think she believes I can take care of this baby. If they're going to give me money every month, then I can take him to the doctor if anything goes wrong, I don't know why I can't take care of him.

They let me out of the hospital. I take my little baby Joseph and I put him in the front seat of my '55 DeSoto, and I drive him to his new home. I've forgotten about my little hairy pot roast dog. Anita and Terry had come by and fed him every day that I was gone.

Joseph seems so small. Everything on him is so — tiny. But what's not tiny on him is his mouth. He can holler, you can hear him for blocks and I know it. I bring him in the house and I put him in the little bassinet I bought him, and Anita and Terry drive up just as I'm going in the door, and they take a picture of me with him. Anita and Terry had cleaned up my house while I was gone, and they put a rug on the floor, a really pretty rug, so it won't be so cold. They said I can play with the baby on the floor without being afraid of him getting slivers from the wood. I'm tired. The place where I had so many stitches hurts like hell, too. I walked in that door with this little teeny tiny baby, and I go to sit down, and I can't. There's no sitting down. Stitches in your crotch makes you go straight from sitting to laying. When I got in the car I screamed like hell when I sat down. You can do it if you really have to, but it hurts. I mean, I either need to be standing up or laying down. Of course, the baby won't care, he can't tell what the hell I'm doing.

The social worker was right. He wakes up a lot. Two or three times a night. I'm so tired. I feel like throwing him outside till he stops that waking up at night. I sleep when he does. At six, eight, and ten in the morning I change his diapers and I feed him. At noon I wash him all over. The book says he's supposed to be hungry every two and a half to three hours. The book says to try to make him wait. He's hungry every two hours, like clockwork. I'm just going to feed him, I can't stand listening to him holler. When I feed him every two hours, he doesn't cry at all. He fusses a little bit if he's wet or dirty, and he fusses when he's hungry, but he doesn't scream like he was doing at first if I feed him every two hours. I wonder if the rest of the stuff in this book is true, or if they just made up their minds and wrote it down like they do for religion. Anita said God gave me this baby. Are you ready for that? Anita, you screwball. Jack gave me this baby. I didn't sleep with God. I told Anita I get to have welfare, and they also make sure that the baby and I get medical care if we need it.

Anita asked me, "Well, what did you put on the birth certificate as the father?"

I told her that the woman in the bed next to me warned me not to put any name down there because the welfare people would go and arrest him or make him pay for the baby or whatever. I put "Name Withheld." Then Anita says, "Well, what's going to happen when he gets older and his father's name's not on the birth certificate?"

I said, "The lady who was taking the information about the birth certificate at the hospital said that I could change the name withheld any time I wanted to. When he gets older I'll tell him who his father is, and then if he wants his name on there, I'll put it on there."

I'm afraid of this little tiny baby Joseph. I'm afraid I'm going to break his teeny little fingers when I put him in his shirt, and I'm afraid I'm going to pick him up wrong or put him down wrong or not feed him enough. I can't even tell if he's healthy or not. The social worker said to watch to see if he gained weight. Well, I want you to know, he's chubby! He's only been home with me a month and he's chubby. He doesn't look like a skeleton anymore so that must mean he's healthy. Plus he just looks around and he's happy. The hairy pot roast dog is happy with him, too. Anytime the little baby moves, the hairy pot roast is standing with his little feet on the bassinet. He can reach the top of the bassinet but he can't get in it because I'll take his head off. He looks down at Joseph squawking, barks away, whines and carries on, so at night whenever Joseph wakes up, he wakes up. I wake up first, then the dog starts making noises. I can't believe I wake up so easy, I usually sleep through everything. Maybe spirit guides shake me because I have a baby I have to take care of. I'm going to do a good job. I just have to figure out what to do and just do it.

Anita gave me this book by Dr. Spock. I want you to know, I can't talk to Joseph like they say. I don't want to talk like that. If little Joseph, when he gets older, starts doing weird things, I'm going to tell him to fucking knock it off. Dr. Spock, a man, too. I'll bet he doesn't ever take care of a baby but the way they want you to talk to 'em in this book is really weird. It's like, "Now Joseph, please don't do such and such." I'm going to say, "Joseph, quit that." That's what I'm going to do.

Men don't take care of babies, so I don't know what they think that they know about it. The doctor at the hospital, when I was in labor, told me that it didn't hurt that much when I was hollering.

He said, "Oh, you know, every woman goes through this and it isn't that bad."

I really told that dumb fool to fuck off.

"It isn't that bad, right? You've been pregnant so many times, it's just an amazement to you why we holler about having labor, everybody in all the cubicles is hollering, dumb ass!"

He left. Then I started to yell at the nurse.

"How the hell would he know whether this hurts very much? He's never had a baby. Stupid man. Never did anything of the kind."

The nurse just laughed, and she said, "Yeah, I don't know why they think they know what's it like to have a baby because they just don't."

Anyway, never mind the Dr. Schmuck book. I'm not doing anything it says in there. I'm also tired of staying in the house and taking care of baby Joseph, but I don't dare say anything because people will think I don't want him. I want him, I'm just tired of this. All I do every day is feed him and change him and wash him off and feed him and change him and wash him and lay down whenever he does.

The social worker's back for a visit. She wants to know the name of the father. I ask her why? She says because then he can pay for the baby instead of the welfare paying for the baby. I say, "How can you make him do that?"

She says, "Well, we get a court order and then we get —" And I think, a court order? I'm not doing that. Jack doesn't want to take this baby and he doesn't want to get a divorce and he doesn't want anything and I'm the dumbbell who believed him. I'm not doing a court order. Besides, Jack would hate me forever. I tell her I'm not doing any court order.

She says, "You don't understand. If you don't do the court order, if you don't give us the name of the baby's father, then we're not going to give you welfare."

I say, "What do you do if a person doesn't even know the name of the baby's father?"

She says, "That isn't true with you, you put on the birth certificate 'Name Withheld'."

I tell her, "I did that because they said you could change that. If you put 'Unknown', you can't change that."

"Well, you put 'Withheld' on the birth certificate, so you do know the name of the father."

I ask her, "What the hell am I going to do if I'm not doing welfare. I don't have any money, at all."

She says, "Well, I don't know, but the law says that if you don't give us the name of the father, we don't give you welfare."

Then she tells me again that I can give Joseph to somebody else to take care of.

I say, "I'm not adopting him to anybody. I want him and I'm keeping him."

She says, "No, I mean a foster home. You can put him in a foster home until you get your own money —"

I can't even let her finish the sentence. I just stand up and tell her to get out, I'm not putting him in a foster home, I'm not doing anything of the kind, I'm just going to take care of him and he's mine. She just looks at me, starts packing up her papers, and tells me I'm making a mistake. It's hard enough to take care of a baby, but it's even worse if you don't have any help and you don't have any money.

I say, "I can do it. I'll just think of something. I always think of something."

She leaves. Now I'm sitting here thinking of something. But I don't know what the hell to do.

DeSoto Nursery

I take the baby and walk back to the back cabin to see Laura and Teddy. Teddy isn't home. I ask Laura if she'd watch the baby during his nap times, you know, like I feed him, and then in two hours I'll be back. I'm going to go see about the nursing home that I wanted to work in. She says she'll watch Joseph while I was working and I can save up. That's what I'm doing. Tomorrow, I'm going to get up, go to that nursing home, and get a job.

At the nursing home, they're glad to see me. Somebody just quit so I have the job. I have to be at work at six in the morning and I get off at two in the afternoon. I go back home and Laura said she'd be glad to help me. Teddy is supposed to be back this weekend, so he can help her. I start work tomorrow. I'll be glad to get out of this damn place and go do something else, instead of just feed the baby and wash the baby and look at the baby. I love this baby, but I'm tired of doing this.

Sometimes I hate this baby, too, it's true. I'm not going to tell anybody that, but sometimes I feel like throwing him outside. Shut the fuck up and go play or something. I'll be glad when he can just go play. I don't have to entertain him. I mean, how much can you do, just staring at him goo-goo-gooing yourself senseless. It makes me nuts.

The nursing home is really neat. It's not like the Geriatrics at the Wyoming State Hospital — they take good care of the people, and they get 'em up and move 'em around in chairs, and they feed them all at the table, and talk to 'em and laugh with 'em. They're geriatrics but it doesn't smell terrible and feel terrible and nobody has to just lay in their bed and scream and cry for nothing because nobody cares. People care about these people.

Right now I only get one day off a week because they're short handed. I work — I'm going to be working at this nursing home for six days a week, only off one.

Oh, goddammit. Teddy's back, and they're shipping him out. This time Laura's going with him. Now what am I going to do? Nobody else here can baby-sit, I checked. I don't know what to do. I have to go to this job or I won't be able to feed him or me. Laura says she'll baby-sit until next week when they both leave. I can't believe this is happening. Baby Joseph looks fat and happy. I don't have a baby-sitter. I don't have any money yet either. The money I'm going to make will just barely take care of us, and pay for the porch and pay for our food. I have to think this over. I wish I could just take him with me to work. I check at the nursing home, I don't really ask 'em, I just kinda say, "Well, what would happen if somebody brought their baby here?"

The boss says, "That wouldn't happen. Nobody can bring their baby here."

Maybe I was wrong. You can't just do what you want. Babies are really a lot of work. Maybe I was wrong, maybe you do have to have a man, maybe that's — that can't be. Other people don't — husbands run off all the time. My mother did the only taking care of us that was done, not my dad. I've gotta think of something.

I woke up with it this morning and I got it. There's a lot of wood around here. I'm going to make the back of that damned '55 DeSoto into a little room for baby Joseph, and then on my breaks at work, I'll go out and feed him because all he does is eat and sleep anyhow. He can't even sit up. That's what I'm going to do.

I get the flat part made so that this board goes all the way up to the front seat, and it has little legs it sits on, it rests on this back seat and has little legs on the floor that hold it up. I made sure there's no way he can get caught in it. I cut up the rug that Anita and Terry gave me, and I put the rug down on the boards so he can't get scratched and he can't get out. Then I put tape over the handles of the door and then I put curtains on the windows. I have to be able to see out the back window a little bit. If I put curtains around then I cut a hole in 'em, one in the back so I can see out when I'm driving. He can't climb up, so he can't get to anything, and he can't roll down the windows, and he can't unlock the doors. Then I just go out and feed him and change him. I have to leave the window a little bit open. He has to have some air. What about if he gets really cold? I stop by the Goodwill place, they have those pajamas with feet in 'em. I buy two of 'em. I'll just dress him in these every day because even if his covers come off, he won't get cold and I won't be there to put his covers back on. He can't get down behind the seats, he can't get wedged between or anything, I fixed it so he can't do anything to hurt himself.

Today's the day I try it out. Laura and Teddy shipped out yesterday. I didn't have to work. Today's my new day with baby Joseph in his new room in the back of the DeSoto. This is really fucking scary. I parked the car at work so it's right outside the nurse's station. If he starts to cry, I'll hear him. I'll be out there in a minute. I hope nobody else hears him.

This is great, I'm already late for work. He decided to cry just as I was pulling in, so I backed out, parked the car, fed him some food, some milk, drove around the block, after I burped him, changed his diaper, and then he went to sleep. I ran into work and I said "I'm sorry I'm late." Nobody said anything. On my break I went out and the window is down a little so he can have fresh air, but you can't really hear him cry very well. I really don't like that. I usually work on the right side of the building, so while I'm out on my break I turn the car around and park it on the right side. This time I open the windows in the front and the back that face the windows of the nursing home. I don't want him to be outside hollering at the top of his lungs and thinking I don't care about him. I changed where I parked the car and then I ran back in after I fed him and changed him and burped him. He burps good. Laura told me that she has a friend whose baby never burps—all he does is throw up. Uck. Baby Joseph spits up all the time, you just have to keep wiping him off with a wet cloth. He doesn't seem to care that he spits up. I care that he spits up. Sometimes I lift him up like I'm playing with him and he spits up all over me. Fun.

The boss at work lets me take a fifteen minute break every two hours. She doesn't know why. I don't tell her. I just ask her instead of lunch could I just have a fifteen minute break every two hours. I'm so tired, I can hardly get up to go to work. I feed baby Joseph before we leave, right before we leave, then at eight o'clock in the morning I get a break, at ten o'clock I get a break, and at noon I get a break and at two I get off. It works out great. He gets a little fussy here and there, I can hear him through the window, so I strung up a bunch of toys on a string between the windows so he can play or look at 'em. He whacks at 'em a lot, smacks 'em around at home, so I thought maybe he'd like it in his car nursery. He's almost like playing with a kitten. If you dangle things, he swats at 'em. I strung those up so maybe he can be happier. It seems to be working out. I wonder how it'll be next week.

Anita and Terry came over and asked me if I had somebody to take care of the baby, and I said, "Yep, me."

They asked me if the people at the nursing home were letting me take Joseph inside, and I said "Nope."

I showed 'em the back of the car and I showed 'em how I rigged it up and they just laughed. They told me again how "zany" I am. Anita just calls me "Zane" now. She thinks that's really funny.

They bought me a thing that props up the baby bottle to the baby's mouth. I can put the bottle in Joseph's mouth with it and he can feed himself. That'll come in handy if anything ever happens and I can't be outside to feed him. Then how in the hell is he going to burp? Besides, he can't change his own diapers that way. At least he won't go hungry. That's what makes him cry the most so I'll use it if I have to.

He stays warm enough: I put on his little shirt and pajamas and his diaper and then I put on the pajamas with feet in 'em. They're almost like blankets. I go out there and sometimes he's all sweaty so he's staying warm enough in the damn car. It scares me to death. I want this baby Joseph and I want to work long enough to have enough money to pay the baby-sitter and pay the rent. I figured it out on paper and I have to keep baby Joseph in this nursery in the car, that's what Anita calls it my car nursery. I have to do this for a whole month before I'll be ahead enough to just keep working and pay somebody to watch him.

The landlady says she knows a lady down the street who watches kids and maybe I could leave baby Joseph there. I went and checked her out, she's a nice lady. She said that she'd help me as soon as I needed her too. I showed her baby Joseph, and she thought he was gorgeous. She called my baby Joseph Gorgeous. Everybody thinks he's cute.

I'm so tired. Terry and Anita came over and asked me what was wrong. They said I looked terrible. I'm just doing the best I can, I told 'em. They said, "Well you look like you need some rest."

I said, "Who can rest with this damn baby, he gets up every two hours?"

"Well, he should quit that pretty soon."

"I just wait for the day when he does!"

They offered to baby-sit for a little while, so I could just sleep, and they'd give him his bottle. So I did. Every time he cried, I woke up. I didn't have to get up. They said they would do that for me on Saturday nights for awhile if I needed it. That really would help. Then I could sleep one whole night.

I wonder if anybody knows that sometimes when he just keeps crying or he wakes up and I'm too tired, I feel like hitting him. I'm not going to hit him. I even go outside and just sit there and let him scream. I feel terrible when I can't help him. He's fed and he's dry and he's clean and I don't know what the hell's wrong with him, and even if I hold him he hollers and that's when I get really upset. I can't be hitting him. Is this why every parent hits their kids? That can't be true. You have to think of something to get out of this.

One night I was sitting outside, I was practically crying myself, and Joseph's in there hollering his lungs out. He ate, he burped, I changed him, I held him, I played with him, he still cried, so I threw him in his bassinet and I'm outside sitting, and the landlady came over and she said, "Here, have a cigarette."

I said, "I hate cigarettes. I always hate 'em. Every time somebody lights 'em up it practically chokes me."

She said, "These won't choke you, they're menthol. Besides, they'll relax you. You can calm down."

I lit up a cigarette and puffed it. She laughed, and said, "You're not inhaling it. That can't calm you down unless you inhale it."

I inhaled it. Bleah. I almost choked to death.

She said, "A few more puffs and you won't be choking on it. Besides, it'll keep you from strangling the baby."

I asked her, "How did you know I feel like strangling him and hitting him and throwing him outside?"

She says, "Oh, everybody feels like that."

I asked her, "How did you keep from hitting your kids?"

She says, "Oh, I just go out on the porch and have a cigarette."

I took a few more drags, then I got dizzy.

She says, "That'll go away too. Just smoke the cigarette and relax."

She said she'd go get some coffee and she brought back a cup of coffee and we sat there and talked and you know, by the time it was over I had two more cigarettes. I did feel calmer. She left me the pack for the night. The next day I bought my own pack. As long as it keeps me calm, I don't give a good goddamn. I just don't want to end up beating up on my baby. I don't want to do that, and I really feel like doing it.

Every day now cigarettes makes it easier. I can calm down. Then I go in and I'm calmer and I sing to Joseph and I play with him, and even if he cries I just sit and hold him sometimes. I guess cigarettes are not that bad.

Baby Joseph smiles now, and sits up, and I made enough money and he has a baby-sitter and no more nursery in the car. He sleeps all night too. We're going to be okay. I mean, I have a baby boy that doesn't do stupid things, and he's not burping and farting and making me miserable in my own house. He's not going to molest people and he's not going to jump up and down on little girls. He's going to laugh a lot. He already laughs a lot, I like to make him laugh. I like to sing to him. I take him everywhere. Do you know, I got this great big shirt from Goodwill, and I put him in it and tuck it into my Levi's and I can take him anywhere I want. Everybody tells me he's starting to look like me. I was kind of hoping he'd look like Jack. I hope he's not mad when he gets older and finds out that he got to look like me instead of good looking like Jack. Can't do anything about it, now.

Dr. Brauma

I'm in the emergency room. I thought I was having a heart attack. The doctor keeps talking to me and he keeps asking me how I feel. As we talk, my heart attack seems to disappear and I start to cry. I don't understand what's happening to me. He says, "It's an anxiety attack. It feels like a heart attack, but it doesn't do anything, you're just scared to death."

I go home. It all starts again. I call my friend. She gives me the number of a shrink because the doctor at the hospital said anxiety attacks are caused by something wrong psychologically. I'm finally going to go crazy, right? Maybe it'll be best to just get it over with.

I start dialing the number. The anxiety attack gets bigger and I put the phone back down. I shake from head to toe. My heart's pounding, I believe I'm going to die. I don't care what that doctor said, maybe he's mistaken. Maybe I'm going to die and he missed finding what's wrong. I'm having a heart attack. I've heard that they always tell women whatever's wrong with 'em is psychological. I'm just going to get in the car and go back to the emergency room.

As I'm driving, my fingers twist up and my hands go numb so I drive with my elbows, I have to get there, I can't die now. I'm a mother. I get to the emergency room, and the same doctor sits and talks to me and says the same thing. He has a nurse come in and give me a shot. In a few minutes, I feel great. I feel calm. I go back home. I go into a sound asleep I don't even remember going to sleep.

I'm awake and the anxiety attack is starting again so I dial the shrink's number, I can't stand this. I just can't stand this. If I'm going to go crazy, I just want to do it and hurry up. I dial the number and a woman answers, and I said, "Is this Dr. Brauma?"

She says yes. I start to cry again.

I tell her, "I feel like something awful's happening to me. Before this, I was feeling like I was going to do something awful to somebody else. A doctor says I'm having anxiety attacks. Do you know about these anxiety attacks? Can you help me?"

She says Yes! She tells me when and how I can get to her office, and she says I'll be okay, she's going to help me.

I go to Dr. Brauma's session after session. She has coffee. I go twice a week. She doesn't want to lock me up. She doesn't think I need to be locked up.

I tell her I hate my job. I feel like hurting everyone. I have a lover who is always jerking me around, and sex is just awful. I tell her I have a roommate who sits and reads the book "Sybil" when I'm having anxiety attacks and I actually fantasize how I'm going to kill her as soon as I'm well enough. I'm just fucked up. I was born fucked up.

I answer her questions about my mom, my dad, and my childhood. She says she thinks I had a horrible childhood. I try to tell her it wasn't that bad, except that I was a hellion. I also tell her about my dog and the lakes and trees and my rag house and I tell her what was good. I know she still thinks I've had a horrible childhood anyway.

I tell her that I'm taking Valium for the anxiety attacks because the doctor at the hospital prescribed 'em. We talk twice a week for two hours at a time. I have never had anyone care so much about what I have to say. I leave the sessions and I go home and go to sleep. Sometimes I cry a lot before I sleep. I don't remember everything we talk about, sometimes I don't remember any of it. I don't know how just talking can make me feel better, but it makes me feel better. She asks questions. She actually wants to know what I think of things, how I feel about things.

She compliments me on how I take care of my child. She tells me I can get through this. She tells me the only way I can get through this is to go into it, and while I go through this she will be right there. She says I have to be right there, too. If I have anxiety, to pay attention. If I cry, to pay attention. If I get mad, to pay attention to what makes me feel like that. She tells me I have to be right there with myself all the time. Why that make me feel so good, I don't know. I don't want to feel any of this!

Many times I tell her, "I don't want to feel any of it."

She tells me she understands. I tell her I don't give a good goddamn if she does understand, I just want it to stop. She tells me she understands that, too. She looks right into my eyes. I get it that she isn't kidding me and I can't help but like her eyes.

"Louise, you should have had help a long time ago, I really don't know how you made it as well as you have this far. It is close to impossible for anyone to work through this alone."

I tell her I wish I had known that I could go get real help somewhere, anywhere. I would have done that. The only thing that ever happened when I tried was that people just made me feel like I was worse for saying anything. I wish they would say people like me could get help in Life magazine. Maybe that's why I hate that Beaver TV show — nothing real happens on it that I can see. My whole life feels more like a mean version of the Three Stooges and The Twilight Zone. Sometimes I just start hollering in the sessions and swearing I'm just going to kill all of them and then I'll feel better.

Dr. Brauma says, "Breathe Louise!" She holds my head and I try to breathe, and calm down and then I just cry.

"I should just line them up and kill 'em. But I am a coward! I know they will just keep doing that ugly shit to someone. They're the ones who should be in pain."

Dr. Brauma says, "There is already enough pain."

"Fine then 'oh great shrink'! Then there should be some other way out for people like me. Why aren't there places, books, movies or something that tells us all about this. How about a class in stupid school that tells the truth about it. Something that says not to kill them but to just run. Run away and get some damn help. So where is it all! And then how about having an 'I didn't kill them' graduation dance."

Dr. Brauma says she doesn't know. She also said thank God for my sense of humor. She says that a lot and it makes me feel better every time.

Sometimes I leave her office thinking I'm never going back, I hate this damn thing, I don't want to talk about it anymore. I go back anyway because somehow or other, this talking about it makes me feel better. I didn't know shrinks really did this. I thought they put you in loony bins or they give you drugs or they tell you how crazy you are or spring a few shock treatments on you or something.

She gives me advice on how to act when I feel like killing somebody, and when I feel like hitting baby Joseph. That acting we do is called "Role Playing." Get this! The trick is to take a break. Just go outside, she says! Take a walk till I feel better. Dig it! I paid for that information! When I feel like doing weird things, she tells me how to think about it. She tells me to write it down, she tells me to draw pictures, so I do it and it works! I don't know why it works.

She feels warm to me. Her eyes are warm. She doesn't ask me creepy questions about details and stuff, she talks about me and how I'm going to work through this. She believes I can. She keeps telling me I can!

I leave the sessions and I go home and I read stories to Joseph and I talk to him and I play with him. I try to be okay. I think maybe I can work through this but I cry a lot and I have anxiety attacks. Dr. Brauma says I can do this if I want to. I have to want to! I can do this.

She calls my spools and strings that I had when I was little a child's meditation. Christ! What the hell does that mean? She talks about the things like my rag house, and all of my hidden treasures, and the dump that I used to go shopping in when I was little, as a way for me to have my own life separate from the hideous things that were going on in my mother's house, a way to survive. She says it's clear to her I was abused over and over.

She says she's going to work with me until I quit coming to her. I don't know why I trust her most of the time, but I trust her. She's not going to get mad that I don't do whatever all she wants me to do and quit talking to me. She promised she'd be right there as long as I was right there. I can't figure her out. Why does she even care about me? She says I'm not going crazy, over and over. She says I'm having a hard time, a very hard time. She says I can learn to do things in a way that doesn't make me feel crazy, that isn't so hard, what makes me happy. She says I'm a good mom, and a good person. She told me I was a good person! I think she just doesn't know me.

She explains to me that I have choices about what I do. I can make up my mind and work toward doing what I want instead of just doing things because I do them. I can know what I'm doing and change the stuff I don't like or the stuff that scares me.

Sometimes I get really pissed off at her and I ask what the hell we're doing, and she says, that more than anything else, she's after the truth. The truth, whatever it is. I like that. Whatever it is. Whatever the damn truth is, we just get to know the truth, and then we get to choose the things we're going to do with it. I want to be okay, but I admit to her that it sounds as possible as flapping my wings and going to the moon.

In the sessions she pisses me off and makes me cry, scream, yell, holler and I want to know, "Where's the applause? I should get a medal for not having killed everybody." She agreed with me. Then she brought me in a medal. It says on it, "Louise's Medal."

There was one time when I told her, "You don't even like me, you don't care about me, you get paid for this, that's why you're doing it." Do you know she didn't even bat an eyelash. She just sat there. Her eyes looking right at me, same as usual, making me think she cares about me. I felt like a total stupid person. I'm screaming at somebody who's nice to me. I don't know why I did that. She always says the same thing, though. "We'll work through that." Sometimes I go to sleep thinking the same words, "We'll work through that." I can't explain it, I don't know why it helps me. It helps me. I've decided, okay, I'm going to be mad, and I'm going to cry, and I'll scream and yell and holler, and sometimes I'm going to be happy, and I'm going to keep right on working through this. If she isn't right, I won't be any worse off. Besides, if she's wrong I tell her she has to give my damn money back. I won't be any crazier, she says, because I worked through it. That sounds true to me. I mean, what could be worse? How could I get any crazier? This stuff is true. Everything that's happened has really happened! I didn't imagine it.

Dr. Brauma looks directly at me and thanks me for telling her things sometimes, especially if it's hard for me. At the end of sessions, she gives me a hug. That feels like trusty old happiness to me. I still wonder sometimes if it's a trick to get me to do what she says. I tell her I'm worried and she better not be tricking me, or I'll knit her damn eyebrows together. She asks me why I think it's all a trick. I tell her it's because I think the whole world just makes up its mind about who's good, who's bad. They're out there, just pretending that they're following the rules. They're out there pretending and at the same time they're doing ugly things. I worry that if I don't pretend too they're going to take my Joseph or kill me or something. I think maybe she thinks that too. She swears she doesn't think that. I'm surprised she answers that question. Lots of damn times I ask her a question and she turns right around and asks me the question I just asked her, then I forget to make her answer me because I'm so busy answering her. I'm back home by the time I realize she didn't answer me. She should have been a baseball player. She has a great curve ball.

I ask her why I can't like sex no matter how I try. I loved Jack and that didn't even help. She says we will figure that out. I think that's a good idea because I won't have to be mad all the time then.

Dr. Brauma doesn't believe that I'm going to have to go to her all the rest of my life. I ask her all the time, "Do I have to come here for the rest of my goddamn life? Do I have to pay for the pleasure of an hour of crying for-goddamn-ever?"

She says no. Yet sometimes I feel like I want to come here. It's like the only safe place and it makes me safe inside of me. She says that I've never been safe. I argued with her. I lost the argument. It's true. I've never been safe. She says there's a way I can make myself safe. I'm going to do it. There's a way to make me safe, so I'll do it. Just like I did when I was little in my rag house.

I have to learn about these choices and I have to learn about what's really true for me. I have to learn about how to be responsible for everything I do as much as I can. She tells me I'm responsible for making my own life better. She says I have tried to be responsible by shopping at the dump, and making rag houses, and being good, and taking good care of my baby and working and paying my bills. She tells me those were my choices, that's me being responsible for my own life. I am going to go back to school and be a counselor. She says I could direct all of my anger at stomping out pain in lives like mine.

How could I have known that no matter how hard I tried to do what I thought was right I'd have to learn about my choices and my boundaries to be as whole and healthy as possible? What a pain in the ass! My history exists unless I have my memory banks erased. I wish I'd known that and what to do about it a long time ago. But no! I have to have dreaded anxiety attacks and fall apart first. There should be a damn billboard on every highway on earth that says -- "If you have been harmed as a child, get real and get help." Or, "If you grew up in an assbite family scream for your friendly neighborhood counselor."

At least now I can go to sleep and sometimes I imagine applause. Sometimes I'm back in the gravel pit, singing to the rocks, and I imagine they applaud. Sometimes I'm in Dr. Brauma's office and I'm in a session—I imagine if people were listening—and imagine they applaud. There is applause. At least, inside of me, there's applause. Dr. Brauma tells me I'm "very fortunate" that I can hear it. I just needed some help.

To Correspond with the Author

Write to:

Louise Burnham
4010 Moorpark Avenue
San Jose, CA 95117
U.S.A.

How to Order this Book

To order additional copies of *Where's the Applause?* send $15.00 (which includes shipping and local taxes) to:

Applause
4010 Moorpark Avenue, Suite 105
San Jose, CA 95117
U.S.A.